ANALYTIC GEOMETRY

ANALYTIC GEOMETRY

Third Edition

CHARLES H. SISAM
Emeritus Professor of Mathematics
Colorado College

WILLIAM F. ATCHISON
Assistant Professor of Mathematics
University of Illinois

HENRY HOLT AND COMPANY · New York

27930–0415
Printed in the United States of America

Preface to the Third Edition

There have been a number of major changes in this edition as well
as many minor changes and a complete revision of the exercises.
These changes have been made with two principal thoughts in mind.
The first has been to clarify and amplify further the text material.
The second has been to bring the book abreast of the current trends
in analytic geometry.

One of the major changes in line with the current trend has been
to put more emphasis on the graphing of curves; consequently the
concepts of intercepts and excluded intervals have been introduced
with simple illustrations in Chapter 1. These concepts, along with
symmetry, have been emphasized again in the chapter on conics.
The single chapter, Higher Plane Curves, in the previous edition
has been expanded into two chapters, one on algebraic curves and
one on transcendental curves. The material on algebraic curves has
been reorganized and greatly amplified in an effort to enable the
student to obtain more quickly an adequate sketch of a curve.

The chapter on conic sections has been rearranged so that more
articles may be omitted if desired without destroying the essential
development. It has also been slightly condensed. At the same time,
the discussions of the equations of the conics as loci have been amplified so that they can serve better as models for the discussions of other
equations.

The chapter on curves in polar coördinates has been amplified to
give a more complete discussion of equivalent equations. The chapter
on tangents, normals, diameters, poles, and polars has been left out
since this material can be more adequately treated in later courses.
Despite the fact that empirical equations are now taught in few
schools, the chapter on this subject has been retained. This is because
recent advances in computing machines have increased the emphasis
on numerical methods.

A new section on the sketching of solids bounded by two or more surfaces has been included in the chapter on surfaces and curves. The material on cylindrical and spherical coördinates has been collected at the end of the chapter on surfaces and its use in the study of surfaces emphasized.

I am deeply grateful for the continued help of Professor C. H. Sisam throughout the preparation of this edition. He has read carefully the entire text and made many helpful suggestions. He is also chiefly responsible for the revised exercises. Answers are given to the odd-numbered exercises; the answers to the even-numbered exercises are published separately.

I wish to express my appreciation to Professor W. A. Ferguson at the University of Illinois for many helpful suggestions made throughout the preparation of the revision. I am also grateful to several other colleagues for their suggestions. I especially appreciate the assistance of my wife in the preparation of the entire revised manuscript.

W. F. A.

University of Illinois
January, 1955

Preface to the First Edition

This textbook has been written with the actual needs and desires of the teachers of analytic geometry constantly in mind. It is primarily intended for a course of three semester hours but it includes ample, carefully selected material for a five hour course. The text has been arranged to facilitate a selection of material with a minimum of inconvenience. The essentials of the first six chapters constitute what is customarily considered to be the basic course in plane analytic geometry. To this should be added as much of the remaining subject matter as time permits. The starred articles may be omitted without interrupting the continuity of the text. As far as is practicable, these articles have been put near the ends of chapters.

The course in analytic geometry has several major objectives, each of which has been fully considered in the preparation of this text. It should follow in a natural way from the student's previous work in mathematics, which it is expected to unify; it must acquaint the student with the methods, the spirit, and the essential facts of analytic geometry; and it should stress the particular types of geometric reasoning that the student will encounter most frequently in his later work. It is for this last reason that a number of devices helpful in the drawing of graphs have been emphasized in chapters eight and ten and their usefulness has been illustrated by applying them to several higher plane curves that the student is likely to meet in subsequent courses.

The exercises are sufficiently numerous and have been graded so that a selection may be made to fit the needs of students of varying ability. In particular, it is hoped that the Selected Exercises at the ends of certain chapters will be found to be stimulating and challenging by distinctly superior students. Answers have been given to approximately one third of the exercises. These have been selected with the purpose of enabling the student to assure himself of the correctness of his methods and to encourage accuracy in his computations.

In preparing this text, the author has received helpful suggestions from so many sources that it is plainly impossible to acknowledge all of them. He is especially indebted, however, to Professor Ralph Beatley, of Harvard University; Professor E. R. Hedrick, of the University of California; Professors A. J. Kempner and C. A. Hutchinson, of the University of Colorado; Professor E. B. Lytle, of the University of Illinois; Professor Virgil Snyder, of Cornell University, and Miss Martha Belschner, of Colorado College, for valuable constructive criticisms of the text.

C. H. S.

Contents

INTRODUCTION   xv

PLANE ANALYTIC GEOMETRY

Chapter I. COÖRDINATES AND GRAPHS

Article   Page
1.1   Introduction   3
1.2   Rectangular Coördinates   3
1.3   Plotting Points   5
1.4   The Locus of an Equation   6
1.5   Symmetry   10
1.6   Intersections of Graphs   12

Chapter II. FUNDAMENTAL DEFINITIONS AND THEOREMS

2.1   Directed Line Segments   15
2.2   Distance Between Two Points   18
2.3   Point Dividing a Segment in a Given Ratio   20
2.4   Inclination and Slope of a Line   23
2.5   Slope of the Line through Two Given Points   23
2.6   Parallel and Perpendicular Lines   26
2.7   Angle from One Line to Another   27
2.8   Applications to Elementary Geometry   29
2.9   The Equation of a Locus   31

Chapter III. THE LINE

3.1   Equation of a Line   37
3.2   Lines Parallel to the Axes   37
3.3   The Point-Slope Form   38
3.4   The Two-Point Form   39
3.5   The Intercept Form   40
3.6   The Slope-Intercept Form   41
3.7   The General Form. Linear Equations   42
3.8   The Linear Function   44
3.9   The Normal Form   46

Article | Page
3.10 Reduction of the Equation of a Line to the Normal Form | 48
3.11 Distance from a Line to a Point | 50
3.12 The Area of a Triangle | 53
3.13 Families of Lines. Parameters | 54
3.14 Family of Lines through the Intersection of Two Given Lines | 56
3.15 Factorable Equations | 57

Chapter IV. THE CIRCLE

4.1 Equation of a Circle in Terms of Its Center and Radius | 61
4.2 General Form of the Equation of a Circle | 62
4.3 Circle Determined by Three Conditions | 65
4.4 Loci Problems Leading to Lines and Circles | 68

Chapter V. POLAR COÖRDINATES

5.1 Introduction | 75
5.2 Polar Coördinates | 75
5.3 Relations between Polar and Rectangular Coördinates | 77
5.4 The Polar Equation of a Line | 79
5.5 The Polar Equation of a Circle | 81

Chapter VI. THE CONIC SECTIONS

6.1 Plane Sections of a Right Circular Cone | 84
6.2 Second Degree Equations and Conic Sections | 85

The Parabola:

6.3 Standard Form of the Equation of the Parabola | 85
6.4 Discussion of the Equation | 87
6.5 Applications | 89
6.6 A Continuous Construction for a Parabola | 89

The Ellipse:

6.7 Standard Form of the Equation of the Ellipse | 91
6.8 Discussion of the Equation | 93
6.9 Some Applications of the Ellipse | 95
6.10 A Second Definition of the Ellipse | 97
6.11 A Continuous Construction for an Ellipse | 98

Article

Page

The Hyperbola:

6.12   Standard Form of the Equation of the Hyperbola   99
6.13   Discussion of the Equation. Asymptotes   101
6.14   Equilateral Hyperbola   104
6.15   A Second Definition of the Hyperbola   106
6.16   A Continuous Construction for a Hyperbola   106
6.17   Standard Equation of a Conic in Polar Coördinates   107

Chapter VII. TRANSFORMATION OF COÖRDINATES

7.1   Changing the Coördinate Axes   114
7.2   Translation of Axes   114
7.3   The Quadratic Function   117
7.4   Rotation of Axes   119
7.5   The Equilateral Hyperbola   120

Chapter VIII. CONICS WITH EQUATIONS NOT IN STANDARD FORM

8.1   The General Equation of Second Degree   123
8.2   Conics with Principal Axis Parallel to a Coördinate Axis   124
8.3   Conics Satisfying Given Conditions   126
8.4   Simplification by Rotation. Removal of the xy-term   127
8.5   Reduction of Numerical Equations to a Standard Form   129
8.6   Determination of the Type of a Conic from Its Equation   132

Chapter IX. ALGEBRAIC CURVES

9.1   Introduction   135
9.2   Symmetries   136
9.3   Intersection with the Coördinate Axes. Polynomial Functions   137
9.4   Horizontal and Vertical Asymptotes. Rational Functions   139
9.5   Excluded Intervals   142
9.6   Multiplicity of the Origin. Tangent Lines at the Origin   143
9.7   Graphs of Equations   145

Chapter X. TRANSCENDENTAL CURVES

10.1   Introduction   150
10.2   The Sine and Cosine Curves   150
10.3   The Tangent Curve   154

Article   Page
10.4   The Cosecant, Secant and Cotangent Curves   154
10.5   The Inverse Trigonometric Functions   155
10.6   The Logarithmic Curves   157
10.7   The Exponential Curves   158
10.8   Applications   160
10.9   Damped Vibrations   161
10.10   Addition of Ordinates   162

Chapter XI. PARAMETRIC EQUATIONS

11.1   Introduction   165
11.2   Parametric Equations of the Circle   165
11.3   Parametric Equations of the Ellipse   166
11.4   Path of a Projectile   167
11.5   Parametric Equations and Curve Plotting   168
11.6   The Cycloid   170
11.7   The Epicycloid   172
11.8   The Hypocycloid   173

Chapter XII. CURVES IN POLAR COÖRDINATES

12.1   Polar Equations   175
12.2   Discussion of the Equation   177
12.3   The Lemniscate   181
12.4   The Cardioid   181
12.5   The Limaçon   181
12.6   The Conchoid of Nicomedes   182
12.7   The Rose Curves   183
12.8   The Spirals   183
12.9   Intersections of Curves in Polar Coördinates   185

Chapter XIII. EMPIRICAL EQUATIONS

13.1   Equations Derived from Experimental Data   189
13.2   Selecting the Type of Equation   190
13.3   Linear Type by the Method of Averages   190
13.4   Linear Type by the Method of Least Squares   192
13.5   Derivation of the Formulas for the Method of Least
        Squares   193
13.6   Parabolic and Hyperbolic Types   197
13.7   Exponential Type   201
13.8   Polynomial Type   203

SOLID ANALYTIC GEOMETRY

Chapter XIV. DEFINITIONS AND THEOREMS

Article   Page

14.1 Rectangular Coördinates   211
14.2 Figures   212
14.3 Distance between Two Points   213
14.4 Direction Cosines of a Directed Line   215
14.5 Direction Numbers of a Line   217
14.6 The Angle between Two Directed Lines   219

Chapter XV. PLANES AND LINES

15.1 Normal Equation of a Plane   224
15.2 General Form of the Equation of a Plane   225
15.3 The Traces of a Plane   226
15.4 Angle between Two Planes   228
15.5 Plane through a Given Point Perpendicular to a Given Line   229
15.6 Distance from a Plane to a Point   229
15.7 Planes Satisfying Three Conditions   231
15.8 Intercept Equation of a Plane   232

The Line in Space:

15.9 Planes and Lines   233
15.10 Line through a Given Point Having a Given Direction. The Symmetric Form   234
15.11 The Two-Point Form   235
15.12 The Parametric Form   235
15.13 The General Form   235
15.14 Family of Planes through a Line. Projecting Planes   237

Transformation of Coördinates:

15.15 Translation of Axes   239
15.16 Rotation of Axes   240

Chapter XVI. TYPES OF SURFACES AND CURVES

16.1 Surfaces and Curves   245
16.2 Cylinders   246
16.3 Surfaces of Revolution   247

Article   Page
16.4   The Sphere   249
16.5   Quadric Surfaces   250
16.6   The Ellipsoid   251
16.7   The Hyperboloid of One Sheet   252
16.8   The Hyperboloid of Two Sheets   253
16.9   The Elliptic Paraboloid   254
16.10   The Hyperbolic Paraboloid   254
16.11   The Quadric Cone   255
16.12   Curves in Space   256
16.13   Parametric Equations of a Curve in Space   257
16.14   The Sketching of Solids Bounded by Surfaces   258
16.15   Cylindrical Coördinates   262
16.16   Spherical Coördinates   262

TABLES

  I. Four-place Table of Logarithms   268
 II. Four-place Table of Natural Trigonometric Functions   270
III. Exact Values of the Trigonometric Functions of Certain
     Angles   271
 IV. Three-place Table of Square Roots   271
  V. Three-place Table of Exponential Functions   272

Answers to Odd-numbered Exercises   273

Index   285

Introduction

In this introduction, we have collected, for reference, a number of definitions, theorems, and formulas from algebra, geometry, and trigonometry that will be useful in this course.

0.1 Quadratic Equations and Completing the Square. An equation of the form

$$ax^2 + bx + c = 0, \qquad a \neq 0$$

in which a, b, and c do not contain x, is a quadratic equation in x. Its roots are:

$$x_1 = \frac{-b + \sqrt{b^2 - 4ac}}{2a} \quad \text{and} \quad x_2 = \frac{-b - \sqrt{b^2 - 4ac}}{2a}.$$

If a, b, and c are real numbers, these roots are real and unequal, real and equal, or imaginary, according as

$$b^2 - 4ac$$

is positive, zero, or negative.

The process of completing the square of the x terms to obtain the roots will be reviewed here because this process will be used frequently in the forthcoming chapters.

Transpose c and then factor a from the left side of the quadratic equation. This gives

$$a\left(x^2 + \frac{b}{a}x\right) = -c.$$

To complete the square of the expression inside the parenthesis we add $\left(\frac{1}{2} \cdot \frac{b}{a}\right)^2$, which means that we must actually add $a\left(\frac{b^2}{4a^2}\right)$ to both sides of the equation. This gives

$$a\left(x^2 + \frac{b}{a}x + \left[\frac{b}{2a}\right]^2\right) = \frac{b^2}{4a} - c$$

or
$$a\left(x + \frac{b}{2a}\right)^2 = \frac{b^2 - 4ac}{4a}.$$

Dividing by a and taking the square root of both sides we get

$$x + \frac{b}{2a} = \pm \sqrt{\frac{b^2 - 4ac}{4a^2}}$$

or

$$x = \frac{-b \pm \sqrt{b^2 - 4ac}}{2a}.$$

0.2 Determinants. The expression

$$\begin{vmatrix} a_1 & b_1 \\ a_2 & b_2 \end{vmatrix}$$

is called a **determinant of the second order.** Its value is defined to be

$$a_1 b_2 - a_2 b_1.$$

Similarly, the expression

$$\begin{vmatrix} a_1 & b_1 & c_1 \\ a_2 & b_2 & c_2 \\ a_3 & b_3 & c_3 \end{vmatrix}$$

is a **determinant of the third order.** Its value may be found from the formula

$$a_1 \begin{vmatrix} b_2 & c_2 \\ b_3 & c_3 \end{vmatrix} - a_2 \begin{vmatrix} b_1 & c_1 \\ b_3 & c_3 \end{vmatrix} + a_3 \begin{vmatrix} b_1 & c_1 \\ b_2 & c_2 \end{vmatrix} =$$

$$a_1 b_2 c_3 - a_1 b_3 c_2 - a_2 b_1 c_3 + a_2 b_3 c_1 + a_3 b_1 c_2 - a_3 b_2 c_1.$$

Determinants of higher orders may be written, and their values found, in a similar way.

0.3 Linear Equations. One of the principal uses of determinants is in solving systems of linear equations. Using determinants, the solutions of

$$a_1 x + b_1 y = c_1$$
$$a_2 x + b_2 y = c_2$$

can be written

$$x = \frac{\begin{vmatrix} c_1 & b_1 \\ c_2 & b_2 \end{vmatrix}}{\begin{vmatrix} a_1 & b_1 \\ a_2 & b_2 \end{vmatrix}} \text{ and } y = \frac{\begin{vmatrix} a_1 & c_1 \\ a_2 & c_2 \end{vmatrix}}{\begin{vmatrix} a_1 & b_1 \\ a_2 & b_2 \end{vmatrix}}, \text{ where } \begin{vmatrix} a_1 & b_1 \\ a_2 & b_2 \end{vmatrix} \neq 0.$$

Similarly the solution of

$$a_1 x + b_1 y + c_1 z = d_1$$
$$a_2 x + b_2 y + c_2 z = d_2$$
$$a_3 x + b_3 y + c_3 z = d_3$$

can be written

$$
x = \frac{\begin{vmatrix} d_1 & b_1 & c_1 \\ d_2 & b_2 & c_2 \\ d_3 & b_3 & c_3 \end{vmatrix}}{\begin{vmatrix} a_1 & b_1 & c_1 \\ a_2 & b_2 & c_2 \\ a_3 & b_3 & c_3 \end{vmatrix}}, \quad y = \frac{\begin{vmatrix} a_1 & d_1 & c_1 \\ a_2 & d_2 & c_2 \\ a_3 & d_3 & c_3 \end{vmatrix}}{\begin{vmatrix} a_1 & b_1 & c_1 \\ a_2 & b_2 & c_2 \\ a_3 & b_3 & c_3 \end{vmatrix}}, \quad \text{and } z = \frac{\begin{vmatrix} a_1 & b_1 & d_1 \\ a_2 & b_2 & d_2 \\ a_3 & b_3 & d_3 \end{vmatrix}}{\begin{vmatrix} a_1 & b_1 & c_1 \\ a_2 & b_2 & c_2 \\ a_3 & b_3 & c_3 \end{vmatrix}}
$$

where the determinant in the denominator must be different from
zero. What happens in case the determinant in the denominator is
zero will be brought out in exercises later.

0.4 Logarithms. If N, x, and a are three numbers (a positive and
not equal to unity) that satisfy the equation

$$N = a^x,$$

then the exponent, x, is called the *logarithm of N to the base a* and we
may write the preceding equation in the form

$$x = \log_a N.$$

The following properties of logarithms are useful:

$$\log_a (MN) = \log_a M + \log_a N, \qquad \log_a \left(\frac{M}{N}\right) = \log_a M - \log_a N,$$

$$\log_a M^n = n \log_a M, \qquad \log_a \sqrt[n]{M} = \frac{1}{n} \log_a M,$$

$$\log_a \frac{1}{M} = - \log_a M, \qquad \log_b M = \frac{\log_a M}{\log_a b}.$$

A table of logarithms to the base 10 will be found in Table I,
page 268.

0.5 Functions. A variable y is said to be a function of a variable
x if to each value of x from a given set of values there is associated
one or more values of y. The variable x is called the **independent
variable** and the variable y is called the **dependent variable.** If to
each value of x there is only one value of y then y is called a **single-
valued function of x.**

Only real values of the variable and the function are normally
considered in analytic geometry. For example, the equation $y^2 = x$

defines "y as a function of x" only for the set of values $x \geqq 0$.* The equation $y^2 = \dfrac{x^2}{x^2 - 1}$ defines y as a function of x only for the set of values $x > 1$, $x < -1$ and $x = 0$.

The notation $y = f(x)$ or $y = \phi(x)$, etc. is used to mean "y is a function of x." Also $f(x_1)$ is used to denote the value of the function when x is assigned the particular value x_1. Thus if $f(x) = x^3 - 2x^2 + 3$, then $f(2) = (2)^3 - 2(2)^2 + 3 = 3$, and $f(a) = a^3 - 2a^2 + 3$.

0.6 Angles. The part of a straight line that extends indefinitely in one direction from a fixed point on it is called a **half-line** (or **ray**).

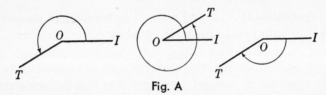

Fig. A

We shall consider an angle, as IOT in Figure A, to be generated by rotating a half-line about its end point O from the position OI to the position OT. The point O is the **vertex,** the half-line OI is the **initial side** and OT is the **terminal side,** of the angle.

The rotation may include one or more complete revolutions, as is indicated in the second figure, and it may be in the clockwise or counter-clockwise direction. An angle is *positive* if the generating half-line rotates counter-clockwise and *negative* in the contrary case.

0.7 Radian Measure. In advanced mathematics, angles are usually measured in **radian** (or **circular**) **measure.** In this system, the unit angle is the **radian** which is defined as an angle which, if placed with its vertex at the center of a circle will intercept on the circumference an arc equal in length to the radius of the circle.

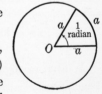

Fig. B

To determine the relation between degrees and radians, we notice that, in an angle of half a revolution, there are 180°. There are also

---

* The symbol $>$ is read "is greater than." The symbol $\geqq$ is read "is greater than or equal to." Similarly, the symbol $<$ is read "is less than" and the symbol $\leqq$ is read "is less than or equal to."

π radians since the length of the semi-circumference is π times the radius. Hence,
$$\pi \text{ radians} = 180°.$$
$$1 \text{ radian} = (180/\pi)° = 57° \ 17' \ 45'', \text{ approximately},$$
$$1° = (\pi/180) \text{ radians} = 0.01745 \text{ radians, approximately}.$$

In practice, the word *radian* is usually omitted in stating the size of an angle in radian measure.

If θ is the number of radians in an angle with its vertex at the center of a circle, a, the length of the radius, and s, the length of the intercepted arc, then
$$s = a\theta.$$

0.8 Trigonometric Functions. To define the trigonometric functions of a given angle θ $(= XOP)$, we may place the angle so that its initial side is horizontal and extends to the right from the vertex O. Choose any point P on the terminal side and drop a perpendicular PL from P to the initial side (produced if necessary).

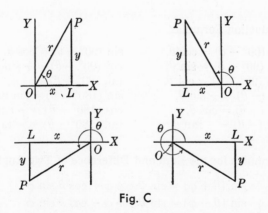

Fig. C

Denote by r the length of the segment OP, which we shall always consider as positive. The length of the segment OL is denoted by x and is positive or negative according as L is to the right or left of O. The length of LP is denoted by y and is positive or negative according as P lies above or below the initial side.

We now define the functions as follows:

$$\sin \theta = \frac{y}{r}, \qquad \csc \theta = \frac{r}{y},$$

$$\cos \theta = \frac{x}{r}, \qquad \sec \theta = \frac{r}{x},$$

$$\tan \theta = \frac{y}{x}, \qquad \cot \theta = \frac{x}{y}.$$

0.9 Trigonometric Identities. The above six functions are connected by the following identities:

$$\csc \theta = \frac{1}{\sin \theta}, \qquad \sin^2 \theta + \cos^2 \theta = 1,$$

$$\sec \theta = \frac{1}{\cos \theta}, \qquad \sec^2 \theta - \tan^2 \theta = 1,$$

$$\cot \theta = \frac{1}{\tan \theta}, \qquad \csc^2 \theta - \cot^2 \theta = 1,$$

$$\tan \theta = \frac{\sin \theta}{\cos \theta}, \qquad \cot \theta = \frac{\cos \theta}{\sin \theta}.$$

0.10 Reduction Formulas.

$$\sin (90° - \theta) = \cos \theta, \qquad \sin (90° + \theta) = \cos \theta,$$
$$\cos (90° - \theta) = \sin \theta, \qquad \cos (90° + \theta) = - \sin \theta,$$
$$\tan (90° - \theta) = \cot \theta, \qquad \tan (90° + \theta) = - \cot \theta,$$
$$\sin (- \theta) = - \sin \theta, \qquad \sin (180° - \theta) = \sin \theta,$$
$$\cos (- \theta) = \cos \theta, \qquad \cos (180° - \theta) = - \cos \theta,$$
$$\tan (- \theta) = - \tan \theta, \qquad \tan (180° - \theta) = - \tan \theta.$$

0.11 Formulas for the Sum and Difference of Two Angles

$$\sin (\theta + \phi) = \sin \theta \cos \phi + \cos \theta \sin \phi$$
$$\sin (\theta - \phi) = \sin \theta \cos \phi - \cos \theta \sin \phi$$
$$\cos (\theta + \phi) = \cos \theta \cos \phi - \sin \theta \sin \phi$$
$$\cos (\theta - \phi) = \cos \theta \cos \phi + \sin \theta \sin \phi.$$

$$\tan (\theta + \phi) = \frac{\tan \theta + \tan \phi}{1 - \tan \theta \tan \phi}$$

$$\tan (\theta - \phi) = \frac{\tan \theta - \tan \phi}{1 + \tan \theta \tan \phi}.$$

0.12 Formulas for the Double and Half Angle.

$$\sin 2\theta = 2 \sin \theta \cos \theta$$
$$\cos 2\theta = \cos^2 \theta - \sin^2 \theta = 1 - 2 \sin^2 \theta = 2 \cos^2 \theta - 1$$
$$\tan 2\theta = \frac{2 \tan \theta}{1 - \tan^2 \theta}$$
$$\sin \frac{\theta}{2} = \pm \sqrt{\frac{1 - \cos \theta}{2}} \qquad \cos \frac{\theta}{2} = \pm \sqrt{\frac{1 + \cos \theta}{2}}$$

0.13 Triangle Formulas.
If we denote the lengths of the sides of a triangle by a, b, and c, and the magnitudes of the opposite angles by α, β, and γ, respectively, then

$$\frac{\sin \alpha}{a} = \frac{\sin \beta}{b} = \frac{\sin \gamma}{c}. \qquad \text{Law of Sines}$$
$$a^2 = b^2 + c^2 - 2bc \cos \alpha. \qquad \text{Law of Cosines}$$

0.14 The Greek Alphabet.

Letters	Names	Letters	Names	Letters	Names
A α	Alpha	I ι	Iota	P ρ	Rho
B β	Beta	K κ	Kappa	Σ σ	Sigma
Γ γ	Gamma	Λ λ	Lambda	T τ	Tau
Δ δ	Delta	M μ	Mu	Υ υ	Upsilon
E ϵ	Epsilon	N ν	Nu	Φ ϕ	Phi
Z ζ	Zeta	Ξ ξ	Xi	X χ	Chi
H η	Eta	O o	Omicron	Ψ ψ	Psi
Θ θ	Theta	Π π	Pi	Ω ω	Omega

REVIEW EXERCISES

Algebra Exercises

1. Simplify the following:

(a) $\frac{1}{2} + \frac{3}{4} - \frac{1}{3}$.

(b) $\frac{1}{x} - \frac{3}{x^2} + \frac{2}{y}$.

(c) $\frac{1}{x - y} - \frac{1}{x + y} + \frac{3}{x^2 - y^2}$.

(d) $1 + \frac{1}{1 - (1/x)}$.

2. Solve by completing the square:

(a) $x^2 + 2x - 3 = 0$.

(b) $2x^2 - 2x - 3 = 0$.

(c) $3x^2 - 7x + 4 = 0$.

(d) $5x^2 + 3x - 8 = 0$.

3. Solve by using the quadratic formula:

(a) $2x^2 - 3x + 5 = 0$.   (b) $x^2 - 6x + 9 = 0$.

(c) $3x^2 + 6x - 2 = 0$.   (d) $5 - 4x - 3x^2 = 0$.

4. Solve for y in terms of x by using the quadratic formula:

(a) $y^2x - x^2y + 2 = 0$.   (b) $y^2x + 2y^2 + xy - x = 0$.

(c) $x^3 - y^2 + 2xy - x - 1 = 0$.

5. Solve simultaneously:

(a) $x^2 - y^2 + 2x - 3y = 2$,   (b) $y = x^2 + x - 2$,

     $x - 2y = 2$. $x - y = 2$.

(c) $x^2 + y^2 = 13$,   (d) $x^2 + y^2 = 25$,

     $3x^2 + 2y^2 = 30$. $5x^2 - 2y^2 = 13$.

6. Determine the real values of x for which the following functions are negative:

(a) $2x - 4$.   (b) $5 - 7x$.

(c) $x^2 + 3x + 2$.   (d) $3x^2 - 2x + 1$.

(e) $(x - 1)(3 - x)(2x + 1)$.   (f) $\dfrac{3x - 2}{(x - 1)(x + 2)}$.

7. Solve simultaneously, using determinants:

(a) $2x - 3y = 4$,   (b) $3x + 5y = 7$,

     $x + 4y = 6$. $4x - 8y = 3$.

(c) $6x - 7y - z + 10 = 0$,   (d) $x + y - 3z = 6$,

     $2x + 3y - 2z - 35 = 0$, $3x + 2y - 7z = 14$,

     $5x - 4y - 3z - 16 = 0$. $x - 3y + 3z = -4$.

8. Solve the following equations and check the results:

(a) $\sqrt{x + 1} = 3$.   (b) $\sqrt{x + 11} = x - 1$.

(c) $\sqrt{x} + \sqrt{x - 1} = 2$.   (d) $\sqrt{x - 3} - \sqrt{x + 2} = 1$.

9. Write the following equations in the logarithmic form:

(a) $10^2 = 100$.   (b) $2^4 = 16$.   (c) $36^{\frac{1}{2}} = 6$.

(d) $\sqrt{49} = 7$.   (e) $\sqrt[3]{8^2} = 4$.   (f) $81^{-0.25} = \frac{1}{3}$.

10. Write the following equations in the exponential form:

(a) $\log_{10} 1000 = 3$.   (b) $\log_5 25 = 2$.   (c) $\log_{64} 8 = \frac{1}{2}$.

(d) $\log_a 1 = 0$.   (e) $\log_{625} 0.2 = -0.25$.

(f) $\log_{32} 0.5 = -0.2$.

11. Express the following as an algebraic sum of the logarithms of integers:

(a) $\log_a \dfrac{\sqrt[3]{16}}{9^{\frac{1}{4}} 7^{\frac{3}{2}}}$.

(b) $\log_a \dfrac{3^4}{5^3}$.

(c) $\log_a \dfrac{\sqrt{5}}{2^3 \sqrt[3]{7}}$.

12. Express the following as the logarithm of a single quantity:

(a) $3 \log_a 48 - 2 \log_a (24) + 4 \log_a 17$.

(b) $\log_a 4 - \log_a 3 + \log_a \pi + 3 \log_a r$.

13. If $f(x) = 3x - 4$, find $f(0)$, $f(1)$, $f(-2)$, $f(\frac{2}{3})$.

14. If $f(t) = \sqrt{t} + \dfrac{1}{\sqrt{t}}$, find $f(1)$, $f(4)$, $f(3)$, $f(\frac{1}{9})$.

15. If $f(z) = 2z - 3$, find $f(y^2)$, $f(1 - y)$, $f(1/y)$.

16. If $f(w) = \dfrac{w - 1}{w + 1}$, find $f(3)$, $f(-3)$, $f(-t)$, $f(1/t)$.

17. Express the volume of a cube as a function of the length of its edge.

18. Express the length of the hypotenuse of an isosceles right triangle as a function of one of its legs.

19. Express the area of a circle as a function of its radius.

Trigonometry Exercises

20. Express the following angles in radians:

(a) $330°$. (b) $225°$. (c) $150°$. (d) $-200°$. (e) $390°$.

21. Convert the following angles from radians to degrees:

(a) $3\pi/4$. (b) $4\pi/5$. (c) 2.5. (d) -3. (e) $10\pi/3$.

22. Express the following as functions of a positive acute angle $\le 45°$:

(a) $\sin 341°$. (b) $\cos 260°$. (c) $\tan 172°$. (d) $\cot 490°$.
(e) $\csc (-200°)$. (f) $\sec (-145°)$.

23. Find the length of arc subtended on a circle of radius 5 feet by an angle at the center of (a) 2.6 radians, (b) 30°.

24. Find the radius of a circle for which an arc 14.4 feet long is subtended by an angle of (a) 1.2 radians, (b) 18°.

25. Find $\sin \theta$ and $\tan \theta$ if $\cos \theta = -\frac{3}{4}$ and θ is in (a) the second quadrant, (b) the third quadrant.

26. Find $\sin \theta$ and $\cos \theta$ where θ is an acute angle if (a) $\tan 2\theta = \frac{3}{4}$, (b) $\tan 2\theta = -\frac{24}{7}$.

27. Solve the following equations for all values of θ:

(a) $2 \sin^2 \theta - \sin \theta - 1 = 0$.   (b) $\sin \theta - \cos 2\theta = 0$.

(c) $\sin 2\theta = \cos \theta$.   (d) $3 \tan \theta = 2 \sin 2\theta$.

(e) $\sin \theta = 1 + 2 \cos \theta$.   (f) $4 \sin \theta = 3 \csc \theta$.

28. Prove the following trigonometric identities by use of the identities given in Art. 0.9:

(a) $\sec \theta = \csc \theta \tan \theta$.   (b) $\csc \theta \cos \theta = \cot \theta$.

(c) $\dfrac{\cos^2 \theta}{\sin \theta + 1} = 1 - \sin \theta$.   (d) $\dfrac{1}{\sec \theta + \tan \theta} = \dfrac{1}{\cos \theta} - \dfrac{1}{\cot \theta}$.

(e) $\dfrac{\tan^2 \theta}{\sec^2 \theta} + \dfrac{\cot^2 \theta}{\csc^2 \theta} = 1$.   (f) $\dfrac{\csc \theta}{\cot \theta + \tan \theta} = \cos \theta$.

(g) $\dfrac{\csc \theta - \sin \theta}{\cos \theta} = \cot \theta$.   (h) $\sec^4 \theta + \tan^4 \theta = 1 + 2 \sec^2 \theta \tan^2 \theta$.

PLANE
ANALYTIC
GEOMETRY

Coördinates and Graphs

1.1 Introduction. Analytic Geometry is a subject in which algebra, geometry, and trigonometry are studied together in such a way that each is helpful in simplifying and clarifying the solution of problems arising in the others. We learn, for example, to solve geometric problems by means of algebra, and to see the geometry behind what otherwise may have appeared as a pure algebraic process. The interrelationships between these subjects is very important in the applications of analytic geometry and should be emphasized throughout the course. The concepts and methods of analytic geometry are constantly employed in more advanced branches of mathematics.

Although several men contributed to the invention of analytic geometry, the chief contributor was René Descartes, a French mathematician and philosopher, whose *La Géométrie*, which appeared in 1637, was the source from which the mathematical world learned the methods of analytic geometry. Because of this work of Descartes, analytic geometry is sometimes called "Cartesian geometry."

1.2 Rectangular Coördinates. Let there be given two lines $X'X$ and $Y'Y$ (Fig. 1.1) which are perpendicular to each other and intersect at a point O. These two lines are called the **coördinate axes;** $X'X$

is the **x-axis** and $Y'Y$, the **y-axis**. The point O is the **origin**. Distances on the x-axis are considered positive if measured from left to

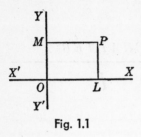

Fig. 1.1

right and negative if measured in the opposite direction. Similarly, distances on the y-axis are positive if measured upward and negative if measured downward. This convention as to signs may be expressed briefly by saying that the x-axis is "directed to the right" and that the y-axis is "directed upward."

Let P be any point in the plane of the coördinate axes. From P drop perpendiculars to the x- and y-axes and denote the feet of these perpendiculars by L and M, respectively. The length of the segment OL, measured from O to L and taken with its proper sign, is denoted by x and is called the **x-coördinate**, or **abscissa**, of P. Similarly, the segment measured from O to M and taken with its proper sign is denoted by y and is called the **y-coördinate**, or **ordinate**, of P. The two numbers x and y are the **coördinates** of P and are written thus: (x, y). Observe that the two coördinates are enclosed by parentheses and separated by a comma.

The coördinates defined above and used to locate a point are called *rectangular* coördinates. A coördinate system to locate points could be set up in which the axes are oblique, but this will not be done in this book. We will, however, in Chapter 5, set up another coördinate system called the polar coördinate system. It locates a point by giving its distance and direction from a fixed point.

It will be seen from Fig. 1.1 that, numerically, $MP = OL$ and $LP = OM$. Moreover, these lengths will agree in sign if MP is considered to be positive if it is measured to the right and LP is positive if it is measured upward. We shall, accordingly, frequently find it convenient to speak of the length of MP and LP, rather than those of OL and OM, as the coördinates of P.

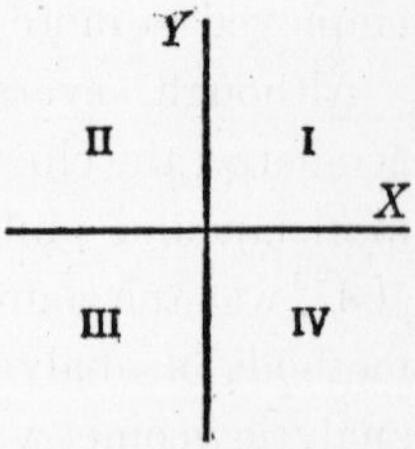

Fig. 1.2

The coördinate axes divide the plane into four parts, called **quadrants,** which are numbered (conforming to the usage familiar from trigonometry) as in the adjoining figure (Fig. 1.2).

1.3 Plotting Points. If we have given a pair of real numbers *
(x, y), we can always find a point P for which x is the abscissa and y
the ordinate. Suppose, for example, that the given pair of coördinates
is $(3, -2)$. We first determine L by laying off on the x-axis three units
to the right from O and then locate P by laying off, on a parallel to
the y-axis, two units downward from L.

When a point P is located in this way by means of its coördinates,
it is said to be **plotted**. Thus, in Fig. 1.3, we have plotted the points
that have the pairs of coördinates $(3, -2)$, $(4, 3)$, $(-2, 2)$, and
$(-1, -3)$. Usually we shall use one of the two expressions "the point
(x, y)" or "the point whose coördinates are (x, y)," instead of the
more accurate expression "the point whose pair of coördinates is
(x, y)."

Whenever it is necessary to plot points, time can be saved, and
greater accuracy secured, by using coördinate
paper; that is, paper that is ruled with equally
spaced lines parallel to the coördinate axes.
Correctly drawn figures greatly simplify the
work in analytic geometry and frequently sug-
gest the method for solving problems. Therefore, an essential part of every exercise is the
drawing of a suitable figure. The habitual use

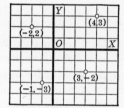

Fig. 1.3

of coördinate paper is the most convenient aid in constructing accurate figures.

EXERCISES

1. Plot the points whose pairs of coördinates are: $(2, 5)$, $(-3, 2)$,
$(-4, -2)$, $(4, -3)$, $(0, 5)$, $(-2, 0)$.

2. Plot the points: $(3, 1)$, $(-1, 5)$, $(-3, -2)$, $(2, -6)$, $(-4, 0)$,
$(0, 6)$.

---

* If either of the numbers x or y is imaginary, the corresponding point P cannot be plotted by the methods used in this course. When we are drawing graphs
of equations (as in Art. 1.4), we shall often obtain solutions of the given equation for which at least one of the coördinates x or y is imaginary. Such a solution
does not determine a point on the required graph. Geometric interpretations of
these imaginary solutions will be found in advanced courses in analytic geometry,
but they lie beyond the scope of this book.

Draw the triangle having the given points as vertices:

3. $(5, 1)$, $(2, -2)$, $(3, 5)$.

4. $(2, -1)$, $(7, 2)$, $(4, 6)$.

Draw the triangle and find its area, given that its vertices are:

5. $(-3, 2)$, $(5, 2)$, $(5, 8)$.

6. $(-1, 1)$, $(-1, 7)$, $(4, 3)$.

7. Draw the rectangle and find its area, given that its vertices are: $(7, 3)$, $(-2, 3)$, $(-2, -4)$, and $(7, -4)$.

8. Draw the rectangle and find the coördinates of its fourth vertex, given that three of its vertices are: $(6, 1)$, $(-4, 1)$, and $(6, 7)$.

9. Draw the right triangle and find the length of its hypotenuse, given that its vertices are: $(2, 3)$, $(8, 3)$, and $(8, 11)$.

10. Find the coördinates of the midpoint of each of the three sides of the triangle in Ex. 9.

11. The center of a square is at the origin and its sides are parallel to the coördinate axes. If the length of a side of the square is 6, find the coördinates of its vertices.

12. Find the coördinates of a point that lies 4 units to the right of, and 5 units below, the point $(2, 9)$.

13. What is the locus of a point for which $x = 0$?

14. What is the locus of a point for which $y = 0$?

15. In what quadrant does a point lie (*a*) if both of its coördinates are negative; (*b*) if x is negative and y is positive?

16. What is the locus of a point such that (*a*) $y = 2$; (*b*) $x = -1$?

17. Draw a line through the point $(2, -3)$ parallel to the y-axis. What is the abscissa of any point on this line?

18. Two vertices of an equilateral triangle are $(1, 0)$ and $(3, 0)$. Find the coördinates of the third vertex, given that it lies in the first quadrant.

1.4 The Locus of an Equation. The following two problems are of fundamental importance in the study of analytic geometry: (*a*) given an equation in x and y, to find its locus (or graph), and (*b*) given a locus (defined by a single geometric condition) to find its equation.

Various procedures and devices for dealing with each of these problems will be exemplified as we proceed with this course. In the examples given in the present article, we shall use a very general (but frequently quite laborious) method for dealing with the first of these problems. The second problem will be considered in Art. 2.9.

The locus (or graph) of an equation in x and y is the assemblage of

those points (and no others) whose coördinates satisfy the given equation.
If we have given such an equation,

$$F(x, y) * = 0,$$

we can draw its graph, at least approximately, by assigning values to
x, computing the corresponding values of y from the given equation,
plotting the points whose coördinates have been found in this way,
and drawing a smooth curve through them. Sometimes it is more
convenient to assign values to y and compute the corresponding
values for x. In either case, it may happen that the resulting equation
is difficult to solve.

The points where the graph intersects the axes are usually easier
to determine than any others. The abscissas of the points obtained
by putting $y = 0$ are called the **x-intercepts,** and the ordinates of the
points obtained by putting $x = 0$ are called the **y-intercepts.**

Some methods for drawing approximately the graphs of given
equations will be illustrated by means of the following examples.

Example 1. Draw the graph of the equation $2x + y - 4 = 0$.

We first solve the given equation for one of the variables. In this case,
it is easier to solve for y as a function of x. We find

$$y = 4 - 2x.$$

We now assign to x an arbitrary set of values, substitute each of these
in the above equation, determine the resulting values of y, and make a
table of the corresponding pairs of values, as follows:

x	-2	-1	0	1	2	3	4
y	8	6	4	2	0	-2	-4

The result of plotting on coördinate paper the pairs of values of x and y
from this table is shown in Fig. 1.4a. A smooth curve drawn through these
points represents the required graph (Fig. 1.4b).

The x-intercept is 2 and the y-intercept is 4.

---

* We shall use symbols such as

$$F(x, y), \qquad f(x, y), \qquad G(x, y), \qquad \phi(x, y),$$

and so on, to indicate any expression in x and y.

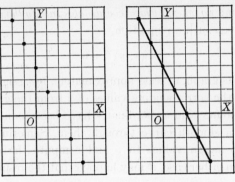

Fig. 1.4a   Fig. 1.4b

It is seen from the figure that the graph of $2x + y - 4 = 0$ is a line.*
It belongs, in fact, to the class of equations of the form

$$Ax + By + C = 0,$$

which, as we shall show in Chapter 3, are the equations of lines.
Equations of this form are called *linear equations.*

Example 2. Draw the graph of $y = x^2 + 2x - 3$.

By tabulating the values of y corresponding to integral values of x from
-4 to $+2$, we have

x	-4	-3	-2	-1	0	1	2
y	5	0	-3	-4	-3	0	5

The graph of the given equation (Fig. 1.5) is represented by plotting
these points and drawing a smooth curve through them.

The graph of the above equation is called a
parabola, a curve we shall study more fully in
Chapter 6.

Notice that the x-intercepts of this graph are
the roots of the quadratic equation

$$x^2 + 2x - 3 = 0.$$

Similarly, if the roots of any given quadratic
equation,

$$ax^2 + bx + c = 0,$$

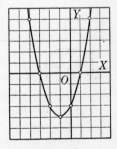

Fig. 1.5

* We shall use the world *line*, throughout, to mean a straight line.

are real, one can find them approximately by drawing the graph of

$$y = ax^2 + bx + c,$$

and measuring the abcissas of the points of intersection of the graph with the x-axis.

Example 3. Draw the graph of $x^2 + y^2 = 25$.

By solving the given equation for y as a function of x, we obtain *

$$y = \pm \sqrt{25 - x^2}.$$

For a given value of x, there are thus two values of y, as shown by the following table:

x	-5	-4	-3	-2	-1	0	1	2	3	4	5
$y = \sqrt{25-x^2}$	0	3	4	$\sqrt{21}$	$2\sqrt{6}$	5	$2\sqrt{6}$	$\sqrt{21}$	4	3	0
$y = -\sqrt{25-x^2}$	0	-3	-4	$-\sqrt{21}$	$-2\sqrt{6}$	-5	$-2\sqrt{6}$	$-\sqrt{21}$	-4	-3	0

The graph is a circle (Fig. 1.6) with center at the origin and radius 5.

In this example, if we had assigned to x values greater than $+5$ or less than -5, $25 - x^2$ would have been negative. By taking the square root of a negative number we would have obtained imaginary values for y, so that no corresponding points could have been plotted. These two sets of values of x for which we get no real values of y, namely $x > 5$ and $x < -5$, are called *excluded intervals.*† They are very useful in determining where the graph of the curve cannot be plotted and will be discussed more fully later in the book.

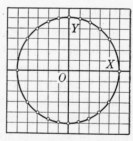

Fig. 1.6

The accuracy of the graph of a given equation can always be increased by increasing the number of values assigned to x and thus

---

* By the symbol $\sqrt{}$, unless preceded by a sign, we shall always mean the *positive* square root of the quantity under the radical.

† The word "interval" will also be used for the following sets of real values of x, where a and b are any two real numbers such that $a < b$: $x \leq a$, $x \geq b$, $a \leq x \leq b$, $a < x \leq b$, $a < x < b$, $a \leq x < b$.

increasing the number of points plotted, assuming, of course, that no errors are made in obtaining these points. It is particularly important to obtain additional points on the curve at places where the form of the curve is not clearly determined by the points already plotted.

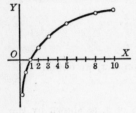

Fig. 1.7

Example 4. Draw the graph of the logarithmic equation $y = \log_{10} x$.

To draw the graph of this equation, we first assign to x any set of positive values we please. The value of y corresponding to each of these values of x may then be found with the aid of a table of logarithms. In this way, we have obtained the following table of coördinates of points on the required curve.

x	0.1	0.5	1	2	3	5	8	10
y	-1	-0.3	0	0.3	0.5	0.7	0.9	1

The graph defined by plotting these points and drawing a smooth curve through them is shown in Figure 1.7. Since the logarithms of negative numbers are imaginary, we see that $x < 0$ is an excluded interval here. This curve is called a *logarithmic curve*. It will be considered further in Art. 10.6.

Since, from the definition of a logarithm, the equation $y = \log_{10} x$ is equivalent to $x = 10^y$, it follows that Fig. 1.7 is also the graph of the exponential equation $x = 10^y$.

1.5 Symmetry. Two points are said to be *symmetric* with respect to a line if that line is the perpendicular bisector of the line segment joining the two points. Hence the two points (x, y) and $(x, -y)$, whose x-coördinates are equal and whose y-coördinates differ only in sign are symmetric with respect to the x-axis. Similarly, the points (x, y) and $(-x, y)$ are symmetric with respect to the y-axis.

We have seen, in Example 3 of the preceding article, that if (x, y) is any point on the graph of the given equation then its symmetric point with respect to the x-axis, $(x, -y)$, also lies on the graph. This circle is thus an illustration of a curve that satisfies the following definition: *any curve possessing the property that the symmetric point, with respect to the x-axis, of every point on it also lies on the curve is said to be symmetric with respect to the x-axis.* Stated in another way, this means that the curve is such that for every point it has above the *x*-axis it also has the mirror image of that point below the *x*-axis with the *x*-axis serving as the mirror.

Similarly, a curve is *symmetric with respect to the y-axis,* if the symmetric point with respect to the *y*-axis of every point on it also lies on the curve. It will be seen from Fig. 1.6 that the circle $x^2 + y^2 = 25$ is also symmetric with respect to the *y*-axis.

It can be shown that: *the graph of an equation is symmetric with respect to the x-axis if an equivalent equation* * *is obtained when y is replaced by — y; and the graph of an equation is symmetric with respect to the y-axis if an equivalent equation is obtained when x is replaced by — x.*

Considerations of symmetry are very helpful in drawing the graphs of given equations. If, for example, the part of the curve that lies above the *x*-axis has been drawn, and if the graph is known to be symmetric with respect to the *x*-axis, then we can locate as many points as we please on the lower half by choosing points on the part already drawn and plotting their symmetrical points with respect to the *x*-axis. Similarly, if the curve is symmetric with respect to the *y*-axis, we first draw the part of it to the right of the *y*-axis, then locate points on it to the left of the *y*-axis by symmetry.

EXERCISES

Draw the graphs of the following linear equations. Determine the intercepts.

1. $y = x$. **2.** $y = x - 3$. **3.** $y = 6 - 2x$.
4. $y + 5 = 0$. **5.** $x = 8$. **6.** $3y + 2x = 6$.
7. $5y + 2x = 10$. **8.** $7y = 3x + 4$. **9.** $3x + 4y + 12 = 0$.

Draw the graphs of the following functions for values of x in the interval indicated. State any symmetries with respect to either axis.

10. $y = x^2 + 4$, $(-3 \text{ to } 3)$. **11.** $y = x^2 - 4$, $(-4 \text{ to } 4)$.
12. $y = x^2 - 2x$, $(-3 \text{ to } 5)$. **13.** $y = x^2 - 2x + 2$, $(-3 \text{ to } 5)$.

---

* Two equations in *x* and *y* are called *equivalent* if exactly the same pairs of values satisfy both equations. For example, multiplying an equation by a non-zero constant or rearranging the terms gives an equivalent equation.

14. $y = x^2 - 3x$, $(-2$ to $5)$.   **15.** $y = x^2 - 3x + 4$, $(-2$ to $5)$.

16. $y = x^3$, $(-3$ to $3)$.   **17.** $y = x^3 - 4x$, $(-3$ to $3)$.

18. $y^2 = 3x$, $(0$ to $12)$.   **19.** $y^2 = 3x + 6$, $(-2$ to $10)$.

20. $y^3 = x^2$, $(-8$ to $8)$.   **21.** $x^2 + y^2 = 16$, $(-4$ to $4)$.

22. $y = x^4$, $(-2$ to $2)$.   **23.** $y = (x^2 - 4)^2$, $(-3$ to $3)$.

24. $y = \cos x$, $(-\pi$ to $\pi)$.   **25.** $y = \sin x$, $(-\pi$ to $\pi)$.

26. $y = \cot x$, $(-\pi$ to $\pi)$.   **27.** $y = \sec x$, $(-\pi$ to $\pi)$.

28. The formula for changing from Centigrade to Fahrenheit thermometer readings is $F = \frac{9}{5}C + 32$. Exhibit this formula graphically and explain the meaning of the intercepts.

★ **1.6 Intersections of Graphs.*** The graphs of the two equations,

$$5x - 3y = 1,$$
$$3x + 2y = 12,$$

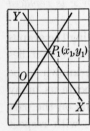

Fig. 1.8

are seen, from Fig. 1.8, to be two lines that intersect in some point P_1. It is required to find the coördinates of this point.

Let the coördinates of P_1 be (x_1, y_1). Since P_1 lies on the graph of the first equation, its coördinates satisfy this equation, that is,

$$5x_1 - 3y_1 = 1;$$

and since it lies on the graph of the second equation, we have similarly,

$$3x_1 + 2y_1 = 12.$$

To find the coördinates of P_1, we, accordingly, solve these two equations as simultaneous. We find

$$x_1 = 2, \quad y_1 = 3,$$

that is, the required intersection is the point $(2, 3)$. This result should be checked by measuring the coördinates of the point of intersection in the figure.

By precisely similar reasoning we find in general that: *to determine the coördinates of the points of intersection of the graphs of any two equations, solve the two equations as simultaneous. The solutions, if there are any, for which x and y are both real, are the coördinates of the points common to the two graphs.*

---

* Articles marked with a ★ may be omitted.

This method of determining the points of intersection of two curves is illustrated by the following examples. The results may be checked, approximately, by measuring the coördinates of the points of intersection of the graphs.

Example 1. Determine the intersections of the graphs of the equations $x - 2y + 2 = 0$ and $x^2 + 4y^2 = 100$.

If we substitute the value of x from the first equation in the second and simplify, we obtain

$$y^2 - y - 12 = 0.$$

The roots of this equation, $y = 4$ and $y = -3$, are the ordinates of the required points of intersection.

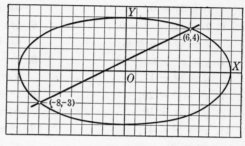

Fig. 1.9

If we substitute these values of y successively in the first of the given equations and solve for x, we find that the required intersections are $(6, 4)$ and $(-8, -3)$.

If we had substituted one of the values of y, as $y = 4$, in the second of the given equations, instead of the first, and solved for x, we would have obtained $x = 6$ and $x = -6$. One of these values of x is correct for the abscissa of a point of intersection but the other is not. The reason for this extraneous value of x, when we attempt to complete the solution in this way, may be seen from the figure. There are two points, $(6, 4)$ and $(-6, 4)$, on the graph of $x^2 + 4y^2 = 100$ that have the ordinate $y = 4$. Only the first of these points lies on the line $x - 2y + 2 = 0$.

Example 2. Find the intersections of the graphs of the equations $x + y = 10$ and $x^2 + y^2 = 16$.

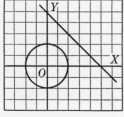

Fig. 1.10

From the figure, we see that the graphs of these equations do not intersect. To determine this algebraically, we solve the two equations simultaneously and obtain $(5 + \sqrt{-17}, 5 - \sqrt{-17})$ and $(5 - \sqrt{-17}, 5 + \sqrt{-17})$ as the solutions. As these values of x and y are imaginary, the corresponding points cannot be plotted and the curves do not intersect.

EXERCISES

Solve the following problems algebraically and check by solving them graphically:

1. $x + y = 5,$
$\qquad 3x - 2y = 5.$

2. $5x + 3y = 7,$
$\qquad 2x - y = 5.$

3. $3x - 2y = 7,$
$\qquad x + 3y = 6.$

4. $2x - 3y - 4 = 0,$
$\qquad 5x + 2y + 9 = 0.$

5. $7x + 5y + 2 = 0,$
$\qquad x + 4y - 3 = 0.$

6. $14x + 3y + 2 = 0,$
$\qquad 4x + 5y + 13 = 0.$

7. $y = x^2 + 4x - 13,$
$\qquad y = 3x - 1.$

8. $2y = x^2 + 7x - 4,$
$\qquad y = 2x + 3.$

9. $x^2 + y^2 = 20,$
$\qquad y = 3x + 10.$

10. $x^2 + y^2 = 13,$
$\qquad 5x + y = 13.$

11. $x^2 + y^2 = 41,$
$\qquad xy = 20.$

12. $x^2 + y^2 = 25,$
$\qquad x^2 + 3y^2 = 57.$

Draw the graphs of the following pairs of equations and show algebraically that the graphs do not intersect:

13. $y = x^2,$
$\qquad y = 2x - 3.$

14. $x^2 + y^2 = 5,$
$\qquad y = x^2 + 7.$

Fundamental Definitions and Theorems

2.1 Directed Line Segments. One important difference between elementary geometry and analytic geometry is that, in the latter, constant use is made of directed line segments. This concept is used in trigonometry in defining the signs of the trigonometric functions (Art. 0.8) and we have encountered it in this course in the definitions of the coördinates of a point; but we shall use it frequently, from now on, for segments not beginning at the origin and on lines lying anywhere in the plane.

If a line segment with end points A and B (Fig. 2.1) is thought of as generated by a point which traverses the line in a definite direction, either from A to B or from B to A, it is called a **directed line segment** for which the direction is that in which the generating point

Fig. 2.1

moves. A **directed line** is one for which it is agreed that the lengths of all segments on it that are directed in one way are to be considered positive and those directed the opposite way are negative. The positive direction on a line is sometimes indicated by an arrow, as in Fig. 2.1.

A thermometer scale offers a familiar example of directed segments on a directed line. If the top of the mercury column rises $10°$ from A to B, we say that the temperature change is $+ 10°$ but, if it falls $10°$, from B to A, the change is $- 10°$.

In Fig. 2.1, let us denote by $\overline{AB}$ and $\overline{BA}$ the lengths of the directed segments from A to B and from B to A, respectively, each with its proper sign.* The length of the undirected segment, we shall denote by AB. It follows from the definition that, in the given figure

$$\overline{AB} = AB, \qquad \overline{BA} = - AB.$$

Hence
$$\overline{BA} = - \overline{AB} \quad \text{or} \quad \overline{AB} + \overline{BA} = 0.$$

Let A, B, and C be any three points on a directed line (Figs. 2.2*a*, *b*, *c*). Then, for all relative positions of these three points, the following relation holds between the directed segments.

$$\overline{AC} + \overline{CB} = \overline{AB}. \tag{1}$$

$$\underset{\text{Fig. 2.2a}}{\overset{A\;\;C\qquad B}{\longrightarrow}} \qquad \underset{\text{Fig. 2.2b}}{\overset{A\qquad B\;\;C}{\longrightarrow}} \qquad \underset{\text{Fig. 2.2c}}{\overset{C\quad A\qquad B}{\longrightarrow}}$$

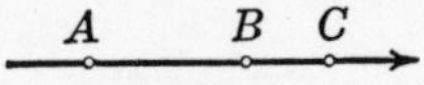

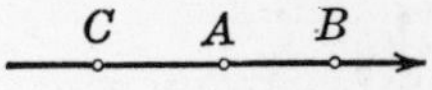

For, if C lies between A and B (Fig. 2.2*a*), the three lengths have the same sign and $\overline{AB}$ equals the sum of the other two. If C lies outside of the segment AB (Figs. 2.2*b* and 2.2*c*), then $\overline{AC}$ and $\overline{CB}$ have opposite signs but their algebraic sum remains equal to $\overline{AB}$.

Let $L_1(x_1, y_0)$ and $L_2(x_2, y_0)$ be any two points on a line parallel to the x-axis and cutting the y-axis at $L(0, y_0)$. From the definition of the coördinates of a point (Art. 1.2), we have

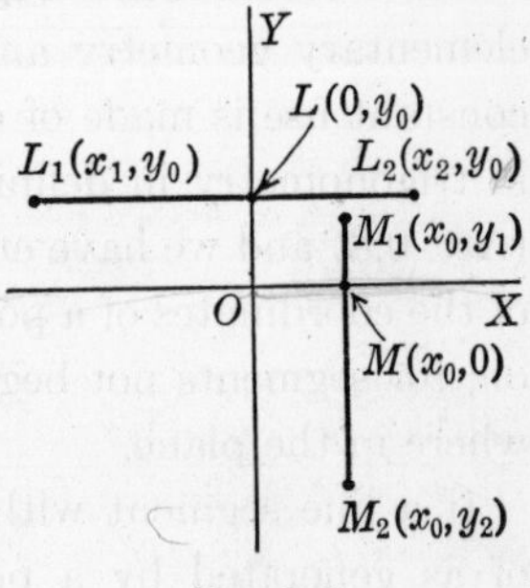

$$\overline{LL_1} = x_1 \quad \text{and} \quad \overline{LL_2} = x_2.$$

Fig. 2.3

Hence from (1),
$$\overline{L_1L_2} = \overline{L_1L} + \overline{LL_2} = - \overline{LL_1} + \overline{LL_2} = - x_1 + x_2$$
or
$$\overline{L_1L_2} = x_2 - x_1, \tag{2}$$

---

* We shall also refer to the directed segments themselves by the symbols $\overline{AB}$ and $\overline{BA}$. The undirected segment will similarly be referred to as the segment AB.

that is, *the length of the directed segment $\overline{L_1L_2}$, on a line parallel to the x-axis, equals the abscissa of L_2 minus the abscissa of L_1.*

Similarly, if $M_1(x_0, y_1)$ and $M_2(x_0, y_2)$ are any two points on a line parallel to the y-axis, we find in exactly the same way that

$$\overline{M_1M_2} = y_2 - y_1, \tag{3}$$

that is, *the length of the directed segment $\overline{M_1M_2}$, on a line parallel to the y-axis, equals the ordinate of M_2 minus the ordinate of M_1.*

One main advantage of the use of directed line segments is that formulas (2) and (3) are valid regardless of the relative positions of the points. These formulas will be used frequently in this and subsequent chapters. Important special cases of (2) and (3) arise when the lines coincide with the axes, that is in (2) when $y_0 = 0$ and in (3) when $x_0 = 0$.

EXERCISES

Find the length of the directed segment $\overline{L_1L_2}$ by using formula (2). Check your result by measurement of your figure.

1. $L_1(2, 0)$, $L_2(8, 0)$.   2. $L_1(-3, 2)$, $L_2(2, 2)$.
3. $L_1(-6, 7)$, $L_2(-1, 7)$.   4. $L_1(10, -3)$, $L_2(4, -3)$.
5. $L_1(1, -1)$, $L_2(-7, -1)$.   6. $L_1(-3, 3)$, $L_2(-7, 3)$.

Find M_1M_2 by using formula (3). Check by measurement of your figure.

7. $M_1(0, -2)$, $M_2(0, 3)$.   8. $M_1(2, 3)$, $M_2(2, 7)$.
9. $M_1(-1, 6)$, $M_2(-1, 3)$.   10. $M_1(4, -8)$, $M_2(4, -6)$.
11. $M_1(3, 5)$, $M_2(3, -1)$.   12. $M_1(-2, -2)$, $M_2(-2, -8)$.

Let the feet of the perpendiculars from P_1 and P_2 on the x-axis be L_1 and L_2, respectively, and on the y-axis be M_1 and M_2, respectively. Find the lengths of the directed segments L_1L_2 and M_1M_2.

13. $P_1(2, 7)$, $P_2(6, 4)$.   14. $P_1(-3, -1)$, $P_2(9, 4)$.
15. $P_1(5, -3)$, $P_2(-1, 2)$.   16. $P_1(-7, 4)$, $P_2(-3, -2)$.
17. $P_1(4, -7)$, $P_2(-3, -4)$.   18. $P_1(x_1, y_1)$, $P_2(x_2, y_2)$.

19. In Ex. 13 and 14, compute the length of P_1P_2 by using the results of these two exercises and the Pythagorean Theorem. Check your results by measurement.

20. Prove formula (1) for all six possible relative positions of the points A, B, C.

2.2 Distance between Two Points. Let $P_1(x_1, y_1)$ and $P_2(x_2, y_2)$ be two given points (Fig. 2.4). Draw the undirected segment P_1P_2. It

is required to find the length of this segment in terms of the coördinates of P_1 and P_2.

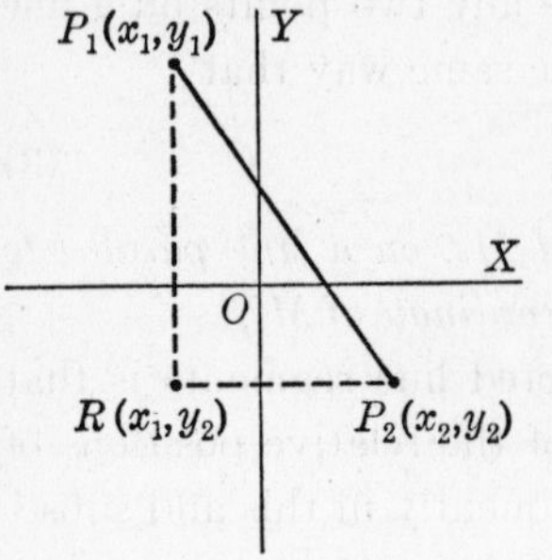

Draw a line through P_1 parallel to the y-axis and a line through P_2 parallel to the x-axis. Call their point of intersection R. Then R has coördinates (x_1, y_2). (Why?)

Since the angle at R is a right angle, we have by the Pythagorean theorem,

Fig. 2.4

$$(P_1P_2)^2 = (RP_2)^2 + (RP_1)^2.$$

But

$$(RP_2)^2 = (\overline{RP_2})^2 = (x_2 - x_1)^2,$$

and

$$(RP_1)^2 = (\overline{RP_1})^2 = (y_2 - y_1)^2.$$

Hence

$$(P_1P_2)^2 = (x_2 - x_1)^2 + (y_2 - y_1)^2,$$

or

$$P_1P_2 = \pm \sqrt{(x_2 - x_1)^2 + (y_2 - y_1)^2}. \tag{4}$$

This formula gives the length of the undirected segment P_1P_2. If a positive direction has been assigned on the line then the sign for the directed distance $\overline{P_1P_2}$ has to be selected accordingly. Thus if $\overline{P_1P_2}$ has the same direction as the assigned direction, then the positive sign would be chosen; otherwise the negative sign would be used.

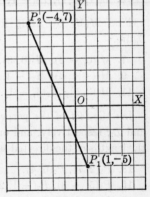

Fig. 2.5

Example 1. Find the undirected distance between the points whose coördinates are $P_1(+1, -5)$ and $P_2(-4, +7)$.

Applying (4) we get:

$$P_1P_2 = \sqrt{(-4 - 1)^2 + (7 - [-5])^2} = \sqrt{5^2 + 12^2}$$
$$= \sqrt{169} = 13.$$

Hence 13 is the undirected distance P_1P_2.

Example 2. State by an equation that the point $P(x, y)$ is equidistant from $P_1(5, -4)$ and $P_2(1, 2)$.

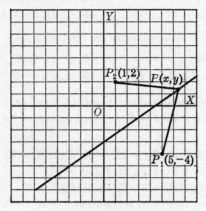

Fig. 2.6

In drawing the figure for this example let $P(x, y)$ be any point on the graph equidistant from P_1 and P_2. Thus we must have $PP_1 = PP_2$. Applying (4) we get:

$$PP_1 = \sqrt{(x - 5)^2 + (y + 4)^2} \text{ and } PP_2 = \sqrt{(x - 1)^2 + (y - 2)^2}$$

Thus we must have

$$\sqrt{(x - 5)^2 + (y + 4)^2} = \sqrt{(x - 1)^2 + (y - 2)^2}$$

Squaring both sides and simplifying, we get:

$$x^2 - 10x + 25 + y^2 + 8y + 16 = x^2 - 2x + 1 + y^2 - 4y + 4$$

$$- 8x + 12y = - 36$$

or

$$2x - 3y = 9$$

for the equation we sought.

EXERCISES

Find the undirected distance between the given points:

1. $(2, 7), (6, 4)$.   **2.** $(-7, -2), (5, 3)$.

3. $(-1, -4), (-9, 2)$.   **4.** $(5, 9), (-3, -6)$.

5. $(4, -6), (-3, -2)$.   **6.** $(8, 1), (3, -1)$.

Find the lengths of the sides of the triangle whose vertices are:

7. $(3, 2), (6, -3), (4, 4)$.   **8.** $(-4, -1), (1, 3), (-2, 1)$.

9. $(5, 6), (1, -2), (-2, 3)$.   **10.** $(-4, 0), (5, 2), (0, 3)$.

Show that the following triangles are isosceles:

11. $(2, 1)$, $(9, 3)$, $(4, -6)$.
12. $(5, -2)$, $(6, 5)$, $(2, 2)$.
13. $(-1, 2)$, $(4, -3)$, $(5, 4)$.
14. $(0, 2)$, $(-1, 4)$, $(-3, 3)$.

Show that the following triangles are right triangles:

15. $(4, 6)$, $(7, 5)$, $(1, -3)$.
16. $(1, 2)$, $(4, 6)$, $(-3, 5)$.
17. $(2, 1)$, $(3, -1)$, $(1, -2)$.
18. $(4, 5)$, $(-3, 9)$, $(1, 3)$.

Each of the following sets of four points are on a line. In each case let the positive direction be from A to B, and then determine the directed distance $\overline{P_1P_2}$.

19. $A(-4, 0)$, $B(0, 3)$, $P_1(-12, -6)$, $P_2(-8, -3)$.
20. $A(3, 2)$, $B(-1, 6)$, $P_1(2, 3)$, $P_2(10, -5)$.
21. $A(-2, -6)$, $B(2, -3)$, $P_1(10, 3)$, $P_2(2, -3)$.
22. Find y, given that $(4, y)$ is equidistant from $(-5, 2)$ and $(13, -6)$.
23. Find the coördinates of a point that is equidistant from $(5, 6)$ and $(1, 8)$ and also from $(-1, 9)$ and $(6, 8)$.
24. Find two points whose ordinates are 4 that lie at a distance 13 from $(3, -1)$.
25. State by an equation that the point (x, y) is equidistant from $(7, -1)$ and $(3, 5)$. What is the graph of this equation?
26. State by an equation that the point (x, y) lies at a distance 3 from $(4, 1)$. What is the graph of this equation?

2.3 Point Dividing a Segment in a Given Ratio. Let $P_1(x_1, y_1)$ and $P_2(x_2, y_2)$ be the end points of the given segment and let $P(x, y)$ be the point of the segment such that

$$\frac{\overline{P_1P}}{\overline{PP_2}} = \frac{n_1}{n_2}$$

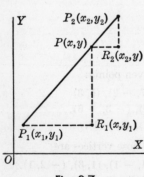

Fig. 2.7

where n_1/n_2 is the given ratio. It is required to determine the coördinates of P in terms of n_1, n_2, and the coördinates of P_1 and P_2.

Draw lines through P and P_2 parallel to the y-axis and lines through P_1 and P parallel to the x-axis. Let their intersections be R_1 and R_2 respectively, as shown in the figure. Then $P_1R_1 = x - x_1$ and $PR_2 = x_2 - x$.

The triangles P_1R_1P and PR_2P_2 are similar. (Why?) Hence we have, both in magnitude and sign,*

$$\frac{n_1}{n_2} = \frac{\overline{P_1P}}{\overline{PP_2}} = \frac{\overline{P_1R_1}}{PR_2} = \frac{x - x_1}{x_2 - x}. \tag{5}$$

From the same similar triangles, we also find that:

$$\frac{n_1}{n_2} = \frac{\overline{P_1P}}{\overline{PP_2}} = \frac{\overline{R_1P}}{R_2P_2} = \frac{y - y_1}{y_2 - y}. \tag{6}$$

If we equate the first and last members of (5) and solve for x, and the first and last members of (6) and solve for y, we obtain

$$x = \frac{n_2x_1 + n_1x_2}{n_1 + n_2}, \quad y = \frac{n_2y_1 + n_1y_2}{n_1 + n_2}, \tag{7}$$

as the coördinates of the point $P(x, y)$ that divides the segment from $P_1(x_1, y_1)$ to $P_2(x_2, y_2)$ in the ratio n_1/n_2.

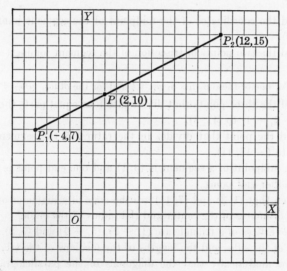

Fig. 2.8

---

* The elementary geometry theorem concerning the proportionality of the corresponding sides of two similar triangles shows only that the ratios of the lengths of these segments are numerically equal. That the signs of these ratios are also equal must be determined independently by considering the directions of the segments in the figure. This difficulty will arise in all cases in which theorems of elementary geometry are applied to directed segments.

In particular, if P is the midpoint of the segment P_1P_2, then $n_1 = n_2$. (Why?) By substituting $n_1 = n_2$ in (7), and simplifying, we find that *the coördinates of the midpoint of the segment P_1P_2 are*

$$x = \frac{x_1 + x_2}{2}, \quad y = \frac{y_1 + y_2}{2}, \tag{8}$$

that is, *the coördinates of the midpoint of a segment are the averages of the coördinates of the end points.*

Example. Find the point that divides the segment from $(-4, 7)$ to $(12, 15)$ in the ratio $\frac{3}{5}$.

Here $n_1 = 3$ and $n_2 = 5$. Thus

$$x = \frac{5(-4) + 3(12)}{3 + 5} = 2 \quad \text{and} \quad y = \frac{5(7) + 3(15)}{3 + 5} = 10.$$

Hence the point is $P(2, 10)$.

EXERCISES

1. Find the coördinates of the midpoint of the segment joining $(1, 6)$ to $(5, -2)$.

2. Find the two points of trisection of the segment joining $(-1, 7)$ to $(5, -2)$.

Note: For one of these points $n_1/n_2 = \frac{1}{2}$ and for the other, $n_1/n_2 = \frac{2}{1}$.

3. Find the three points that divide into four equal parts the segment joining $(-5, -4)$ to $(11, 8)$.

4. Find the point that divides in the ratio 4:5 the segment joining $(10, -7)$ to $(-17, 11)$.

5. The midpoint of a segment is $(3, 1)$ and one end point is $(5, -7)$. Find the other end point.

6. Given that $(1, 3)$ and $(7, 11)$ are the ends of a diameter of a circle, find the coördinates of the center and the radius of the circle.

7. The vertices of a triangle are $(1, -2)$, $(5, -4)$ and $(7, 2)$. Find the midpoints of the sides and the lengths of the medians of the triangle.

8. Show analytically that the diagonals of the parallelogram whose vertices are $(-3, -1)$, $(5, -1)$, $(7, 3)$ and $(-1, 3)$ bisect each other.

9. In what ratio does the point $(5, 1)$ divide the segment from $(-3, -5)$ to $(17, 10)$?

10. The vertices of a triangle are (x_1, y_1), (x_2, y_2), and (x_3, y_3). Find the point on each median twice as far from each vertex as from the midpoint of the opposite side. State the theorem that follows from your results.

11. Show that formula (7) is valid when (*a*) $n_1 = 0$ or $n_2 = 0$ and (*b*) n_1 or n_2 is negative. In (*b*) distinguish between the cases when $n_1 + n_2$ is positive and when it is negative.

2.4 Inclination and Slope of a Line. The **inclination** of a line *l* (not parallel to the *x*-axis) is defined as the smallest positive angle for which the initial side (Art. 0.6) extends in the positive direction along the *x*-axis and the terminal side extends along *l*. If *l* is parallel to the *x*-axis, its inclination is defined to be zero.

The tangent of the angle of inclination is called the **slope** of the line. In analytic geometry, we deal with the slope more frequently than with the inclination.

We shall denote the inclination of a line by α and its slope by m, so that

$$m = \tan \alpha. \tag{9}$$

If the inclination, α, is an acute angle, then tan α, or m, is *positive* and the line extends *upward to the right;* but if α is obtuse, m is *negative* and the line extends *upward to the left.* Finally, if $\alpha = 90°$, so that *l* is perpendicular to the *x*-axis, tan α ceases to exist; that is, *lines perpendicular to the x-axis have no slope.* When we speak of the slope of a line we

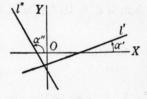

Fig. 2.9

shall suppose, accordingly, that the line is not perpendicular to the *x*-axis.

Care must be taken in order not to confuse the case of lines parallel to the *x*-axis which have zero slope with lines perpendicular to the *x*-axis which have no slope.

2.5 Slope of the Line through Two Given Points. Let $P_1(x_1, y_1)$ and $P_2(x_2, y_2)$ $(x_1 \neq x_2)$ * be the two given points and let *l* be the line that passes through them.

Through P_1 draw a line parallel to the *x*-axis and choose some point *K* on this line to the right of P_1. Denote by ϕ the smallest positive (or zero) angle having the half-line from P_1 through *K* as initial side and the half-line from P_1 through P_2 as terminal side.

---

* The symbol $\neq$ is read "is not equal to."

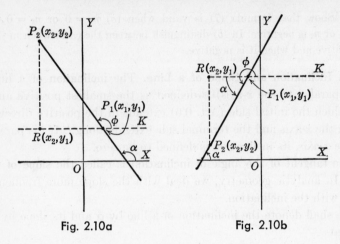

Fig. 2.10a   Fig. 2.10b

If α is the inclination of l, we now have, if $\phi < 180°$ (Fig. 2.10a)

$$\phi = \alpha \qquad \text{(Why?)}$$

but, if $\phi \geqq 180°$ (Fig. 2.10b)

$$\phi = \alpha + 180°. \qquad \text{(Why?)}$$

In either case,

$$\tan \phi = \tan \alpha = m. \qquad (10)$$

From Figs. 2.10a and 2.10b and the definition of the tangent of an angle

$$\tan \phi = \frac{\overline{RP_2}}{\overline{P_1 R}} = \frac{y_2 - y_1}{x_2 - x_1} = \frac{y_1 - y_2}{x_1 - x_2}$$

where the last ratio is obtained from the preceding one by multiplying the numerator and denominator by -1 and rearranging. Thus using (10), the slope m of the line through $P_1(x_1, y_1)$ and $P_2(x_2, y_2)$ is

$$m = \frac{y_2 - y_1}{x_2 - x_1} = \frac{y_1 - y_2}{x_1 - x_2}, \qquad (11)$$

that is, *the slope of the line through two given points equals the difference of the ordinates of the points divided by the difference of the abscissas of the points, the differences being taken in the same order.*

We have supposed throughout this article that $x_1 \neq x_2$. If $x_1 = x_2$, the line is parallel to the y-axis and has no slope (Art. 2.4).

Example. Find the slope and the inclination of the line through (2, 1) and (− 2, 6).

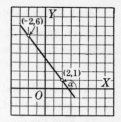

Fig. 2.11

From (11), we find, as the required slope,

$$m = \frac{6 - 1}{-2 - 2} = -\frac{5}{4} = -1.25.$$

To determine the inclination α, we substitute this value of m in (9). We obtain

$$\tan \alpha = -1.25.$$

By trigonometry, we have

$$\tan (180° - \alpha) = -\tan \alpha = 1.25.$$

From the table of tangents on page 270 we find, to the nearest degree,

$$180° - \alpha = 51° \quad \text{or} \quad \alpha = 129°.$$

EXERCISES

A table of the trigonometric functions from 0° to 90° will be found on page 270. If an angle is to be found, find it to the nearest degree.

Find the slope of a line whose inclination is:

1. 30°.   2. 135°.   3. 37°.   4. 108°.
5. $\pi/4$.   6. $\pi/3$.   7. $5\pi/6$.   8. $3\pi/4$.

Find the inclination of a line whose slope is:

9. 1.   10. 0.   11. $-\sqrt{3}$.   12. $-\sqrt{3}/3$.
13. 0.2126   14. 1.8807.   15. -3.4874.   16. -0.4663.

Find the slope and the inclination of the line through the two given points:

17. (3, 1), (5, 6).   18. (2, 4), (− 5, 1).   19. (− 3, − 1), (2, − 5).
20. (1, 2), (− 3, 8).   21. (− 1, 2), (4, 2).   22. (− 1, 6), (1, − 4).
23. (3.648, 1.187), (0.839, 3.361).
24. The vertices of a triangle are (2, − 1), (5, 6) and (7, 2). Find the slopes and inclinations of its sides.
25. Plot the point (3, 2). Find the coördinates of the point 5 units to the right and 3 units above this point. Find, also, the slope of the line through the two points.

Draw through the given point the line having the slope indicated:

26. $(1, 3)$, $m = 1$.

27. $(2, -1)$, $m = \frac{3}{2}$.

28. $(-2, -1)$, $m = -\frac{2}{3}$.

29. $(-1, 4)$, $m = -\frac{5}{2}$.

30. $(-2, 2)$, $m = 2$.

31. $(2, 1)$, $m = -1$.

32. An equilateral triangle has one vertex at the origin, another on the x-axis, and the third in the first quadrant. Find the slopes of its sides.

33. Find the slopes of two of the bisectors of the angles of the triangle in Ex. 32, and show that the third bisector has no slope.

34. Three vertices of a square are $(0, 0)$, $(a, 0)$ and $(0, a)$. Find the co-ordinates of the fourth vertex and the slopes of the diagonals.

35. Express by an equation the condition that the slope of the line through (x, y) and $(-1, 2)$ equals $\frac{3}{2}$.

2.6 Parallel and Perpendicular Lines. Let l_1 and l_2 be two given lines neither of which is parallel to the y-axis.

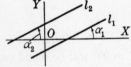

If the lines l_1 and l_2 are parallel to each other, their inclinations, and hence their slopes, are equal. (Why?)

Conversely, if

Fig. 2.12

$$m_1 = m_2, \quad \text{then} \quad \alpha_1 = \alpha_2,$$

and the lines are parallel.

Hence, *the condition that l_1 and l_2 are parallel is that*

$$m_1 = m_2. \tag{12}$$

If the lines l_1 and l_2 are perpendicular, we have either

$$\alpha_2 = \alpha_1 + 90°, \quad \text{(Fig. 2.13}a\text{)}$$

or

$$\alpha_1 = \alpha_2 + 90°. \quad \text{(Fig. 2.13}b\text{)}$$

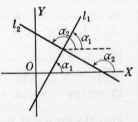

Fig. 2.13a

In either case

$$\tan \alpha_1 = -\cot \alpha_2 = -\frac{1}{\tan \alpha_2};$$

or, since $\tan \alpha_1 = m_1$ and $\tan \alpha_2 = m_2$,

$$m_1 = -\frac{1}{m_2}, \quad \text{or} \quad m_1 m_2 = -1. \tag{13}$$

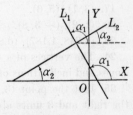

Fig. 2.13b

Conversely, if

$$m_1 = -\frac{1}{m_2}, \text{ then } \tan \alpha_1 = -\frac{1}{\tan \alpha_2} = -\cot \alpha_2,$$

from which it follows that $\alpha_1 = \alpha_2 \pm 90°$ so that the given lines are perpendicular. Hence, *the condition that l_1 and l_2 are perpendicular is that the product of their slopes equals minus one.*

2.7 Angle from One Line to Another. In order to choose a definite one among all the angles formed by two given intersecting lines l_1 and l_2, we make the following definition: *the angle from the line l_1 to the line l_2 is the smallest positive angle through which l_1 must be rotated in order to coincide with l_2. This angle is also called the angle l_2 makes with l_1.*

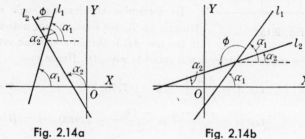

Fig. 2.14a   Fig. 2.14b

If ϕ is this angle, and if m_1 and m_2 are the slopes of l_1 and l_2, respectively, we shall show that

$$\tan \phi = \frac{m_2 - m_1}{1 + m_1 m_2}. \quad ^* \tag{14}$$

We have, in fact,

Case I. If $\alpha_2 > \alpha_1$ (Fig. 2.14a)
$$\alpha_2 = \alpha_1 + \phi. \text{ (Why?)}$$
So that
$$\phi = \alpha_2 - \alpha_1.$$
Hence,
$$\tan \phi = \tan (\alpha_2 - \alpha_1)$$
$$= \frac{\tan \alpha_2 - \tan \alpha_1}{1 + \tan \alpha_1 \tan \alpha_2}.$$

Case II. If $\alpha_1 > \alpha_2$ (Fig. 2.14b)
$$\alpha_1 = \alpha_2 + (180° - \phi). \text{ (Why?)}$$
So that
$$\phi = 180° + \alpha_2 - \alpha_1.$$
Hence,
$$\tan \phi = \tan (180° + \alpha_2 - \alpha_1)$$
$$= \tan (\alpha_2 - \alpha_1)$$
$$= \frac{\tan \alpha_2 - \tan \alpha_1}{1 + \tan \alpha_1 \tan \alpha_2}.$$

---

* If $1 + m_1 m_2 = 0$, this formula should not be used. (Why not?) In this case, it follows from formula (13) of Art. 2.6 that l_1 and l_2 are perpendicular.

Since $\tan \alpha_1 = m_1$ and $\tan \alpha_2 = m_2$, we have, accordingly, in either case,

$$\tan \phi = \frac{m_2 - m_1}{1 + m_1 m_2},$$

which is the required formula (14).

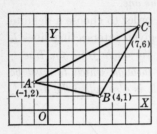

Fig. 2.15

Example. Find, to the nearest degree, the angles of the triangle whose vertices are $A(-1, 2)$, $B(4, 1)$, and $C(7, 6)$.

The slopes m_1, m_2, and m_3, of BC, CA, and AB, respectively, are found by (11) to be

$$m_1 = \tfrac{5}{3}, \quad m_2 = \tfrac{1}{2}, \quad m_3 = -\tfrac{1}{5}.$$

To determine the interior angle of the triangle at A, for example, we notice that, if the line AB is turned about the vertex A through the required angle, it will coincide with AC. Hence

$$\tan A = \frac{\frac{1}{2} + \frac{1}{5}}{1 - \frac{1}{10}} = \frac{7}{9} = 0.7778. \qquad A = \quad 38°$$

Similarly, $$\tan B = \frac{-\frac{1}{5} - \frac{5}{3}}{1 - \frac{1}{3}} = \frac{-14}{5} = -2.8000. \qquad B = 110°$$

and $$\tan C = \frac{\frac{5}{3} - \frac{1}{2}}{1 + \frac{5}{6}} = \frac{7}{11} = 0.6364. \qquad C = \quad \frac{32°}{180°}$$

EXERCISES

Find the angle from the line l_1 to the line l_2, given:

1. $m_1 = \frac{2}{5}$, $m_2 = \frac{3}{2}$.   **2.** $m_1 = 2$, $m_2 = -\frac{3}{2}$.

3. $m_1 = -\frac{4}{3}$, $m_2 = \frac{2}{3}$.   **4.** $m_1 = \frac{5}{2}$, $m_2 = \frac{1}{3}$.

Find the slope of the line l_1, given:

5. $m_2 = \frac{4}{3}$, $\phi = 45°$.   **6.** $m_2 = \frac{2}{3}$, $\phi = \arctan \frac{5}{2}$.

Show by finding the slopes that the three given points lie on a line:

7. $(4, 2)$, $(-2, -1)$, $(6, 3)$.   **8.** $(1, 7)$, $(4, 1)$, $(6, -3)$.

9. Is the line through $(3, 5)$ and $(1, 9)$ parallel to the line through $(5, 8)$ and $(11, -4)$?

10. Show that $(1, -3)$, $(-2, -1)$, $(6, 0)$ and $(3, 2)$ are vertices of a parallelogram and find its acute angle.

11. Show by using the slopes of the sides that $(2, -3)$, $(5, -1)$, $(1, 5)$, and $(-2, 3)$ are the vertices of a rectangle. Find also the acute angle between the diagonals.

12. Show that $(-2, 3)$, $(3, -2)$ and $(2, 5)$ are the vertices of an isosceles triangle and find its equal angles.

Find the angles of the triangle whose vertices are:

13. $(2, -1)$, $(7, 2)$, $(4, 6)$.   **14.** $(-5, 8)$, $(-2, -8)$, $(9, 5)$.

15. $(-3, -2)$, $(7, 1)$, $(-9, 7)$.   **16.** $(4, -5)$, $(7, 2)$, $(2, 6)$.

17. Find y, given that the angle from the line determined by the points $(3, y)$ and $(-1, 2)$ to the line determined by the points $(4, 1)$ and $(-2, 3)$ is $135°$.

18. Discuss what must be done in place of using formulae (12), (13), and (14) when either or both of l_1 and l_2 are parallel to the y-axis.

★ **2.8 Applications to Elementary Geometry.** Many of the theorems of elementary geometry can be proved more easily by the methods of analytic geometry than by those with which the student is already familiar. In this article, we shall show how the formulas derived in this chapter may be used to demonstrate some of these theorems.

In proving geometric theorems analytically one should first draw a figure of the type needed making sure it has no special properties. For example, if the theorem is about a triangle do not draw a right triangle or an isosceles triangle, or if the theorem is about a right triangle be sure it is not an isosceles right triangle. Next, select the coördinate axes in such a way that the computations will be as simple as possible. If, for example, it is known that the figure is a rectangle, we may take the coördinate axes along two adjacent sides, or if it is a triangle, we may take the x-axis through two vertices and the y-axis through the third. When this is done, some of the coördinates will of necessity be zero. To the others, literal values should customarily be assigned, chosen in such a way that they conform to the known facts in the statement of the problem. The process is best illustrated by examples.

Example 1. Prove analytically that the midpoint of the hypotenuse of a right triangle is equidistant from the vertices.

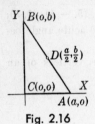

Fig. 2.16

Let ABC be the given triangle with a right angle at C and let the lengths of the legs be $CA = a$ and $CB = b$.

If we choose the line CA as x-axis and CB as y-axis (Fig. 2.16), we find, as the coördinates of the vertices, $C(0, 0)$, $A(a, 0)$, and $B(0, b)$. Let D be the midpoint of AB. By (8), the coördinates of D are $(a/2, b/2)$.

By the distance formula, we now have

$$DC = \sqrt{\left(\frac{a}{2} - 0\right)^2 + \left(\frac{b}{2} - 0\right)^2} = \frac{1}{2}\sqrt{a^2 + b^2},$$

$$DA = \sqrt{\left(\frac{a}{2} - a\right)^2 + \left(\frac{b}{2} - 0\right)^2} = \frac{1}{2}\sqrt{a^2 + b^2},$$

$$DB = \sqrt{\left(\frac{a}{2} - 0\right)^2 + \left(\frac{b}{2} - b\right)^2} = \frac{1}{2}\sqrt{a^2 + b^2}.$$

Hence, $DC = DA = DB$, which proves the theorem.

Example 2. Prove that, if the diagonals of a parallelogram are equal, the figure is a rectangle.

Let $ABCD$ be the given parallelogram. We choose the line AB as x-axis and the line perpendicular to it at A as y-axis. Since we do not know that the angle at A is a right angle, we should not take D as a point on the y-axis. The coördinates of A are $(0, 0)$; of B are $(a, 0)$, where a is the length of the side AB of the parallelogram. Denote the coördinates of D by (b, c); then those of C are $(a + b, c)$. (Why?)

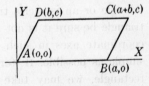

Fig. 2.17

If we equate the expressions for the lengths of the diagonals AC and DB, as found from the distance formula, we obtain

$$\sqrt{(a + b - 0)^2 + (c - 0)^2} = \sqrt{(a - b)^2 + (0 - c)^2}$$

By squaring both sides and simplifying, we find that this equation reduces to $4ab = 0$. But $a \neq 0$, since it is the length of a side of the given parallelogram. Hence $b = 0$, so that D lies on the y-axis, the angle at A is a right angle, and the figure is a rectangle.

EXERCISES

Prove the following theorems analytically:

1. The segment joining the midpoints of two sides of a triangle is parallel to the third side and equal in length to half the third side.

2. If the diagonals of a rectangle are perpendicular to each other, the rectangle is a square.

3. If a median of a triangle is perpendicular to the side it bisects, the triangle is isosceles.

4. Two medians of an isosceles triangle are equal.

5. If two medians of a triangle are equal, the triangle is isosceles.

6. The diagonals of a parallelogram bisect each other.

7. If the diagonals of a trapezoid bisect each other, the figure is a parallelogram.

8. The distance between the midpoints of the non-parallel sides of a trapezoid equals half the sum of the parallel sides.

9. The lines joining the midpoints of successive sides of a rectangle form a rhombus.

10. The lines joining the midpoints of successive sides of any quadrilateral form a parallelogram.

11. The lines joining the midpoints of opposite sides of any quadrilateral bisect each other.

12. The sum of the squares of the four sides of a parallelogram equals the sum of the squares of the diagonals.

13. Three times the sum of the squares of the sides of any triangle equals four times the sum of the squares of the three medians.

Solve the following exercises, taking the coördinate axes without any particular reference to the figure:

14. The theorem of Ex. 1.   **15.** The theorem of Ex. 5.

16. The theorem of Ex. 10.   **17.** The theorem of Ex. 11.

2.9 The Equation of a Locus.

In Art. 1.4, we considered the problem of finding the locus (or graph) of a given equation. In this article, we shall take up the converse problem: given a locus defined by a single geometric condition, find the equation of that locus, that is, find the equation that is satisfied by the coördinates of those points (and no others) that lie on the locus.

To find the equation of the locus, first take a point $P(x, y)$ on the locus.

Next, state, by an equation in the coördinates of $P(x, y)$, the geometric condition that defines the locus. This equation, if stated so that it is satisfied by the coördinates of the points on the locus and no others, is the equation of the locus.

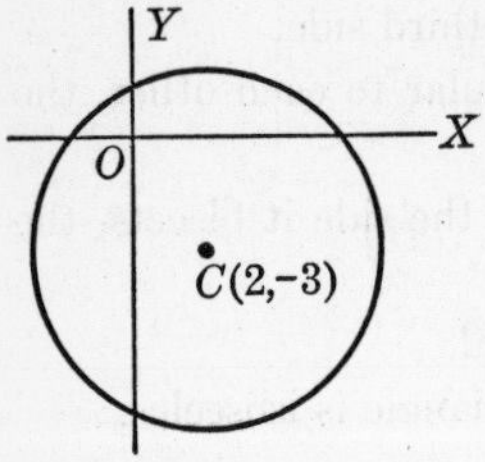

Frequently the equation, as obtained from the geometric definition, can be simplified. Care must be taken, in this process of simplification, that no points of the locus are lost and that no extraneous points are introduced.

Fig. 2.18

Example 1. Find the equation of the circle (Fig. 2.18) with center at $(2, -3)$ and radius 5

By geometry, this circle is the locus of a point $P(x, y)$ whose distance from $(2, -3)$ is equal to 5. Hence by the distance formula, which gives an undirected distance,

$$\sqrt{(x-2)^2 + (y+3)^2} = 5,$$

or

$$(x-2)^2 + (y+3)^2 = 25.$$

This equation may be further simplified to the form

$$x^2 + y^2 - 4x + 6y - 12 = 0.$$

The coördinates of every point on the circle satisfy any one of these equations, and conversely, any point whose coördinates satisfy any one of the equations is at a distance 5 from $(2, -3)$ and lies on the circle. Hence, any one of these equations is an equation of the given circle and no points of the circle have been gained or lost by the process of simplification.

Exercise. Determine the equation of the locus of points for which the sum of the positive square roots of the x- and y-coördinates is 1. Show that if this equation is simplified to remove radicals, points are obtained whose coördinates do not satisfy the given condition.

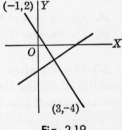

Fig. 2.19

Example 2. Find the equation of the perpendicular bisector of the line segment (Fig. 2.19) joining the points $(-1, 2)$ and $(3, -4)$.

By geometry, this line is the locus of a point $P(x, y)$ whose distance from $(-1, 2)$ is equal to its distance from $(3, -4)$. Hence,

$$\sqrt{(x+1)^2 + (y-2)^2} = \sqrt{(x-3)^2 + (y+4)^2},$$

or $x^2 + y^2 + 2x - 4y + 5 = x^2 + y^2 - 6x + 8y + 25.$

This equation may be simplified to

$$2x - 3y - 5 = 0.$$

This equation is satisfied by the coördinates of every point on the bisector and not by the coördinates of any other point. Hence it is the required equation of the bisector.

Example 3. Find the equation of the line which passes through the point $(1, -2)$ and has the slope $-\frac{2}{3}$.

Let (x, y) be the coördinates of any point on the given locus. By Art. 2.5, the slope of the line through (x, y) and $(1, -2)$ is $\dfrac{y+2}{x-1}$. Since this slope must equal $-\frac{2}{3}$, the required equation is $\dfrac{y+2}{x-1} = -\dfrac{2}{3}$ or $2x + 3y + 4 = 0$. This is the required equation of the line.

Sometimes we shall be able to draw the graph of a given equation by recognizing the equation as the equation of a known locus.

Example 4. Find the locus of the equation $\dfrac{y-3}{x+2} = \dfrac{5}{4}$. The first member of this equation is the slope of the line through the points (x, y) and $(-2, 3)$. Since this slope must equal $\frac{5}{4}$, the required locus is the line through $(-2, 3)$ of slope $\frac{5}{4}$.

Example 5. Find the locus of the equation $(x+2)^2 + (y-7)^2 = 16$.

If we write this equation in the equivalent form

$$\sqrt{(x+2)^2 + (y-7)^2} = 4,$$

we see that its graph is the locus of a point whose distance from $(-2, 7)$ is 4. Hence, the required graph is a circle with center at $(-2, 7)$ and radius 4.

The two forms of the equation are equivalent since the latter form expresses the equality of undirected distances and the former expresses the equality of the squares of these undirected distances.

EXERCISES

Find the equations of the following loci. Simplify the equation whenever possible.

1. A line parallel to the x-axis and passing through $(5, -2)$.

2. A line parallel to the y-axis and passing through $(2, -1)$.

3. A circle with center at the origin and radius 4.

4. A circle with center at $(2, -1)$ and radius 5.

5. A circle with center at the origin and passing through $(-2, 3)$.

6. A circle with center at $(-5, 1)$ and passing through $(-1, 4)$.

7. The perpendicular bisector of the segment joining $(4, 1)$ and $(-2, 3)$.

8. The line through $(2, 4)$ of slope $\frac{3}{2}$.

Hint. Find the slope of the line through (x, y) and $(2, 4)$. Equate this slope to $\frac{3}{2}$.

9. The line through $(-1, 3)$ of slope $-\frac{2}{5}$.

10. The line through $(2, 5)$ of inclination $45°$.

11. The line through $(0, -4)$ of inclination $120°$.

Identify the locus of each of the following equations:

12. $(x - 1)^2 + (y - 3)^2 = 9.$ **13.** $(x - 3)^2 + (y + 2)^2 = 16.$

14. $\sqrt{(x - 1)^2 + (y - 3)^2} = \sqrt{(x - 5)^2 + (y - 7)^2}.$

15. $\sqrt{(x + 2)^2 + (y - 1)^2} = \sqrt{(x - 4)^2 + (y + 5)^2}.$

16. $\dfrac{y - 1}{x - 4} = 3.$ **17.** $\dfrac{y - 5}{x + 1} = -\dfrac{4}{3}.$

18. $y - 2 = 2(x - 3).$

Find the equation of the locus of a point that satisfies the given condition and draw its graph:

19. Its directed distance from the x-axis equals twice its directed distance from the y-axis.

20. The sum of its directed distances from the coördinate axes equals 2.

21. The sum of the squares of its distances from the coördinate axes equals 9.

22. The square of its distance from the origin plus 6 times its directed distance from the x-axis equals zero.

23. Its distance from the origin equals 3 times its distance from $(4, 0)$.

24. Twice its directed distance from the y-axis plus 3 times its directed distance from the x-axis equals 6.

MISCELLANEOUS EXERCISES

1. Find the length of the perimeter of the triangle whose vertices are $(5, 3)$, $(-7, -2)$, and $(5, -2)$.

2. The center of a circle is $(4, 1)$ and one end of a diameter is $(-2, 7)$. Find the coördinates of the other end of this diameter.

3. Show that the triangle whose vertices are $(-3, 3)$ $(1, 9)$ and $(5, 2)$ is isosceles and find the equal angles.

4. Prove in two ways that $P_1(-9, 5)$, $P(6, -5)$ and $P_2(12, -9)$ lie on a line. In what ratio does P divide the segment P_1P_2?

5. Prove in two ways that $(12, 1)$, $(2, 7)$ and $(-7, -8)$ are vertices of a right triangle and find its acute angles.

6. Show that $(2, 1)$, $(6, 4)$, $(3, 8)$ and $(-1, 5)$ are the vertices of a square. Find the coördinates of the center of the square and its area.

7. The diagonals of a square lie on the coördinate axes. The area of the square is 32. Find the vertices.

8. Find the angle from the line through $(4, 2)$ and $(9, 5)$ to the line through $(3, 1)$ and $(1, 7)$.

9. Three vertices of a rectangle are $(9, 3)$, $(5, 9)$ and $(-7, 1)$. Find the fourth vertex and the area of the rectangle.

10. Express by an equation the condition that the line through (x, y) and $(-5, 0)$ is perpendicular to the line through (x, y) and $(5, 0)$. What is the graph of this equation?

11. The center of a regular hexagon is at the origin and one vertex is $(6, 0)$. Find the other vertices.

12. Show analytically that, if the diagonals of a parallelogram are perpendicular to each other, the parallelogram is a rhombus.

13. If D is the midpoint of the side AB of the triangle ABC, show that $AC^2 + BC^2 = 2(CD^2 + AD^2)$.

14. Show that the sum of the squares of the four sides of a quadrilateral equals the sum of the squares of the diagonals plus four times the square of the segment joining the midpoints of the diagonals.

SELECTED EXERCISES

1. Find the coördinates of the center of the circle that passes through the points $P_1(x_1, y_1)$, $P_2(x_2, y_2)$, and $P_3(x_3, y_3)$.

2. Let O be the origin and let $P_1(x_1, y_1)$ and $P_2(x_2, y_2)$ be any two given points in the plane. Find the cosine of the angle P_1OP_2 in terms of the coördinates of P_1 and P_2.

3. In a triangle ABC determine a point D such that angle $DAB =$ angle $DBC =$ angle DCA and a point D' such that angle $D'BA =$ angle $D'CB$ $=$ angle $D'AC$. The points D and D' are called the *Brocard points* of the triangle.

4. If the angle $\omega = XOY$ between the coördinate axes is not a right angle, and if the line through a given point P parallel to OY intersects OX at L (Fig. 2.20) and the one through P parallel to OX intersects OY at

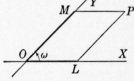

Fig. 2.20

M, then $\overline{OL} = x$ and $\overline{OM} = y$ are called the **Cartesian** (or **oblique**) co-ordinates of P.

Derive the formula for the distance between two points in terms of their Cartesian coördinates.

5. Find the Cartesian coördinates (Ex. 4) of the point $P(x, y)$ that divides the segment from $P_1(x_1, y_1)$ to $P_2(x_2, y_2)$ in the ratio $n_1 : n_2$.

6. If $ABCD$ is a parallelogram and E and F are the midpoints of BC and CD, respectively, show, by using Cartesian coördinates (Ex. 4), that the points on AE and AF that are twice as far from A as from the latter points are the points of trisection of BD.

The Line

3.1 Equation of a Line. The equation of a line is an equation such that (1) the coördinates of every point on the line satisfy the equation and (2) every point whose coördinates satisfy the equation is on the line.

In the applications of analytic geometry, it is necessary that we be able to write the equation of a line whenever enough geometric conditions have been given us to fix its position. This information may be stated to us in any one of a number of ways, but in each instance only two distinct conditions have to be given. For example, we may be given its direction and the position of one point on it, or the position of two of its points. We shall begin this chapter, accordingly, by showing how the equation of a line may be found when its position has been fixed in various ways.

3.2 Lines Parallel to the Axes. If the line is parallel to the y-axis, it meets the x-axis in some point $(a, 0)$. It follows from the definition of the coördinates of a point (Art. 1.2), that the abscissa of any point on the line is $x = a$ and, conversely, that any point that has its abscissa equal to a lies on the given line. (Why?) Hence the equation of any line parallel to the y-axis is

$$x = a. \tag{1}$$

By similar reasoning, we find that the equation of the line parallel to the x-axis that intersects the y-axis at $(0, b)$ is

$$y = b. \tag{2}$$

3.3 The Point-Slope Form. If the line l whose equation is required passes through a given point $P_1(x_1, y_1)$ and has for its slope a given number m, we shall show that its equation is

$$y - y_1 = m(x - x_1). \tag{3}$$

This equation is called the *point-slope form* of the equation of the line.

To show that (3) is the equation of l, we must show that (3) is satisfied by the coördinates of every point that lies on l and that every point whose coördinates satisfy (3) lies on l.

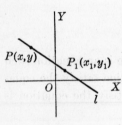

The point P_1 itself lies on l and its coördinates clearly satisfy (3) since, if we assign to x and y the values x_1 and y_1, respectively, both members of the equation are zero.

Next, let $P(x, y)$ be any point on l other than P_1. Then the slope of the line through P_1 and P is m, that is (Art. 2.5)

$$m = \frac{y - y_1}{x - x_1}, \tag{4}$$

Fig. 3.1

or $y - y_1 = m(x - x_1).$

Hence, the coördinates of P satisfy (3).

Conversely, if the coördinates of any point P, other than P_1, satisfy (3), then they also satisfy (4). Hence the slope of the line P_1P is m and P lies on l.

Example. Find the equation of the line through $(2, 1)$ perpendicular to the line through $(-3, -1)$ and $(-1, 2)$.

The slope of the line through $(-3, -1)$ and $(-1, 2)$ is $\frac{3}{2}$. Hence (Art. 2.6) the slope of the required line is $-\frac{2}{3}$ and, since it passes through $(2, 1)$, its equation is

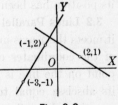

Fig. 3.2

$$y - 1 = -\tfrac{2}{3}(x - 2) \quad \text{or} \quad 2x + 3y - 7 = 0.$$

3.4 The Two-Point Form. If $P_1(x_1, y_1)$ and $P_2(x_2, y_2)$ are two given points on a line, and if $x_1 \neq x_2$, then the slope of the line through these two points is (Art. 2.5)

$$m = \frac{y_2 - y_1}{x_2 - x_1}.$$

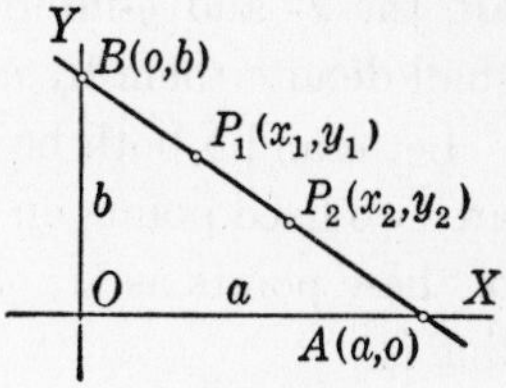

If we substitute this value of the slope in equation (3), we have

$$y - y_1 = \frac{y_2 - y_1}{x_2 - x_1}(x - x_1). \qquad (5)$$

Fig. 3.3

This is the *two-point form* of the equation of a line.

If $x_1 = x_2$, the line through P_1 and P_2 is parallel to the y-axis and its equation is, by Art. 3.2,

$$x = x_1. \qquad (6)$$

If we multiply equation (5) through by $x_2 - x_1$, transpose all the terms to the left-hand member, and simplify, we find that the resulting equation may be written in the following form,

$$\begin{vmatrix} x & y & 1 \\ x_1 & y_1 & 1 \\ x_2 & y_2 & 1 \end{vmatrix} = 0, \qquad (7)$$

as may be seen by expanding this determinant by the rule for evaluating a determinant of the third order (Art. 0.2)

The student should verify that this determinant form for the equation of a line through two given points holds also when $x_1 = x_2$, that is, when the line is parallel to the y-axis.

Example. Find the equation of the line through the intersection of $x + 2y - 4 = 0$, $x - 3y + 1 = 0$ and also through the midpoint of the segment joining $(2, 5)$ and $(4, 3)$.

The point of intersection of the given lines is found, by solving their equations as simultaneous, to be $(2, 1)$ and the midpoint of the given segment, by Art. 2.3, is $(3, 4)$. The equation of the line through these two points is

$$y - 1 = \frac{4 - 1}{3 - 2}(x - 2),$$

or

$$y = 3x - 5.$$

3.5 The Intercept Form. The directed distances $\overline{OA}$ and $\overline{OB}$ (Fig. 3.3) from the origin to the intersections of a line with the axes are the x- and y-intercepts (Art. 1.4), respectively, of the line. We shall denote them by a and b.

Let a and b both be different from zero. Then $A(a, 0)$ and $B(0, b)$ are two fixed points on the line and we find, by taking the coördinates of these points as (x_1, y_1) and (x_2, y_2) in (6), that the equation of this line is

$$y - 0 = \frac{b - 0}{0 - a}(x - a),$$

or

$$-ay = bx - ab.$$

If we rearrange this equation, and divide by ab which, by hypothesis, is different from zero, we obtain

$$\frac{x}{a} + \frac{y}{b} = 1, \tag{8}$$

which is the *intercept form* of the equation of the line.

If $ab = 0$, equation (8) fails. The line then goes through the origin and if it is not the y-axis its equation can be put in the form $y = mx$ where m is the slope. Equation (8) is also not applicable if the line is parallel to either axis (see Art. 3.2).

Example. Find the intercepts of the line $3x - 2y - 12 = 0$ and write its equation in the intercept form.

The x-intercept is found, by putting $y = 0$ and solving for x, to be $a = 4$. Similarly, by putting $x = 0$, we find for the y-intercept $b = -6$. Hence the intercept form of the equation is $\frac{x}{4} + \frac{y}{-6} = 1$.

EXERCISES

Find the equation of the line through the given point having the given slope:

1. $(5, 2)$, $m = 2$.   **2.** $(4, -1)$, $m = \frac{3}{2}$.   **3.** $(-3, 4)$, $m = -2$.
4. $(2, 3)$, $m = -\frac{1}{2}$.   **5.** $(4, 7)$, $m = 0$.   **6.** $(0, -3)$, $m = 2$.

Find the equation of the line through the given point having the given inclination:

7. $(2, 4)$, $\alpha = 45°$.   **8.** $(5, -2)$, $\alpha = 30°$.
9. $(3, 5)$, $\alpha = 3\pi/4$.   **10.** $(2, -2)$, $\alpha = \pi/2$.

Find the equation of the line through the given points:

11. $(2, 3)$, $(4, 7)$.   **12.** $(-3, 2)$, $(1, 5)$.   **13.** $(7, 6)$, $(-5, -2)$.

14. $(7, 1)$, $(-3, 5)$.   **15.** $(2, -5)$, $(-4, 7)$.   **16.** $(7, 3)$, $(-3, 4)$.

17. Find the equation of a line through $(4, -1)$ parallel (a) to the x-axis and (b) to the y-axis.

18. Find the equations of two lines parallel to the y-axis and at a distance from it numerically equal to 2.

19. The equations of the sides of a triangle are $2x - 3y - 7 = 0$, $3x + 2y - 17 = 0$, and $5x - y + 2 = 0$. Find the vertices.

20. Show that the lines $2x - y + 6 = 0$, $4x - 3y + 2 = 0$, and $5x - 2y + 20 = 0$ meet in a point.

21. Find the equation of the line through $(-3, 5)$ and through the intersection of the lines $x - y - 3 = 0$ and $3x + 5y - 17 = 0$.

22. Find the equation of the line through $(7, -2)$ for which the x- and y-intercepts are equal and $\neq 0$.

23. Find the abscissa of a point whose ordinate is 3 that lies on the line through $(2, -7)$ and $(-4, 8)$.

24. Find the equation of a line through $(3, -5)$ whose x-intercept is $\neq 0$ and 3 times its y-intercept.

25. Three vertices of a rectangle are $(1, -3)$, $(-1, -2)$ and $(3, 6)$. Find the equations of the sides and the coördinates of the fourth vertex.

26. The vertices of a parallelogram are $(5, -1)$, $(6, 2)$, $(2, 7)$, and $(1, 4)$. Find the equations (a) of the sides and (b) of the diagonals.

27. The vertices of a triangle are $(-3, 6)$, $(5, 2)$ and $(7, 4)$. Find the equations of the sides.

28. Find the equations of the medians of the triangle in Ex. 27 and find the point at which these medians meet.

29. Find the equations of the altitudes of the triangle in Ex. 27 and find the point at which these altitudes meet.

30. Show analytically that the medians of the triangle whose vertices are $(a, 0)$, $(b, 0)$, and $(0, c)$ meet in a point. This point is called the *centroid* of the triangle.

31. Show analytically that the altitudes of the triangle in Ex. 30 meet in a point.

3.6 The Slope-Intercept Form. If a given line has slope m and y-intercept b then $B(0, b)$ is a given point on the line and we may apply the point slope form (3) to obtain

$$y - b = m(x - 0),$$
or
$$y = mx + b. \tag{9}$$

as the equation of the line. This is called the *slope-intercept form* of the equation of the line.

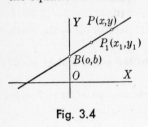

Fig. 3.4

Example. Find the equation of a line whose slope is -2 and whose y-intercept is 6.

The required line is $y = -2x + 6$ or $2x + y = 6$ by direct application of (9).

3.7 The General Form. Linear Equations. Any equation of the form

$$Ax + By + C = 0, \qquad (10)$$

wherein A, B, and C are constants and A and B are not both zero, is an *equation of the first degree in x and y*.

We have seen in Art. 3.6 that, if a line is not parallel to the y-axis, it has an equation $y = mx + b$ and, if it is parallel to the y-axis, it has an equation $x = a$ (Art. 3.2). Both of these equations are of the first degree in x and y. Hence, we have

Theorem I: *Every line has an equation of the first degree in x and y.*

We shall now prove

Theorem II: *Every equation of the first degree in x and y, with real coefficients, is the equation of a line.*

There are two cases, according as $B \neq 0$ or $B = 0$.

If $B \neq 0$, we can solve (10) for y, giving

$$y = -\frac{A}{B}x - \frac{C}{B}. \qquad (11)$$

By Art. 3.6, this is the equation of a line in the slope-intercept form

$$y = mx + b$$

for which the slope and y-intercept have the values

$$m = -\frac{A}{B} \quad \text{and} \quad b = -\frac{C}{B}. \qquad (12)$$

If $B = 0$, then, since A and B are not both zero, we can solve (10) for x, giving

$$x = -C/A.$$

This is the equation of a line parallel to the y-axis (Art. 3.2) having its x-intercept equal to $-C/A$.

Hence, in both cases, (10) is the equation of a line. It is called the **general form** of the equation of a line.

Because of Theorems I and II, equation (10) is also called a *linear equation* in x and y.

Since the equation of every line, except those lines parallel to the y-axis, can be reduced to the form (9), every such line has associated with it two constants, m and b. In order to determine the equation of a line, these two constants, m and b, must be determined. On the other hand to fix the position of a line, two geometric conditions must be given; for example, two points on the line, or one point and the slope. The number of geometric conditions is exactly the same as the number of constants to be determined in the equation. Normally each given geometric condition can be used to determine an equation in m and b.

For the lines parallel to the y-axis the two geometric conditions determining the line are, first, that it is parallel to the y-axis and, second, that it has a fixed directed distance from the y-axis. Algebraically, referring back to (10), these conditions are expressed by the equations $B = 0$ and $-C/A = a$, where a is the directed distance from the y-axis. Using these conditions, (10) reduces to $x = a$.

Example 1. Determine the equation of the line through the points $(2, 2)$ and $(3, 1)$.

Since the coördinates $(2, 2)$ must satisfy the equation of the line we must have

$$2 = 2m + b.$$

Similarly for $(3, 1)$ we must have

$$1 = 3m + b.$$

Solving these two equations for m and b we obtain $m = -1$ and $b = 4$. Thus the required line is $y = -x + 4$.

From equations (11) and (12), we obtain the following useful result: *If the equation of a line is solved for y, the coefficient of x is the slope and the constant term is the y-intercept.*

Example 2. Given the line $3x + 4y - 24 = 0$. Find its slope and its intercepts and reduce its equation to the slope-intercept and to the intercept form.

We first solve the equation for y, giving

$$y = -\tfrac{3}{4}x + 6.$$

This is the slope-intercept form. From it we obtain at once $m = -\tfrac{3}{4}$ and $b = 6$. To find a, we put $y = 0$ and solve for x. We obtain $x = 8$. Hence

$$\frac{x}{8} + \frac{y}{6} = 1$$

is the intercept form of the equation of the given line.

3.8 The Linear Function. An expression of the form

$$mx + b, \qquad m \neq 0$$

is called a *linear function* of x.

To find the graph of a linear function, we equate it to y and plot the graph of the resulting equation. We thus find that *the graph of a linear function is a line.*

In the applications of mathematics, two variable quantities are often related in such a way that a change of a given amount in one produces a proportional change in the other. Under such circumstances, the second is a linear function of the first.

Example. An automobile, traveling at a constant rate of 40 miles per hour, has gone 100 miles by noon. Express the distance traveled as a function of the time after noon and draw the graph.

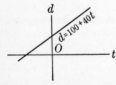

Fig. 3.5

We have

$$d = 100 + 40t$$

where d is the distance traveled in miles and t is the time in hours.

The graph of d, as a function of t, is given in Fig. 3.5. In drawing this graph, we have used a different scale on the d-axis to indicate miles than we have used on the t-axis to indicate hours. In the applications, it is often desirable to use different scales in this manner in order to produce a satisfactory graph.

EXERCISES

Find the equation of the line, given:

1. $m = 2, b = 4.$ **2.** $m = \tfrac{3}{2}, b = \tfrac{5}{6}.$

3. $m = 0, b = -3.$ **4.** $m = -\tfrac{4}{5}, b = -\tfrac{3}{5}.$

Write each of the given equations in the slope-intercept form and in the intercept form:

5. $2x + 3y = 6$.   **6.** $5x - 2y + 10 = 0$.   **7.** $4x - 3y - 5 = 0$.

Find the slopes and the intercepts of the given lines:

8. $4x + 3y = 12$.   **9.** $3x + 2y = 12$.

10. $4x - 5y = 40$.   **11.** $3x - 5y + 15 = 0$.

12. $9x - 6y + 13 = 0$.   **13.** $7x + 2y + 9 = 0$.

14. Find the equation of the line through $(8, 2)$ parallel to the line

$$2x - 3y + 7 = 0.$$

15. Find the equation of the line through $(-2, 5)$ perpendicular to the line $3x + 4y - 17 = 0$.

Find the equations of the lines through the given point parallel and perpendicular, respectively, to the given line:

16. $(4, 1)$, $x + 2y - 9 = 0$.   **17.** $(2, -1)$, $3x - 8y - 5 = 0$.

18. $(3, 2)$, $3x - 9y + 7 = 0$.   **19.** $(-1, -3)$, $2x + 5y - 11 = 0$.

20. $(2, 3)$, $3x + 4y = 8$.   **21.** $(5, -2)$, $5x - 3y + 2 = 0$.

Find the angle from the first of the given lines to the second:

22. $3x - 2y + 1 = 0$, $2x + y - 3 = 0$.

23. $4x + y - 6 = 0$, $x + 2y - 1 = 0$.

24. $3x + 5y + 2 = 0$, $x - 2y + 1 = 0$.

25. $7x - 4y + 8 = 0$, $2x - 6y + 9 = 0$.

26. Given the line $3x - 2y + 6 = 0$. Find its slope, its y-intercept, and the ordinate of the point on the line whose abscissa is 4.

27. Show that $7x - 5y - 43 = 0$, $7x - 5y + 105 = 0$, $5x + 7y - 73 = 0$, and $5x + 7y + 1 = 0$ are the equations of the sides of a rectangle and find the coördinates of the vertices.

28. The equations of two sides of a parallelogram are $3x + 8y + 4 = 0$ and $4x - 5y + 7 = 0$. Find the equations of the other two sides, given that $(-3, 4)$ is a vertex. Find also the acute angle of the parallelogram.

29. Two opposite vertices of a rectangle are $(6, 2)$ and $(-5, 4)$. Two sides of the rectangle are parallel to the line $8x - 6y + 5 = 0$. Find the equations of the four sides and the coördinates of the other two vertices.

30. Find the slope of a line in terms of its intercepts a and b.

31. Find the equation of a line whose x-intercept is a and whose slope is m.

32. The ends of a diagonal of a square are $(0, 0)$ and $(2a, 0)$. Find the equations of the sides.

33. Draw the graph of the linear function $5x + 30$. For what value of x is the function equal to -10? For what values of x is it positive?

34. Express the amount due at the end of N years on \$240 at 5% simple interest.

35. An iron bar, one meter long at 0° C., expands 0.012 millimeters for every degree centigrade rise in temperature. A certain bar is 1.6 meters long at 0° C. Express its length as a function of the temperature. How long would it be if immersed in boiling water (100° C.)?

36. Show that the condition that the lines $Ax + By + C = 0$ and $A'x + B'y + C' = 0$ are parallel is $AB' - BA' = 0$.

37. Show that the condition that the lines in Ex. 36 are perpendicular is $AA' + BB' = 0$.

38. Show that, if $C' \neq C$, the lines $Ax + By + C = 0$ and $Ax + By + C' = 0$ are parallel.

39. Show that the lines $Ax + By + C = 0$ and $Bx - Ay + C' = 0$ are perpendicular.

40. Show that the equations $Ax + By + C = 0$ and $A'x + B'y + C' = 0$ determine the same line if, and only if, $A:B:C = A':B':C'$.

3.9 The Normal Form. Let l (Fig. 3.6) be the given line. Draw through O a line ON perpendicular to l and let ω be the *inclination*

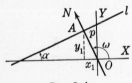

of this perpendicular. From Art. 2.4, we have, $0° \leqq \omega < 180°$. We shall consider ON as a directed line, its positive direction being that of the terminal half-line of ω.

Fig. 3.6

Let $A(x_1, y_1)$ be the intersection of ON with l and denote the length of the directed segment OA by p. Then p is positive if A lies above O and negative if it lies below.

From the definitions of $\sin \omega$ and $\cos \omega$, we find that

$$x_1 = p \cos \omega, \qquad y_1 = p \sin \omega.$$

Let m be the slope of l. Since ON is perpendicular to l, we have

$$m = -\cot \omega.$$

If we substitute these values of x_1, y_1, and m in the point slope equation (3) of a line, we have

$$y - p \sin \omega = -\cot \omega (x - p \cos \omega).$$

In this equation, we replace cot ω by its value $\cos \omega/\sin \omega$ and multiply through by $\sin \omega$. We thus obtain

$$y \sin \omega - p \sin^2 \omega = - x \cos \omega + p \cos^2 \omega,$$

or $\qquad x \cos \omega + y \sin \omega - p(\sin^2 \omega + \cos^2 \omega) = 0,$

that is $\qquad\qquad \boldsymbol{x \cos \omega + y \sin \omega - p = 0.}$ $\qquad$ (13)

This is the *normal form* of the equation of a line. Its importance arises chiefly from the fact (which we shall prove in Art 3.11) that, whenever we are required to determine the distance from a line to a point, we shall need the equation of the line in the normal form.

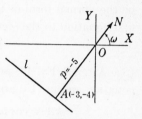

Example 1. Find the normal form of the equation of the line through $A(-3, -4)$ perpendicular to the line through A and the origin.

Draw the line ON through O and A. From **Fig. 3.7**

Fig. 3.7, ω is an acute angle and OA, or p, is negative. Hence we have

$$p = - \sqrt{(-3)^2 + (-4)^2} = -5, \quad \sin \omega = \frac{-4}{-5} = \frac{4}{5},$$

$$\cos \omega = \frac{-3}{-5} = \frac{3}{5},$$

and the required equation is

$$\frac{3x}{5} + \frac{4y}{5} + 5 = 0.$$

Fig. 3.8

Example 2. Two lines of inclination $60°$ lie at a distance from the origin numerically equal to 10. Find their equations in the normal form.

From Fig. 3.8 we find $\omega = 60° + 90° = 150°$, so that $\sin \omega = \sin 150° = \frac{1}{2}$ and $\cos \omega = \cos 150° = -\sqrt{3}/2$. For one of the required lines, $p = 10$ and, for the other, $p = -10$. Hence the required equations are

$$-\frac{\sqrt{3}}{2}x + \frac{1}{2}y - 10 = 0 \quad \text{and} \quad -\frac{\sqrt{3}}{2}x + \frac{1}{2}y + 10 = 0.$$

Exercise. Show that the derivation of equation (13) given in the text fails if l is parallel to the y-axis but that equation (13) still holds for these lines also.

3.10 Reduction of the Equation of a Line to the Normal Form.

Let
$$Ax + By + C = 0 \tag{14}$$

be the equation of a line and let

$$x \cos \omega + y \sin \omega - p = 0 \tag{15}$$

be the normal form of the equation of the same line. To reduce the first equation to the second, we multiply it by a constant k

$$kAx + kBy + kC = 0, \tag{16}$$

(See Art. 3.8, Ex. 40) and determine k so that the coefficients in this equation and in (15) are equal, that is,

$$kA = \cos \omega, \qquad kB = \sin \omega, \qquad kC = -p. \tag{17}$$

If we square the members of the first two of equations (17) and add, we obtain

$$k^2 A^2 + k^2 B^2 = \cos^2 \omega + \sin^2 \omega = 1.$$

If we solve this equation for k, we find that

$$k = \frac{1}{\pm \sqrt{A^2 + B^2}}. \tag{18}$$

To determine the sign of the radical, we note that, since $0° \leqq \omega < 180°$, $\sin \omega$ is always positive or zero. Hence, by the second equation of (17), if $B \neq 0$, k and B have the same signs. If, however, $B = 0$, then $\sin \omega = 0$, so that $\omega = 0$, $\cos \omega = 1$ and k agrees in sign with A.

If we substitute the value of k from (18) in (16), we obtain, as the normal form of the equation of the line defined by (14),

$$\frac{A}{\pm \sqrt{A^2 + B^2}} x + \frac{B}{\pm \sqrt{A^2 + B^2}} y + \frac{C}{\pm \sqrt{A^2 + B^2}} = 0, \tag{19}$$

where the signs before the radicals agree with that of B if $B \neq 0$, and with that of A if $B = 0$.

Hence, *to reduce the equation of a line to the normal form, divide each term by* $\pm \sqrt{A^2 + B^2}$, *choosing the sign before the radical so as to make the coefficient of y positive if B ≠ 0, and the coefficient of x positive if B = 0.*

Example. Reduce the equation $x - 3y - 7 = 0$ to the normal form and find the values of ω and p.

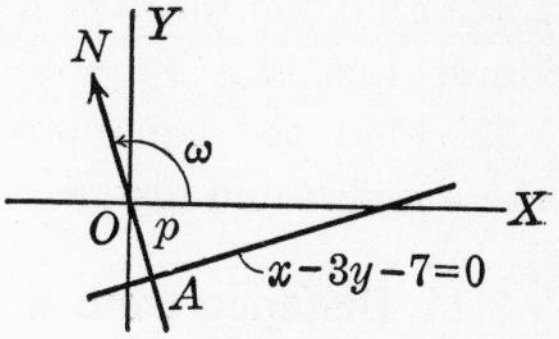

Since $B = -3 < 0$, divide each term by

$$-\sqrt{1^2 + (-3)^2} = -\sqrt{10}.$$

The required equation is thus found to be

Fig. 3.9

$$\frac{-x}{\sqrt{10}} + \frac{3y}{\sqrt{10}} + \frac{7}{\sqrt{10}} = 0.$$

By comparing this equation with the normal form (13), we find

$$\cos \omega = -\frac{1}{\sqrt{10}}, \qquad \sin \omega = \frac{3}{\sqrt{10}}, \qquad p = -\frac{7}{\sqrt{10}}.$$

Since ω lies in the second quadrant, we find by the aid of the tables, $\omega = 108°$.

EXERCISES

Write the equation of the given line in the normal form:

1. $\omega = 60°, p = 5$.
2. $\omega = 135°, p = -2$.
3. $\omega = 0°, p = -4$.
4. $\omega = 5\pi/6, p = 3$.
5. $\omega = \pi/4, p = -2$.
6. $\omega = \pi/2, p = 7$.
7. $\alpha = 150°, p = 5$.
8. $\alpha = 60°, p = 7$.
9. $\alpha = \pi/4, p = -6$.

Write the equations of the following lines in the normal form and find the values of ω and p:

10. $4x + 3y + 20 = 0$.
11. $15x - 8y + 34 = 0$.
12. $3x - 3y - 10 = 0$.
13. $2x + 5y - 58 = 0$.
14. $4x + 7 = 0$.
15. $3y - 5 = 0$.

Write the equation of a line in the normal form given that its intercepts are:

16. $a = 5, b = 12$.   17. $a = 6, b = -6$.   18. $a = 5, b = 4$.
19. Find the equation of the line through $(7, -2)$ for which (a) $\omega = 135°$, and (b) $\omega = \pi/6$.

20. Find the equation of the line through $(24, -7)$ perpendicular to the line joining this point to the origin.

21. Find the directed distance from the line $3x + 4y - 15 = 0$ to the parallel line $3x + 4y - 35 = 0$.

22. Find the equations of the lines parallel to $5x - 12y - 60 = 0$ whose undirected distances from this line are (a) 5 and (b) 3.

3.11 Distance from a Line to a Point. Let $P_1(x_1, y_1)$ be the given point and let the normal form of the equation of the given line be

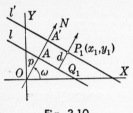

$$x \cos \omega + y \sin \omega - p = 0,$$

where $p = \overline{OA}$ (Fig. 3.10).

If l' is the line through P_1 parallel to l, we may write its equation in the normal form

$$x \cos \omega + y \sin \omega - p' = 0, \quad \text{(Why?)}$$

Fig. 3.10

where $p' = \overline{OA'}$.

Since P_1 lies on l', its coördinates satisfy this equation, that is,

$$x_1 \cos \omega + y_1 \sin \omega - p' = 0. \tag{20}$$

Let Q_1 be the foot of the perpendicular from P_1 on l and let us choose the positive direction on the line through Q_1 and P_1 to agree with that on ON. Then we have, for the required distance d,

$$d = \overline{Q_1P_1} = \overline{AA'} = \overline{OA'} - \overline{OA} = p' - p.$$

If we substitute for p' in this equation its value from (20), we have

$$d = x_1 \cos \omega + y_1 \sin \omega - p, \tag{21}$$

that is, *to find the distance from a line to a point, substitute the coördinates of the point in the left-hand member of the normal form of the equation of the line. The resulting number is the required distance.*

The distance d, or $\overline{Q_1P_1}$, determined by (21), is a directed distance. It is positive if $\overline{Q_1P_1}$ agrees in direction with the positive direction on ON and it is negative in the contrary case. Thus d is positive if P_1 is above the line and negative if P_1 is below the line.

If the equation of the line is given in the general form

$$Ax + By + C = 0$$

and we wish to find the distance of the point $P_1(x_1, y_1)$ from it, we first reduce the equation of the line to the normal form,

$$\frac{Ax + By + C}{\pm \sqrt{A^2 + B^2}} = 0,$$

and then substitute the coördinates of P_1 in the left-hand member. The result is

$$d = \frac{Ax_1 + By_1 + C}{\pm \sqrt{A^2 + B^2}}, \tag{22}$$

where the sign before the radical agrees with that of B if $B \neq 0$, and agrees with that of A if $B = 0$.

Example. Find the distance from the line $2x - y - 4 = 0$ to each of the points $P_1(-1, -2)$, $P_2(5, 0)$, and $P_3(3, 5)$.

We first reduce the given equation to the normal form by dividing both sides of the equation by $-\sqrt{2^2 + (-1)^2} = -\sqrt{5}$. The result is

$$\frac{2x - y - 4}{-\sqrt{5}} = 0.$$

By substituting the coördinates of the given points in the left-hand member of this equation, we find as the required distances

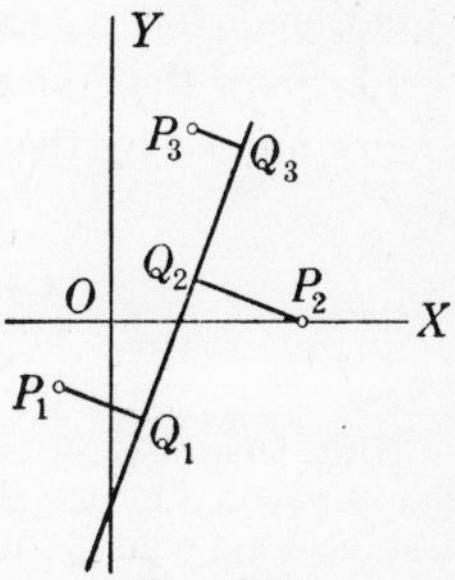

Fig. 3.11

$$d_1 = \frac{4}{\sqrt{5}}, \qquad d_2 = -\frac{6}{\sqrt{5}}, \qquad d_3 = \frac{3}{\sqrt{5}}.$$

Since d_1 and d_3 are positive and d_2 is negative, the points P_1 and P_3 lie above the line and P_2 lies below it (Fig. 3.11).

EXERCISES

Find the directed distance from the given line to the given point and state whether the point lies above or below the line:

1. $(8, 4)$, $5x + 12y - 36 = 0$.   2. $(2, 1)$, $4x - 3y + 10 = 0$.
3. $(4, 3)$, $15x - 8y + 15 = 0$.   4. $(7, 3)$, $2x - 3y - 9 = 0$.
5. $(2, -13)$, $2x + 5y + 3 = 0$.   6. $(4, -2)$, $5y + 7 = 0$.

7. Do the points $(3, 7)$ and $(5, 16)$ lie on the same side of the line $3x - 2y + 12 = 0$?

8. Show that $(-3, 4)$ lies between the parallel lines $2x + y - 5 = 0$ and $6x + 3y + 11 = 0$.

9. Find the equation of the locus of a point whose distances from the parallel lines in Ex. 8 are numerically equal but opposite in sign. What is this locus?

Find the undirected distance between the parallel lines:

10. $3x - 4y + 20 = 0$, $3x - 4y - 10 = 0$.
11. $\sqrt{3}x + y - 8 = 0$, $\sqrt{3}x + y - 14 = 0$.
12. $5x + 3y - 6 = 0$, $10x + 6y - 11 = 0$.
13. $x - 2y + 4 = 0$, $2x - 4y + 19 = 0$.
14. Find the radius of the circle with center at $(3, 7)$ that is tangent to the line $5x - 12y + 4 = 0$.
15. Write the equation of the locus of a point whose directed distance from $4x - 3y + 7 = 0$ is (a) 6, (b) -4. What is the locus of each of these equations?
16. Show that the equations of the lines that bisect the pairs of vertical angles formed by the lines $A_1x + B_1y + C_1 = 0$ and $A_2x + B_2y + C_2 = 0$ are

$$\frac{A_1x + B_1y + C_1}{\sqrt{A_1^2 + B_1^2}} = \pm \frac{A_2x + B_2y + C_2}{\sqrt{A_2^2 + B_2^2}}.$$

Hint. One bisector is the locus of the points whose distances from the given lines are equal in magnitude and sign; the other is the locus of the points whose distances are equal in magnitude but opposite in sign.

Using the formula of Ex. 16, find the equations of the bisectors of the pairs of vertical angles formed by the given lines:

17. $3x + 2y - 9 = 0$, $2x + 3y + 4 = 0$.
18. $7x - y + 3 = 0$, $x + y - 3 = 0$.

Find the bisector of that pair of vertical angles formed by the given lines in which the given point lies:

19. $(8, -2)$; $x + y - 9 = 0$, $x + 7y - 3 = 0$.
20. $(3, 9)$; $4x - 3y + 12 = 0$, $3x + 4y - 18 = 0$.
21. $(1, -1)$; $x + 2y + 4 = 0$, $11x - 2y - 10 = 0$.
22. $(-1, 1)$; $4x + 3y + 5 = 0$, $3x - 4y - 2 = 0$.
23. Find the equations of the bisectors of the angles of the triangle whose sides are $9x - 2y - 5 = 0$, $2x - 9y + 16 = 0$, and $7x + 6y - 59 = 0$.
24. Find the coördinates of the center and the radius of the circle inscribed in the triangle given in Ex. 23.

3.12 The Area of a Triangle. Let $P_1(x_1, y_1)$, $P_2(x_2, y_2)$, and $P_3(x_3, y_3)$ be the vertices of a triangle. If we consider the side P_2P_3 as the base, the length of the base is, by the distance formula,

$$b = \sqrt{(x_2 - x_3)^2 + (y_2 - y_3)^2}.$$

To find the altitude, we first find the equation of the line through P_2 and P_3. By equation (5), Art. 3.4, this is

$$(y_2 - y_3)x - (x_2 - x_3)y + x_2y_3 - y_2x_3 = 0.$$

The altitude, h, is the distance of P_1 from this line. Hence,

$$h = \frac{(y_2 - y_3)x_1 - (x_2 - x_3)y_1 + x_2y_3 - y_2x_3}{\pm \sqrt{(x_2 - x_3)^2 + (y_2 - y_3)^2}}.$$

For the area, we have $S = \frac{1}{2}bh$. Replace b and h by their values just given. We have

$$S = \pm \tfrac{1}{2}(x_1y_2 - x_1y_3 - x_2y_1 + x_3y_1 + x_2y_3 - x_3y_2).$$

This formula is more easily remembered if it is written as a determinant, as follows,

$$S = \pm \tfrac{1}{2} \begin{vmatrix} x_1 & y_1 & 1 \\ x_2 & y_2 & 1 \\ x_3 & y_3 & 1 \end{vmatrix}. \tag{23}$$

The sign should be chosen so as to make S positive.

Exercise. Obtain the equation of the line through two given points, $P_1(x_1, y_1)$ and $P_2(x_2, y_2)$, in the form given in equation (7), Art. 3.4, by imposing the condition that the area of the triangle whose vertices are (x, y), (x_1, y_1), and (x_2, y_2) is equal to zero.

EXERCISES

Find the area of the triangle whose vertices are the given points:

1. $(2, 5)$, $(5, 9)$, $(7, 3)$.   **2.** $(6, 1)$, $(7, 5)$, $(3, 7)$.
3. $(-5, 6)$, $(5, -7)$, $(7, 9)$.   **4.** $(5, 4)$, $(7, -3)$, $(3, 1)$.
5. $(-4, -1)$, $(-6, 2)$, $(8, -3)$.   **6.** $(1, 6)$, $(-2, 7)$, $(-8, -1)$.
7. $(-4, -3)$, $(1, 4)$, $(-3, 5)$.   **8.** $(2, 1)$, $(5, 4)$, $(3, -5)$.

Show by areas that the given points lie on a line, and check by finding the slopes:

9. $(3, 9)$, $(6, 4)$, $(15, -11)$.   **10.** $(1, -4)$, $(5, 3)$, $(13, 17)$.

11. Express by an equation that the area of the triangle whose vertices are (x, y), $(4, 1)$ and $(2, 5)$ is zero. What is the locus of this equation?

12. Find x, given that the area of the triangle whose vertices are $(x, 5)$, $(2, 1)$, and $(4, 7)$ equals 10. (Two solutions).

3.13 Families of Lines. Parameters. If, in the equation

$$3x + 5y + k = 0, \qquad (24)$$

we substitute for k any real number we please, we determine a line. For example, if we put $k = 10$, we obtain

$$3x + 5y + 10 = 0$$

which is the equation of a line; and similarly for any other real value we may assign to k (Fig. 3.12).

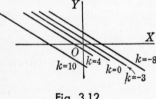

Fig. 3.12

All the lines that can be determined by substituting values for k in (24) are parallel since their slopes all equal $-\frac{3}{5}$. Moreover, by substituting a suitable value for k in (24), we can obtain the equation of any given line of slope $-\frac{3}{5}$. Equation (24) is, consequently, called the equation of the *family* of lines of slope $-\frac{3}{5}$ and k is the *parameter* of the family.

More generally, if the coefficients in the equation of a line contain a quantity k such that, by letting k run through all possible values, we obtain a whole system of lines satisfying some geometric condition, then we say that the given equation defines a **family** of lines and that k is the **parameter** of the family.

For our purposes, the importance of the consideration of families of lines lies in the fact that, if the required line is known to belong to a given family, we may first

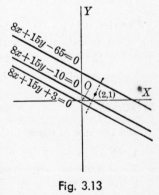

Fig. 3.13

write the equation of this family and then find from the conditions of the problem the value of k that fixes the required line. The following examples will indicate the procedure.

Example 1. Find the equations of the lines parallel to $8x + 15y - 10 = 0$ that lie at a distance from $(2, 1)$ numerically equal to 2.

The equation of the family of lines parallel to the given line is

$$8x + 15y + k = 0.$$

Since we have to do with the distance from this line to a point, we first reduce its equation to the normal form

$$\frac{8}{17}x + \frac{15}{17}y + \frac{k}{17} = 0.$$

The condition that the distance from this line to $(2, 1)$ is equal to ± 2 is now found, by substituting the coördinates of $(2, 1)$ in the left-hand member of the above equation and equating the result to ± 2, to be $\dfrac{31 + k}{17}$ $= \pm 2$. Hence $k = 3$ or $k = -65$ and the required lines are

$$8x + 15y + 3 = 0 \quad \text{and} \quad 8x + 15y - 65 = 0.$$

Example 2. Find the line perpendicular to $x + 2y - 4 = 0$ that passes through $(4, 1)$.

The equation of the family of lines perpendicular to $x + 2y - 4 = 0$ is $y = 2x + k$. (Why?)

To determine the value of k which gives the particular line of the family containing the point $(4, 1)$, we substitute the coördinates of this point in the equation of the family and solve for k. We obtain $1 = 2 \cdot 4 + k$ or $k = -7$. The equation of the required line is, accordingly, $y = 2x - 7$.

Example 3. Find the equations of the lines through $(6, -1)$ for which the product of the intercepts equals 3.

Let a and b be the intercepts. From the statement of the problem, $ab = 3$, or $b = 3/a$. If we substitute this value of b in the intercept form $\dfrac{x}{a} + \dfrac{y}{b} = 1$ of the equation of a line, we obtain

$$\frac{x}{a} + \frac{ay}{3} = 1 \quad \text{or} \quad a^2y + 3x - 3a = 0.$$

This is the equation of the family of lines for which the product of the intercepts is equal to 3.

The condition that a line of this family passes through $(6, -1)$ is that the coördinates of this point satisfy the equation of the family, that is, that $-a^2 - 3a + 18 = 0$. Hence $a = 3$ or $a = -6$ and, by substituting these values of a in the equation of the family, we obtain as the equations of the required lines

$$x + 3y - 3 = 0 \quad \text{and} \quad x + 12y + 6 = 0.$$

3.14 Family of Lines through the Intersection of Two Given Lines. If

$$A_1x + B_1y + C_1 = 0 \quad \text{and} \quad A_2x + B_2y + C_2 = 0$$

are the equations of two intersecting lines, then we shall show that the coördinates of their point of intersection satisfy the equation

$$A_1x + B_1y + C_1 + k(A_2x + B_2y + C_2) = 0 \qquad (25)$$

for *all* values of k. For, the coördinates of the point of intersection satisfy both of the given equations (Why?) and hence, when substituted in (25), reduce this equation to $0 + k \cdot 0 = 0$ which is true for all values of k.

Moreover, (25) is of first degree in x and y and thus, by Art. 3.7, defines a line for all real values of k. It is the equation of the *family of lines through the intersection of the given lines.* Its importance lies in the fact that it enables us to find the equation of a line through the point of intersection of two given lines without ever actually determining the coördinates of this point.

Example. Find the equation of the line through the intersection of $8x - 2y + 3 = 0$ and $5x + 10y + 17 = 0$ that makes an angle of $135°$ with the x-axis.

It is unnecessary actually to find the point of intersection. Instead, we proceed as follows: The required line belongs to the family

$$8x - 2y + 3 + k(5x + 10y + 17) = 0,$$

or $\qquad (8 + 5k)x + (-2 + 10k)y + 3 + 17k = 0.$

The slope of the required line is $\tan 135°$ or -1, so that

$$-\frac{8 + 5k}{-2 + 10k} = -1$$

or $\qquad 8 + 5k = 10k - 2.$

On solving, we find that $k = 2$, so that the required equation is

$$8x - 2y + 3 + 2(5x + 10y + 17) = 0 \quad \text{or} \quad 18x + 18y + 37 = 0.$$

EXERCISES

Write the equations of the following families of lines. Assume, in each case, four values for the parameter and draw the corresponding lines.

1. Having $\alpha = 60°$.

2. Having $\omega = 3\pi/4$.

3. With y-intercept -2.

4. With x-intercept -7.

5. Of slope $\frac{3}{4}$.

6. Passing through $(-1, 2)$.

7. Parallel to $x = 2y$.

8. Perpendicular to $2x = 3y$.

9. Having the sum of its intercepts equal to zero.

10. Having its y-intercept greater by 1 than its x-intercept.

11. Passing through the intersection of $5x - 3y + 11 = 0$ and $2x - 9y + 7 = 0$.

12. Having its slope equal to its y-intercept.

13. Tangent to the circle with center at the origin and radius 3.

Draw four lines of each of the following families of lines and state a geometric property common to all the lines of each family:

14. $y = 3x + b$.

15. $ax + y = a^2$.

16. $y = b$.

17. $x \cos 30° + y \sin 30° - p = 0$.

18. $y - 2 = m(x - 5)$.

19. $x \cos \omega + y \sin \omega \pm 6 = 0$.

20. $x - y + k(3x + 5y - 11) = 0$.

21. Find the line of the family in Ex. 18 that is (*a*) parallel and (*b*) perpendicular to $3x + y - 7 = 0$.

22. Find the line of the family in Ex. 20 that passes through the midpoint of the segment joining $(-1, 5)$ and $(3, 3)$.

23. Find two lines of the family in Ex. 19 of inclination $\pi/4$.

24. Find two lines of the family in Ex. 15 that pass through $(1, 6)$.

3.15 Factorable Equations. The equation $x^2 - 4y^2 = 0$ may be written in the equivalent form

$$(x - 2y) \cdot (x + 2y) = 0.$$

The coördinates of a point will satisfy this equation if, and only if, they make one of the factors of the left-hand member equal to zero.* It follows that the graph of this equation consists of the two lines

$$x - 2y = 0 \quad \text{and} \quad x + 2y = 0.$$

---

* It is an axiom of algebra that the product of two numbers is zero if, and only if, one of the numbers is equal to zero.

Similarly, we may write the equation $x^2y + xy^2 + 3xy = 0$ in the equivalent form

$$x \cdot y \cdot (x + y + 3) = 0$$

from which it follows that the given equation is satisfied by the coördinates of those points, and no others, that lie on the lines

$$x = 0, \quad y = 0, \quad \text{and} \quad x + y + 3 = 0.$$

The graph of the given equation thus consists of these three lines.

EXERCISES

Draw the graphs of the following equations:

1. $(x - 1)(y + 3) = 0$.   **2.** $25x^2 - 4y^2 = 0$.

3. $x^2 - xy - 6y^2 = 0$.   **4.** $9(x - 1)^2 - y^2 = 0$.

5. $x^2 - 4xy + 4y^2 = 9$.   **6.** $(x + 2y)^2 - 3x - 6y = 0$.

7. $x^2 + 2xy + y^2 + 2x + 2y = 0$.

8. $x^2 + xy - 2y^2 + 3x + 6y = 0$.

Write a single equation whose graph is the two given lines:

9. $2x + 3y = 0, 2x - 3y + 5 = 0$.

10. $x + 2y + 3 = 0, 2x - 5y - 1 = 0$.

11. Explain the fallacy of the following statement. The graph of the equation $xy = 1$ consists of the two lines $x = 1$ and $y = 1$.

MISCELLANEOUS EXERCISES

1. Find the equation of a line inclined to the x-axis at an angle of $45°$ and having its y-intercept equal to 3.

2. Find the intercepts of the line through $(6, 2)$ and $(1, -8)$.

3. Find the intercepts of the line through $(1, -6)$ having its slope equal to 3.

4. Write the equation of the locus of a point equidistant from $(3, -1)$ and $(5, 7)$.

5. Find the point P on the y-axis equidistant from $(-2, 1)$ and $(6, 3)$. Find also the interior angle at the vertex P of the isosceles triangle formed by these three points.

6. Find the equations of the lines through the origin and the points of trisection of the segment joining $(1, -9)$ and $(7, 15)$.

7. Find the equation of the locus of a point whose directed distance from $5x - 12y - 9 = 0$ is 4.

8. Find two points on the y-axis at a distance 6 from $4x - 3y + 6 = 0$.

9. Find the equation of the locus of a point whose directed distances from $8x + y - 5 = 0$ and $14x - 8y + 11 = 0$ are numerically equal but opposite in sign.

Find the equation of the family of lines:

10. Passing through $(5, -2)$.

11. Perpendicular to $11x - 3y + 21 = 0$.

12. Whose distances from $(0, 3)$ are numerically equal to 4.

13. Passing through the intersection of $x - y - 2 = 0$ and $5x + 7y + 2 = 0$.

14. Having the y-intercept $\neq 0$ and equal to -5 times the x-intercept.

15. Having the sum of the directed distances from it to $(-3, 0)$ and $(3, 0)$ equal to zero.

16. Find the line of the family in Ex. 13 that is parallel to $3x + 5y - 1 = 0$.

17. Find the equations of two lines of inclination 45° whose undirected distances from $(1, 3)$ are equal to $4\sqrt{2}$.

18. Find two lines parallel to $3x + 4y - 1 = 0$ whose undirected distances from the origin are equal to 2.

19. Find a point whose directed distances from $x + y - 5 = 0$ and $7x - y + 5 = 0$ are equal and whose directed distances from $8x - y + 9 = 0$ and $4x + 7y - 3 = 0$ are equal but opposite in sign.

20. Find the lengths of the altitudes of the triangle whose sides are $4x + 3y + 11 = 0$, $4x - y - 9 = 0$, and $4x - 3y + 5 = 0$.

21. Find the area of the triangle whose vertices are $(3, -5)$, $(-2, 7)$, and $(-5, 3)$ by finding the length of one side and the length of the perpendicular from the third vertex to that side. Check by the formula of Art. 3.12.

22. The equal sides of an isosceles triangle lie on $2x + y - 3 = 0$ and $11x - 2y - 8 = 0$. Find the equation of the third side given that it passes through $(3, 5)$. (Two solutions.)

23. A triangle has a right angle at $(-2, 5)$. The hypotenuse lies on $x - 5y + 1 = 0$ and one end point is at $(4, 1)$. Find the other end point.

24. Two vertices of a rectangle are $(1, 4)$ and $(-6, -5)$. Two sides are parallel to $3x + 2y = 0$. Find the equations of all the sides.

25. The equations of two sides and the diagonal of a parallelogram are $5x + 2y - 1 = 0$, $x + 2y - 13 = 0$, and $x - 6y + 19 = 0$, respectively. Find the coördinates of the vertices and the equations of the other two sides.

26. The ends of one side of a square are $(-2, -4)$ and $(4, -1)$. Find the other two vertices given that they lie above the side joining the given points.

SELECTED EXERCISES

1. Find the coördinates of the foot of the perpendicular from (x_1, y_1) on the line $Ax + By + C = 0$. Derive the formula for the distance from the given line to the given point as the distance between these two points.

2. Show that, if $B^2 - 4AC > 0$, the equation $Ax^2 + Bxy + Cy^2 = 0$ defines two lines through the origin. Find the condition that these two lines are perpendicular.

3. Find the equation of a family of lines such that the directed distances of any line of the family from two given points are (*a*) equal, (*b*) equal but opposite in sign.

4. Show analytically that, in any triangle, the following sets of three lines meet in a point (*a*) the altitudes, (*b*) the medians, (*c*) the perpendicular bisectors of the sides.

5. Show that the three points defined in Ex. 4 lie on a line and find the ratio in which the intersection of the medians divides the segment joining the other two points.

6. Show that, if the algebraic sum of the distances from any line to the vertices of a triangle is zero, then the centroid of the triangle lies on the line, and conversely.

7. Let $A_1x + B_1y + C_1 = 0$, $A_2x + B_2y + C_2 = 0$, and $A_3x + B_3y + C_3 = 0$ be the equations of three lines. Show that these lines meet in a point or are parallel if, and only if, $\begin{vmatrix} A_1 & B_1 & C_1 \\ A_2 & B_2 & C_2 \\ A_3 & B_3 & C_3 \end{vmatrix} = 0.$

8. Discuss all cases arising in the algebraic solution of

$$\begin{cases} A_1x + B_1y = C_1 \\ A_2x + B_2y = C_2 \end{cases} \text{ where } \begin{vmatrix} A_1 & B_1 \\ A_2 & B_2 \end{vmatrix} = 0.$$

Interpret each case geometrically.

The Circle

4.1 Equation of a Circle in Terms of Its Center and Radius. A circle is defined as the locus of a point that moves so that its distance from a fixed point, the center, is equal to a constant, the radius.

To find the equation of a circle from its definition, we let $C(h, k)$ be its center and let a be the radius. If $P(x, y)$ is any point on the circle, the expression for its distance from $C(h, k)$ is

$$\sqrt{(x - h)^2 + (y - k)^2}$$

and, since this distance is equal to a, we have, as the equation of the circle,

$$\sqrt{(x - h)^2 + (y - k)^2} = a \qquad (1)$$

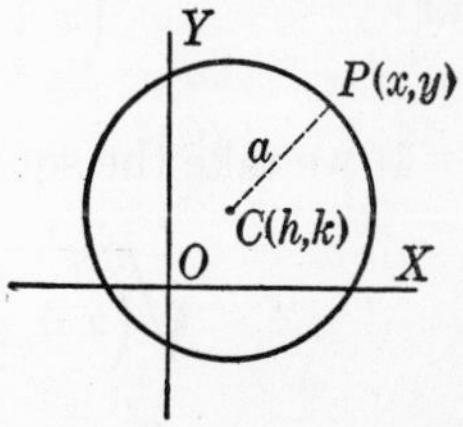

or

$$(x - h)^2 + (y - k)^2 = a^2. \qquad (2)$$

Fig. 4.1

Conversely, if the coördinates of a point $P(x, y)$ satisfy (2) they also satisfy (1) so that the distance between P and C is equal to a and P lies on the circle. Equation (2) is thus the *equation of the circle with center $C(h, k)$ and radius a.*

In particular, if h and k are both equal to zero, equation (2) reduces to

$$x^2 + y^2 = a^2 \qquad (3)$$

which is the equation of the circle in the important special case when the center of the circle lies at the origin.

4.2 General Form of the Equation of a Circle. If we expand equation (2), we obtain

$$x^2 + y^2 - 2hx - 2ky + h^2 + k^2 - a^2 = 0. \tag{4}$$

This equation is of the form

$$x^2 + y^2 + Dx + Ey + F = 0 \tag{5}$$

so that every circle has an equation of the form (5).

We now wish to find out whether, conversely, every equation of the form (5) is the equation of a circle. For this purpose, we rewrite (5) in the equivalent form

$$(x^2 + Dx \quad) + (y^2 + Ey \quad) = \quad - F$$

and complete the squares in the two parentheses by adding $\dfrac{D^2}{4}$ and $\dfrac{E^2}{4}$ to both sides of the equation. We now have

$$\left(x^2 + Dx + \frac{D^2}{4}\right) + \left(y^2 + Ey + \frac{E^2}{4}\right) = \frac{D^2}{4} + \frac{E^2}{4} - F,$$

or

$$\left(x + \frac{D}{2}\right)^2 + \left(y + \frac{E}{2}\right)^2 = \frac{D^2 + E^2 - 4F}{4}.$$

If we take the square root of both sides of this equation, we obtain

$$\sqrt{\left(x + \frac{D}{2}\right)^2 + \left(y + \frac{E}{2}\right)^2} = \frac{1}{2}\sqrt{D^2 + E^2 - 4F}. \tag{6}$$

The left-hand member of (6) is the formula for the distance of the point (x, y) from the point $(- D/2, - E/2)$ and the right-hand member is a constant. The appearance of the graph of the equation is accordingly found to depend on the value of the quantity $D^2 + E^2 - 4F$, as follows:

(a) If $D^2 + E^2 - 4F > 0$, the right-hand member of (6) is real and greater than zero, so that the locus of (6), and hence of (5), is a circle with

Center $(- D/2, - E/2)$ and radius $\frac{1}{2}\sqrt{D^2 + E^2 - 4F}$. (7)

(b) If $D^2 + E^2 - 4F = 0$, the graph of the given equation reduces to a single point, the center $(-D/2, -E/2)$. In this case, (5) is said to define a **point circle,** or **circle of zero radius.**

(c) If $D^2 + E^2 - 4F < 0$, there can be no points on the graph since neither $(x + D/2)^2$ nor $(y + E/2)^2$ can be negative. In this case, (5) is said to define an **imaginary circle,** with the center and radius defined by (7).

If the definition of a circle is extended as in (b) and (c), equation (5) defines a circle for all real values of D, E, and F. It is called the **general form** of the equation of a circle. It is often a more convenient form to work with than equation (2) is, because the coefficients enter in it to the first power only.

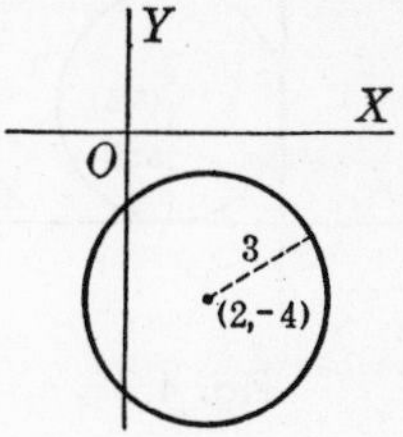

Example 1. Find the center, the radius, and the co-ordinates of the intersections with the axes, of the circle $x^2 + y^2 - 4x + 8y + 11 = 0$.

Fig. 4.2

To complete the squares in the left-hand member, we first write the equation in the form

$$(x^2 - 4x \quad) + (y^2 + 8y \quad) = \quad -11.$$

Inside the parentheses, the coefficients of x^2 and y^2 are unity. Hence these expressions become perfect squares by adding the square of half the coefficient of x and of y, respectively. On making these additions, we obtain

$$(x^2 - 4x + 4) + (y^2 + 8y + 16) = 4 + 16 - 11$$

or
$$(x - 2)^2 + (y + 4)^2 = 9.$$

The given equation thus defines a circle with center $(2, -4)$ and radius 3.

To find the intersections with the x-axis, put $y = 0$ and solve for x.

We have
$$x^2 - 4x + 11 = 0.$$

Hence
$$x = 2 \pm \sqrt{-7}.$$

Since these values of x are imaginary, the curve does not intersect the x-axis (Fig. 4.2).

Similarly, on putting $x = 0$, we obtain

$$y^2 + 8y + 11 = 0$$

so that
$$y = -4 \pm \sqrt{5}.$$

Hence the intersections with the y-axis are $(0, -4 + \sqrt{5})$ and $(0, -4 - \sqrt{5})$.

Example 2. Find the equation of the circle of radius 5 that lies in the first quadrant and is tangent to both axes.

Since the distance from the center of a circle to a tangent is numerically equal to the radius, the coördinates of the center of the required circle are (5, 5) (Fig. 4.3), and its equation is, from (2),

$$(x - 5)^2 + (y - 5)^2 = 5^2$$

or $$x^2 + y^2 - 10x - 10y + 25 = 0.$$

To verify that the circle defined by this equation is tangent to the x-axis, we put $y = 0$ in the final equation, giving

$$x^2 - 10x + 25 = 0.$$

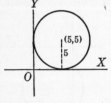

Fig. 4.3

Since the roots of this equation are equal, the circle is tangent to the x-axis. The point of tangency is found, by solving the above equation, to be (5, 0).

The corresponding discussion for the y-axis is left as an exercise for the student.

EXERCISES

Write the equation of the circle with the given point as center and the given radius:

1. $(4, 1)$, radius 3.   2. $(5, -3)$, radius 6.
3. $(-4, 3)$, radius 5.   4. $(-3, -3)$, radius 3.
5. $(5, -2)$, radius 5.   6. $(\frac{7}{2}, \frac{3}{2})$, radius 3.

Write the equation of the circle having the given point as center and satisfying the given condition:

7. $(12, -5)$, through $(0, 0)$.   8. $(2, -6)$, through $(-6, 9)$.
9. $(-4, 7)$, tangent to $x = 0$.   10. $(-5, -3)$, tangent to $y = 0$.
11. $(-4, -2)$, tangent to $5x + 12y + 5 = 0$.
12. $(5, -7)$, tangent to $3x - y + 8 = 0$.

Find the center and radius and state whether the circle is a real circle, a point circle or an imaginary circle. Draw the circle if it exists.

13. $x^2 + y^2 + 6x - 12y + 20 = 0$.   14. $x^2 + y^2 + 12x - 6y + 9 = 0$.
15. $x^2 + y^2 - 8x + 6y + 25 = 0$.   16. $x^2 + y^2 + 12x - 4y - 5 = 0$.
17. $x^2 + y^2 + 7x + 3y - 10 = 0$.   18. $x^2 + y^2 - 6x - 2y + 14 = 0$.
19. $2x^2 + 2y^2 - 5x - 9y + 11 = 0$. 20. $5x^2 + 5y^2 - 6x + 2y - 3 = 0$.

21. Find the points in which the circle in Ex. 13 intersects the y-axis. Does it intersect the x-axis?

22. Find the points in which the line $x - y + 8 = 0$ intersects the circle in Ex. 13.

23. Find the points in which the line $3x - y + 5 = 0$ intersects the circle in Ex. 16.

24. Write the equation of a circle having $(4, -5)$ and $(6, 1)$, as ends of a diameter.

25. Find the points of intersection of the circles $x^2 + y^2 - 2x + 18y - 87 = 0$ and $x^2 + y^2 + 2x - 2y - 11 = 0$.

26. Find the equation of a circle passing through $(1, -5)$ and concentric with $x^2 + y^2 - 8x + 4y - 5 = 0$.

Find the equation of the family of circles:

27. With center at the origin.

28. With center at $(-2, 3)$.

29. Having the same center as $x^2 + y^2 + 4x + 8y - 5 = 0$.

30. With center on $y = x + 1$ and passing through $(0, 0)$.

4.3 Circle Determined by Three Conditions. Each of the standard forms of the equation of a circle

$$(x - h)^2 + (y - k)^2 = a^2 \quad \text{and} \quad x^2 + y^2 + Dx + Ey + F = 0$$

contains three constants. Thus to determine the equation of a circle we must be able to determine these three constants. This means that we must have three conditions from which we can get three equations to determine these constants. We can, for example, determine the constants if we know that the circle passes through three given points, or that it passes through two known points and that its center lies on a given line, and so on.

In any given problem, we must first decide which of the above two standard forms of the equation of the circle to use. If the coördinates of the center and the radius can be determined conveniently from the statement of the problem, it is usually best to find these numbers and substitute them in the first standard form. In most other cases, it is easier to use the general form of the equation of the circle, since the constants D, E, and F enter in this equation to the first power only.

Example 1. Find the equation of the circle through the points $(5, 3)$, $(6, 2)$, and $(3, -1)$.

In problems of this type, we shall use the general form (5).

To find D, E, and F, we impose the condition that the coördinates of each of the given points satisfy the equation of the circle, that is,

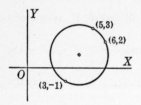

Fig. 4.4

$$25 + 9 + 5D + 3E + F = 0,$$
$$36 + 4 + 6D + 2E + F = 0,$$
$$9 + 1 + 3D - E + F = 0.$$

On solving these equations for D, E, and F, we find that

$$D = -8, \qquad E = -2, \qquad F = 12.$$

When these values of D, E, and F are substituted in equation (5), we have, as the required equation of the circle through the given points,

$$x^2 + y^2 - 8x - 2y + 12 = 0.$$

Example 2. Find the equations of the circles that pass through $(-1, 1)$ and $(1, 3)$ and are tangent to the line $x + 3y = 0$.

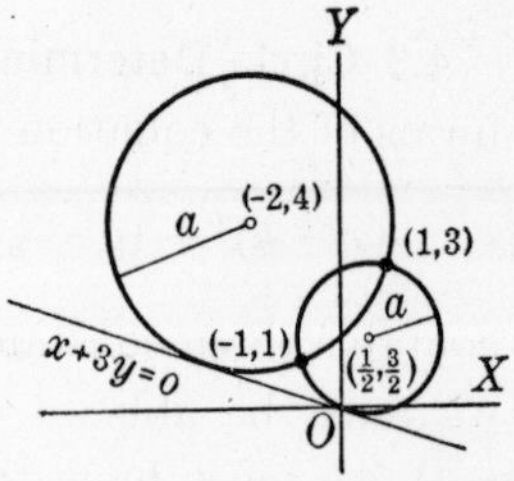

In this case, we shall use equation (2).

Since the coördinates of each of the given points satisfy the equation of the circle, we have

$$(-1 - h)^2 + (1 - k)^2 = a^2$$

and

$$(1 - h)^2 + (3 - k)^2 = a^2.$$

Since the distance from the center to the given tangent line is numerically equal to the radius, we have also

$$\frac{h + 3k}{\sqrt{10}} = \pm a.$$

Fig. 4.5

By subtracting the second equation from the first, and simplifying, we obtain

$$h + k - 2 = 0. \tag{8}$$

If we substitute the value of a from the third equation in the first, and simplify, we have

$$9h^2 - 6hk + k^2 + 20h - 20k + 20 = 0. \tag{9}$$

On solving (8) and (9) as simultaneous and substituting the resulting solutions in the first of the above equations to find a, we obtain

$$h = -2, \; k = 4, \; a = \sqrt{10},$$

and
$$h = \frac{1}{2}, \; k = \frac{3}{2}, \; a = \frac{\sqrt{10}}{2}.$$

By substituting these sets of values of h, k, and a in (2), we obtain, as the equations of the required circles,

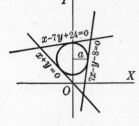

Fig. 4.6

$$(x + 2)^2 + (y - 4)^2 = 10,$$
and $\quad (x - \frac{1}{2})^2 + (y - \frac{3}{2})^2 = \frac{5}{2},$
or $\quad x^2 + y^2 + 4x - 8y + 10 = 0,$
and $\quad x^2 + y^2 - x - 3y = 0.$

Example 3. Find the equation of the circle inscribed in the triangle formed by the lines $x + y = 0$, $\;x - 7y + 24 = 0$, $\;$ and $\;7x - y - 8 = 0$.

The distance from each of the sides of the triangle to the center is numerically equal to the radius a. To find this distance, we first write the equation of each side in the normal form

$$\frac{x + y}{\sqrt{2}} = 0, \quad \frac{x - 7y + 24}{-5\sqrt{2}} = 0, \quad \frac{7x - y - 8}{-5\sqrt{2}} = 0.$$

It is seen from the figure that the center lies above the first and third sides and below the second, hence

$$a = \frac{h + k}{\sqrt{2}} = -\frac{h - 7k + 24}{-5\sqrt{2}} = \frac{7h - k - 8}{-5\sqrt{2}}. \tag{10}$$

On solving these equations, we find $h = 0$, $k = 2$, $a = \sqrt{2}$. Hence the equation of the required circle is

$$x^2 + (y - 2)^2 = 2,$$
or $\quad x^2 + y^2 - 4y + 2 = 0.$

If we change the sign of any one of the directed distances in (10), the resulting equations determine the center and radius of an *escribed circle* — that is, a circle that is exterior to the triangle but is tangent to the three lines that define its sides.

EXERCISES

Write the equation of the circle passing through the given points:

1. $(0, 0)$, $(-4, 0)$, $(0, 6)$.   **2.** $(0, 0)$, $(1, 2)$, $(3, 3)$.

3. $(2, 3)$, $(-1, 7)$, $(1, 5)$.   **4.** $(3, 2)$, $(-1, 4)$, $(2, 5)$.

5. $(4, -1)$, $(2, 3)$, $(-2, 5)$.   **6.** $(2, 1)$, $(4, 5)$, $(-3, -2)$.
7. $(6, 2)$, $(2, 4)$, $(3, -1)$.   **8.** $(1, 2)$, $(3, 4)$, $(-1, 7)$.

Find all the circles that satisfy the given conditions:

9. With center at the intersection of $5x - 2y + 4 = 0$ and $4x - 3y + 13 = 0$ and passing through $(1, 3)$.

10. Circumscribed about the triangle, the equations of whose sides are $x - y + 2 = 0$, $3x - 4y + 11 = 0$, and $2x - 3y + 8 = 0$.

11. Circumscribed about the triangle, the equations of whose sides are $x + 3y - 9 = 0$, $x + 7y - 29 = 0$, and $x + y - 5 = 0$.

12. Having the same center as $x^2 + y^2 - 5x + 3y = 0$ and tangent to $x - y + 1 = 0$.

13. Passing through $(5, 4)$ and $(2, -1)$ and having its center on the line $7x - 2y - 1 = 0$.

14. With center on $2x - 5y - 1 = 0$ and tangent to $4x - 3y + 16 = 0$ at $(-1, 4)$.

15. Passing through $(-2, 7)$ and $(-4, -1)$, radius $\sqrt{34}$.

16. Passing through $(2, 2)$ and $(-2, 6)$ and tangent to $x - 3y = 0$.

17. Passing through $(-8, -1)$ and tangent to both coördinate axes.

18. Inscribed in the triangle whose sides are $x - 1 = 0$, $y - 6 = 0$, and $3x - 4y - 3 = 0$.

19. Inscribed in the triangle whose sides are $11x + 2y + 20 = 0$, $2x + 11y - 7 = 0$, and $2x - y - 19 = 0$.

4.4 Loci Problems Leading to Lines and Circles. Analytic geometry is a particularly useful device for solving problems of loci. It is accordingly important that the student be able to carry through the process of setting up the equation of the locus defined by a given geometric condition. This problem, which was considered in a preliminary way in Art. 2.9, can now be handled with somewhat greater facility. The process usually involves the following sequence of acts:

(1) *Choose a pair of axes located as conveniently as possible with respect to the data.*

(2) *Assume a point anywhere on the locus and call its coördinates* (x, y).

(3) *Write out a simplified statement of the given geometric condition.*

(4) *State, by an equation in x and y, the condition given in No. 3.*

(5) *The graph of this equation is the required locus.*

The equation should be simplified whenever possible.

The following examples will illustrate how the above principles are actually applied.

Example 1. Given two points A and B such that the length of the segment $AB = 2c$. Find the locus of a point such that the sum of the squares of its distances from A and B is equal to $4c^2$.

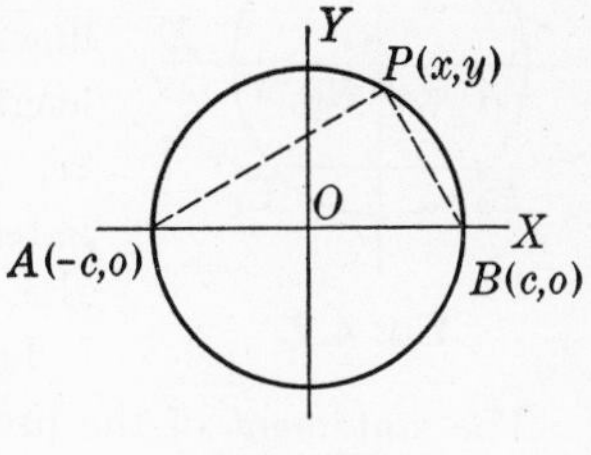

(1) We choose the line through A and B as x-axis and the line perpendicular to it through the midpoint of the segment AB as y-axis. Then the coördinates of A are $(-c, 0)$ and of B $(c, 0)$.

Fig. 4.7

(2) Let $P(x, y)$ be a point anywhere on the locus.

(3) From the statement of the problem, we have

$$AP^2 + BP^2 = 4c^2$$

and, on replacing AP^2 and BP^2 by their values from the distance formula, we obtain, as the equation of the required locus,

(4) $(x + c)^2 + (y - 0)^2 + (x - c)^2 + (y - 0)^2 = 4c^2.$

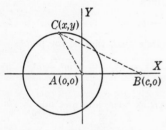

Fig. 4.8

This equation may be simplified to

$$x^2 + y^2 = c^2.$$

(5) The required locus is thus a circle on AB as a diameter as shown in Fig. 4.7.

Example 2. Given two vertices A and B of a triangle. Find the locus of the third vertex C if $CB = 2CA$.

We choose the line through A and B as x-axis, the line perpendicular to it through A as y-axis, and denote the coördinates of B by $(c, 0)$.

Let $C(x, y)$ be any point on the locus.

From the statement of the problem:

$$\sqrt{(x - c)^2 + y^2} = 2\sqrt{x^2 + y^2}.$$

Hence, $x^2 - 2cx + c^2 + y^2 = 4x^2 + 4y^2$

or $x^2 + y^2 + \dfrac{2}{3} cx - \dfrac{c^2}{3} = 0.$

This locus is a circle which has, as a diameter, the segment joining the points $(c/3, 0)$ and $(-c, 0)$ on the line through A and B.

Example 3. Given the base of a triangle and the lengths of the altitude and the median from the vertex to the base. Find the vertex of the triangle.

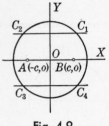

Fig. 4.9

Take the midpoint of the base as origin and the line that contains the base as x-axis. Denote the length of the base, the altitude, and the median by $2c$, h, and m, respectively. Then the coördinates of the ends of the base are $A(-c, 0)$ and $B(c, 0)$.

Let $C(x, y)$ be the required vertex.

The statement of the problem imposes two conditions on C. We shall determine the locus of a point that satisfies each of these conditions separately. Then any point of intersection of the two loci so obtained may be taken as the required vertex.

Since the distance of C from the midpoint $(0, 0)$ of the base is equal to m, the length of the median, C lies on the circle

$$x^2 + y^2 = m^2. \tag{15}$$

Since the distance of C from the x-axis is *numerically* equal to h, the length of the altitude, C lies on one of the lines

$$y = h \quad \text{or} \quad y = -h.$$

The intersections of these lines with the circle (15), that is, the points

$$(\sqrt{m^2 - h^2}, h), \quad (-\sqrt{m^2 - h^2}, h), \quad (\sqrt{m^2 - h^2}, -h), \quad (-\sqrt{m^2 - h^2}, -h)$$

are the required positions of the vertex C.

The four triangles having the segment AB as base, and any one of the above four points as vertex, are congruent.

If $m^2 - h^2 < 0$, the triangle cannot be constructed.

EXERCISES

1. Solve Example 1 when the coördinate axes are taken without special reference to the points A and B.

2. Solve Example 2 when the coördinate axes are taken without special reference to the points A and B.

Find the equation of the locus of a point that satisfies the given conditions:

3. The square of the distance of the point from $(1, 5)$ exceeds by 32 the square of its distance from $(3, -1)$.

4. Three times the square of its distance from (4, 1) equals twice the square of its distances from (1, − 2).

5. The sum of the squares of its distances from the lines $5x + 2y − 8 = 0$ and $2x − 5y − 9 = 0$ equals 9.

6. The square of the distance of the point from (− 2, 5) equals − 39 times its directed distance from $12x − 5y + 1 = 0$.

7. A line segment of length 16 has one end point on the x-axis and the other on the y-axis. Find the locus of the midpoint of the segment.

8. The midpoint of the segment joining $P(x, y)$ to the origin lies on the circle $x^2 + y^2 − 3x + 5y + 6 = 0$. Find the locus of P.

9. The midpoint of the segment joining $P(x, y)$ to (0, b) lies on the circle $x^2 + y^2 = a^2$. Find the locus of P.

Choose a suitable set of coördinate axes and find the equation of the locus of a point satisfying the given conditions:

10. Its distance from a fixed point A equals k times its distance from a fixed point B.

11. The sum of the squares of its distances from two adjacent sides of a square equals the sum of the squares of its distances from the other two sides.

12. The angle from the line joining it to a fixed point A to the line joining it to a fixed point B is a constant.

13. The sum of the squares of its distances from the vertices of a given triangle is a constant.

In the following exercises, two vertices, A and B, of a triangle are given. Find the third vertex C as the intersection of two loci and discuss the number of solutions, given:

14. The length of the side AC and of the median from C to AB.

15. That $AC = 2BC$ and the length of the altitude from AB to C.

16. The length of the median from C to AB and of the radius of the circumscribed circle.

17. The angle ACB and the length of the side AC.

18. The angle ACB and the length of the altitude from A to BC.

19. The angle BAC and the length of the median from C to AB.

MISCELLANEOUS EXERCISES

Find the equations of all the circles satisfying the given conditions:

1. Circumscribed about the triangle whose vertices are (2, − 2), (7, 1), and (− 2, 10).

2. Circumscribed about the triangle the equations of whose sides are $x - 2y + 4 = 0$, $7x + y - 17 = 0$, and $3x - y + 7 = 0$.

3. Having as a diameter the segment from $(-3, -1)$ to the foot of the perpendicular from that point to the line $5x + 2y - 41 = 0$.

4. Passing through $(3, 4)$ and $(-1, 2)$ and having its center on $2x + y - 5 = 0$.

5. Tangent to the y-axis at $(0, 3)$ and passing through $(8, -1)$.

6. Tangent to both axes and having its center on $2x - 5y + 21 = 0$.

7. Tangent to $4x - y - 11 = 0$ at $(3, 1)$ and radius $2\sqrt{17}$.

8. Tangent to the circle $x^2 + y^2 = 9$ and having its center at $(12, -5)$.

Hint. If two circles are tangent, the distance between their centers is equal to the sum or the difference of their radii.

9. Find the points of intersection of the line $4x - y + 1 = 0$ and the circle $x^2 + y^2 + 8x - 4y - 14 = 0$.

10. The midpoint of a chord of the circle $x^2 + y^2 + 2x + 14y - 119 = 0$ is $(2, -3)$. Find the length of the chord.

11. Show that the locus of a point the sum of the squares of whose distances from the vertices of a triangle is a constant is a circle whose center is the centroid of the triangle. (See Art. 3.5, Ex. 30.)

12. Given that $P_1(x_1, y_1)$ lies on the circle $x^2 + y^2 = a^2$; show that $x_1x + y_1y = a^2$ is the tangent line to the circle at P_1.

Hint. The two intersections with the circle of a line tangent to the circle coincide at the point of tangency.

13. Show that all the lines of the family $y = mx + a\sqrt{m^2 + 1}$, m being the parameter, are tangent to the circle $x^2 + y^2 = a^2$. What is the geometric meaning of the parameter m?

14. Find the equations of the two lines tangent to $x^2 + y^2 = 25$ and (*a*) parallel to $2x - 5y + 3 = 0$; (*b*) passing through $(7, -1)$.

15. Let $S \equiv x^2 + y^2 + Dx + Ey + F = 0$

and $S' \equiv x^2 + y^2 + D'x + E'y + F' = 0$

be the equations of two circles. Show that every equation of the form $S + kS' = 0$, where k is a constant $\neq -1$, represents a circle. Since the equation of this system of circles involves a parameter k, these circles constitute a *family* of circles (compare with Art. 3.13).

16. If $S = 0$ and $S' = 0$ are not concentric, show that the centers of all the circles $S + kS' = 0$ lie on the line through the centers of $S = 0$ and $S' = 0$. This line is called the *line of centers* of the family $S + kS' = 0$.

17. Show that if S and S' are not concentric the locus obtained by setting $k = -1$ in Ex. 15 is a straight line perpendicular to the line of centers. This line is called the *radical axis* of the family of circles $S + kS' = 0$.

18. Show that if S and S' intersect then the radical axis passes through the points of intersection of S and S'.

SELECTED EXERCISES

1. Show that, in any triangle, the circle through the midpoints of the sides passes also through the feet of the altitudes and through the points midway between the vertices and the point of intersection of the altitudes. This circle is called the *nine point circle* of the given triangle.

2. A navigator, about to enter a harbor, is uncertain as to his position P. He selects three objects A, B, and C on the shore whose positions are given on the chart and measures the directed angles APB and BPC. Show that his position P is fixed by these angles except when P lies on the circle through A, B, and C.

Note. This problem is of importance in practical navigation.

3. The angle between two intersecting circles is defined as equal to the angle between their tangents at a point of intersection. If ϕ is the angle between the intersecting circles $x^2 + y^2 + Dx + Ey + F = 0$ and $x^2 + y^2 + D'x + E'y + F' = 0$, show that

$$\cos \phi = \pm \frac{DD' + EE' - 2F - 2F'}{\sqrt{D^2 + E^2 - 4F}\sqrt{D'^2 + E'^2 - 4F'}}.$$

Hint. The angles formed by the tangent lines at a point of intersection P_1 are equal to the angles formed by the lines joining P_1 to the centers of the circles.

4. Using the results of Ex. 3, find the condition that the given circles are (*a*) tangent, (*b*) orthogonal, that is, that they intersect at right angles.

5. Let P be any point, other than the origin, and let P' be the point collinear with P and the origin and situated so that, using directed segments,

$$\overline{OP} \cdot \overline{OP'} = k^2$$

where k is a constant. The transformation of the points of the plane obtained by replacing each point P by its corresponding point P' is called an *inversion*. Show that the coördinates of $P'(x', y')$ are determined in terms of those of $P(x, y)$ by the equations

$$x' = \frac{k^2 x}{x^2 + y^2}; \quad y' = \frac{k^2 y}{x^2 + y^2}.$$

6. Show that the locus of a point that is transformed into itself by an inversion is a circle. This circle is called the *circle of inversion*.

7. If P is exterior to the circle of inversion (Ex. 6), show that P' is the intersection with OP of the line joining the points of tangency of the tangents from P to the circle of inversion.

8. Show that, by an inversion:

(a) A line that passes through O is transformed into itself.

(b) A line not passing through O is transformed into a circle through O, and conversely.

(c) A circle not passing through O is transformed into a circle.

Polar Coördinates

5.1 Introduction. Instead of fixing the position of a point by its directed distances from two fixed lines, as in rectangular coördinates, it is sometimes preferable to locate it by its distance and direction from a fixed point. When its position is fixed in this way, the point is said to be located by means of **polar coördinates.**

In principle, the method of fixing the position of a point by its polar coördinates is familiar. We are accustomed, for example, to such statements as that Cleveland is about 300 miles northwest of Washington, or that Buffalo is about 400 miles west of Boston.

5.2 Polar Coördinates. Let O be a fixed point, the **origin,** or **pole,** and let OI be a fixed line through O, the **initial line,** or **polar axis.** The line through the pole perpendicular to the polar axis is the **90° axis.**

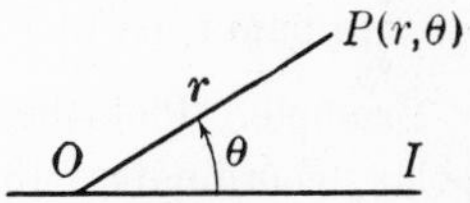

Fig. 5.1

Let P be any point in the plane (other than O) * and draw the line through O and P. The position of P

---

* The polar coördinates of the origin O are defined by taking the radius vector, r, equal to zero and the vectorial angle, θ, to be of any magnitude we please.

is fixed if we know the length r of the segment OP and the angle θ

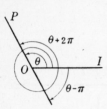

Fig. 5.2

that has the half-line OI for its initial side and the half-line OP for its terminal side. The quantities r and θ are called the **polar coördinates** of P; r is the **radius vector** and θ is the **vectorial angle.**

If the pair of polar coördinates (r, θ) is given, the point P is definitely fixed; but for a given point P, we can find as many pairs of polar coördinates as we please. For, if we add to θ, or subtract from it, any number of complete revolutions, we do not change the terminal side nor the position of P. Thus, (r, θ), $(r, \theta + 2\pi)$, $(r, \theta - 2\pi)$, etc., are all pairs of polar coördinates for the same point P.

Moreover, we can also fix the position of P by choosing, for the terminal side of the vectorial angle, the half-line extending from O in the opposite direction from P and considering the length of the radius vector as negative. Thus $(-r, \theta - \pi)$, $(-r, \theta + \pi)$, $(-r, \theta + 3\pi)$, etc., are also pairs of polar coördinates of the point P. Hence *the radius vector, r, is a directed distance measured along the terminal side of the vectorial angle, θ.*

Summing up the results of the last two paragraphs, we see that the point (r, θ) is also represented by $(r, \theta + 2n\pi)$ and $(-r, \theta + \pi + 2n\pi)$, where n is any integer. These are called **equivalent pairs of polar coördinates.**

For plotting points, or drawing graphs, in polar coördinates, it will be found that both speed and accuracy are improved by the use of **polar coördinate paper,** as in Fig. 5.3.

Example. Plot the points having the polar coördinates $(3, 0°)$, $(4, -240°)$, $(2, 180°)$, $(3, \pi/4)$, $(1, 3\pi/2)$.

From OI, as initial side, we measure off the given angle θ and, on its terminal side, lay off the given length of the radius vector. The resulting points are shown in Fig. 5.3.

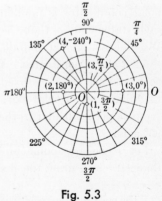

Fig. 5.3

EXERCISES

Plot the points whose polar coördinates are given. Find for each point, one other equivalent pair of polar coördinates for which r is positive and one for which r is negative.

1. $(2, 30°)$.   2. $(7, 45°)$.   3. $(5, 90°)$.   4. $(9, 150°)$.
5. $(6, 60°)$.   6. $(2, -270°)$.   7. $(-4, 60°)$.   8. $(-5, -45°)$.
9. $(-3, -210°)$.   10. $(4, \pi/4)$.   11. $(8, 3\pi/4)$.   12. $(9, \pi)$.
13. $(4, 2\pi)$.   14. $(3, 1)$.   15. $(4, -2)$. ← *RADIANS*

16. Show that the distance between two points $P_1(r_1, \theta_1)$ and $P_2(r_2, \theta_2)$ is $d = \sqrt{r_1^2 + r_2^2 - 2r_1r_2 \cos (\theta_2 - \theta_1)}$.

Hint. Apply the law of cosines (Art. 0.13) to the triangle OP_1P_2.

17. Show that the area of the triangle whose vertices are the origin and the points $P_1(r_1, \theta_1)$ and $P_2(r_2, \theta_2)$ is $S = \frac{1}{2}r_1r_2 \sin (\theta_2 - \theta_1)$.

Using the results of Ex. 16 and 17, find the distance P_1P_2 and the area of the triangle OP_1P_2, given:

18. $P_1(4, 45°)$, $P_2(6, 90°)$.   19. $P_1(2, 60°)$, $P_2(5, 120°)$.
20. $P_1(3, 120°)$, $P_2(7, 27°)$.   21. $P_1(5, 29°)$, $P_2(9, 53°)$.

5.3 Relations between Polar and Rectangular Coördinates. If a system of polar coördinates is so related to a system of rectangular coördinates that they have the same origin and the directions OI on the initial line and OX on the x-axis coincide, as in Fig. 5.4, then the relations between the polar coördinates, r and θ, and the rectangular coördinates, x and y, of a given point P may be found in the following way.

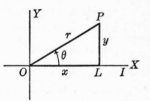

Fig. 5.4

From the definitions * of $\sin \theta$ and $\cos \theta$, we have

$$\cos \theta = \frac{x}{r} \quad \text{and} \quad \sin \theta = \frac{y}{r},$$

so that the values of x and y in terms of r and θ are

$$x = r \cos \theta, \quad y = r \sin \theta. \tag{1}$$

---

* In defining the trigonometric functions the radius vector was restricted to positive values. However, these same relations hold when the radius vector is a directed distance.

To find r and θ in terms of x and y, we notice (Fig. 5.4) that $\tan \theta = y/x$ and that the numerical value of r is the hypotenuse of a right triangle whose legs are x and y. Hence

$$r = \pm \sqrt{x^2 + y^2}; \quad \tan \theta = \frac{y}{x} \quad \text{or} \quad \theta = \text{arc} \tan \frac{y}{x}. \qquad (2)$$

When we determine θ from the last of equations (2), we must bear in mind that there are two angles, differing by 180°, for which $\tan \theta$ has the given value. Before we can determine θ from this equation we must accordingly first find out, by plotting the point on the figure, in what quadrant the given point lies.

Example 1. Find the rectangular coördinates of a point given that its polar coördinates are (4, 60°).

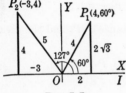
Fig. 5.5

Since $\cos 60° = \frac{1}{2}$ and $\sin 60° = \sqrt{3}/2$, we have, from equations (1),

$$x = 4 \cdot \tfrac{1}{2} = 2, \quad y = 4 \cdot \frac{\sqrt{3}}{2} = 2\sqrt{3}.$$

Hence, the required coördinates are $(2, 2\sqrt{3})$ (Fig. 5.5).

Example 2. Find the polar coördinates of a point, given that its rectangular coördinates are $(-3, 4)$.

From equations (2), we have
$$r = \sqrt{(-3)^2 + 4^2} = 5, \quad \tan \theta = -\tfrac{4}{3} = -1.3333.$$
Moreover, it is seen from Fig. 5.5 that P_2 lies in the second quadrant. Hence we may take $\theta = 127°$ and the required coördinates are (5, 127°).

Example 3. Transform the equation $3x - y - 5 = 0$ to polar coördinates.

By substituting for x and y their values in terms of r and θ from (1), we have
$$3r \cos \theta - r \sin \theta - 5 = 0 \quad \text{or} \quad r(3 \cos \theta - \sin \theta) - 5 = 0.$$

Example 4. Transform the polar equation $r = 2 \cos \theta + 3 \sin \theta$ to rectangular coördinates.

In this case, it will be convenient, first, to multiply the given equation by r, giving
$$r^2 = 2r \cos \theta + 3r \sin \theta.$$

From equations (1) and (2) we now obtain

$$x^2 + y^2 = 2x + 3y.$$

The student should show that the graph of this equation is a circle with center at $(1, \frac{3}{2})$ (in rectangular coördinates) and radius $\sqrt{13}/2$.

EXERCISES

Find the rectangular coördinates of the point having the given polar coördinates:

1. $(6, 30°)$.   **2.** $(7, 120°)$.   **3.** $(8, -45°)$.
4. $(10, \pi/3)$.   **5.** $(5, \pi/2)$.   **6.** $(-4, -5\pi/6)$.

Find polar coördinates for the point having the given rectangular coördinates:

7. $(5, 5)$.   **8.** $(-3, 3\sqrt{3})$.   **9.** $(-6, -6)$.
10. $(0, -2)$.   **11.** $(2\sqrt{3}, -2)$.   **12.** $(-2, 5)$.

13. Show that $(4, 90°)$, $(4, 210°)$, and $(4, 330°)$ are the vertices of an equilateral triangle and find the length of a side of the triangle.

14. The center of a regular octagon is at the origin and one vertex is $(3, 0°)$. Find polar coördinates for the other vertices.

Write the following equations in polar coördinates:

15. $x = 7$.   **16.** $y + 5 = 0$.   **17.** $2x + 5y = 9$.
18. $x^2 + y^2 = 25$.   **19.** $x^2 + y^2 = 6y$.   **20.** $x^2 + y^2 + 8x = 0$.

Write the following equations in rectangular coördinates:

21. $r = 2$.   **22.** $\theta = 3\pi/4$.   **23.** $r \sin \theta = 11$.
24. $r \cos \theta + 5 = 0$.   **25.** $r = 2 \sin \theta$.   **26.** $r \cos \theta + 3 = 0$.

5.4 The Polar Equation of a Line. By substituting the values of x and y in terms of r and θ from equations (1) in the normal form, $x \cos \omega + y \sin \omega - p = 0$, we have

$$r(\cos \theta \cos \omega + \sin \theta \sin \omega) - p = 0.$$

This simplifies to

$$r \cos (\theta - \omega) - p = 0. \qquad (3)$$

which is called the **polar normal form** of the equation of a line.

The following special cases of equation (3) arise frequently. If the given line is perpendicular to the initial line, $\omega = 0$ and equation (3) reduces to:

$$r \cos \theta = p, \quad \text{or} \quad r = p \sec \theta. \qquad (4)$$

If the given line is parallel to the initial line, $\omega = \pi/2$ and equation (3) reduces to:

$$r \sin \theta = p, \quad \text{or} \quad r = p \csc \theta. \tag{5}$$

A special form arises when the line passes through the pole with inclination θ_1. We then get as the equation of the line,

$$\theta = \theta_1. \tag{6}$$

By substituting the values of x and y in terms of r and θ from equations (1) in the general form, $Ax + By + C = 0$, of the equation of a line, we obtain as the **general polar form** of the equation of a line,

$$r(A \cos \theta + B \sin \theta) + C = 0. \tag{7}$$

This form is seldom used since the corresponding rectangular form is usually easier to work with.

Example. Find the polar equation of a line passing through $(5, 120°)$ and perpendicular to the line through the origin and this point.

Equation (3) can be applied directly here. Thus $p = 5$ and $\omega = 120°$ and we get

$$r \cos (\theta - 120°) = 5.$$

EXERCISES

Find the rectangular equations of the following lines:

1. $r(4 \cos \theta - 7 \sin \theta) + 11 = 0.$ **2.** $r(3 \cos \theta + 2 \sin \theta) - 9 = 0.$
3. $r \cos \theta + 5 = 0.$ **4.** $r \cos (\theta - \pi/3) = 6.$
5. $r = 4 \sec (\theta - \pi/4)$ **6.** $\theta = \pi/4.$

Write the following equations in a polar form:

7. $2x - 5y + 8 = 0.$ **8.** $4x + 3y - 9 = 0.$
9. $x - y = 3\sqrt{2}.$ **10.** $\sqrt{3}x + y = 0.$

Write the polar normal form of the equation of a line:

11. Parallel to the 90° axis and passing through (*a*) $(3, 0°)$, (*b*) $(8, 60°)$.
12. Parallel to the polar axis and passing through (*a*) $(-5, 270°)$, (*b*) $(6, \pi/4)$.
13. Passing through $(4, \pi/3)$ and perpendicular to the line through the origin and this point.
14. Passing through $(8, 180°)$ and making an angle of 30° with the polar axis.

15. Through $(8, 30°)$ and perpendicular to a line making an angle of $60°$ with the polar axis.

16. Find the slope of the line $r \cos (\theta + 2\pi/3) = 5$.

17. Find the length of the segment of the line $r \cos (\theta - \pi/6) = 5\sqrt{3}$ included between the coördinate axes.

18. Find polar coördinates for the point of intersection of the lines $r = 5 \sec \theta$ and $r = 5\sqrt{3} \csc \theta$.

19. Find polar coördinates for the point of intersection of the lines $r \cos (\theta - 60°) = 6$ and $r \cos (\theta - 120°) = 6$.

5.5 The Polar Equation of a Circle. Let $C(c, \gamma)$ be the center and a the radius of the circle and let $P(r, \theta)$ be any point on the circle. If we apply the law of cosines (Art. 0.13) to the triangle COP, we obtain

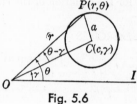

Fig. 5.6

$$r^2 - 2cr \cos (\theta - \gamma) + c^2 = a^2. \qquad (8)$$

This is the polar equation of a circle with center at (c, γ) and radius a. It is seldom used since the corresponding rectangular equation is usually easier to work with.

The following special cases are of importance, and are frequently used.

(*a*) If the center lies on the polar axis and the circle passes through the origin, the coördinates of the center are $(a, 0)$ or (a, π) according as the center lies to the right or left of the origin. Equation (8) now reduces to

$$r = 2a \cos \theta, \quad \text{or} \quad r = - 2a \cos \theta, \qquad (9)$$

the first equation holding if C is to the right of the origin and the second if C is to the left. We are justified in neglecting the factor r which is obtained in reducing equation (8) to either of equations (9) because its locus is only the origin which is already on both of the loci defined by equations (9).

(*b*) If the center lies on the $90°$ axis and the circle passes through the origin, the coördinates of the center are $(a, \pm \pi/2)$ and equation (8) reduces to

$$r = 2a \sin \theta, \quad \text{or} \quad r = - 2a \sin \theta, \qquad (10)$$

according as the center lies above or below the origin.

(*c*) If the center lies at the origin, $c = 0$ and the equation may be simplified to

$$r = a. \tag{11}$$

Example. Find the center and radius of the circle $r = -10 \sin \theta$, and its equation in rectangular coördinates.

Using equation (10) we see that the center is $(5, -\pi/2)$ and the radius is 5. Multiplying $r = -10 \sin \theta$ by r which introduces no new points on the locus, we get

$$r^2 = -10r \sin \theta.$$

Using equations (1) and (2), we get

$$x^2 + y^2 = -10y \quad \text{or} \quad x^2 + (y+5)^2 = 25$$

for the equation of the circle in rectangular coördinates.

EXERCISES

Write the polar equation of the circle having the given point as center and the given radius:

1. $(0, 0°)$, 5.   2. $(3, 0°)$, 3.   3. $(7, \pi/2)$, 7.
4. $(4, \pi/4)$, 4.   5. $(6, \pi/3)$, 4.   6. $(2a, -3\pi/4)$, a.

Find the center and the radius of each of the given circles:

7. $r = 14 \cos \theta$.   8. $r + 6 \sin \theta = 0$.
9. $r = 8 \cos (\theta + \pi/4)$.   10. $r^2 - 4r \sin \theta = 21$.
11. $r^2 - 6r \cos (\theta - 2\pi/3) + 5 = 0$.
12. $r^2 - 10r \cos (\theta - 135°) + 16 = 0$.
13. $r^2 - 12r \cos (\theta + 30°) - 13 = 0$.
14. $r^2 - 8r \cos (\theta - 210°) - 20 = 0$.

Write each of the following equations in rectangular coördinates:

15. $r = 8 \sin \theta$.   16. $r + 10 \cos \theta = 0$.
17. $r = 6 \cos (\theta - 3\pi/4)$.   18. $r^2 - 4r \sin \theta - 12 = 0$.
19. $r^2 - 12r \cos (\theta - 60°) + 27 = 0$.
20. $r^2 - 8r \cos (\theta + 45°) + 7 = 0$.
21. $r^2 + 5r \cos (\theta + \pi/6) + 4 = 0$.
22. $r^2 + 6r \cos (\theta - \pi/4) - 40 = 0$.

Write the equations of the following circles in the form of equation (8):

23. $r = 3 \cos \theta + 3\sqrt{3} \sin \theta$.
24. $r^2 - 5\sqrt{2}r \cos \theta - 5\sqrt{2} \sin \theta - 11 = 0$.

Find the points of intersection of the two loci:

25. $r = 8 \cos \theta$, $r \cos \theta = 2$.

26. $r = 4 \sin \theta$, $r \cos \theta = \sqrt{3}$.

MISCELLANEOUS EXERCISES

1. Find the rectangular coördinates of the points whose polar coördinates are $(6, 120°)$, $(3, 57°)$ and $(-5, 37°)$.

2. Show that $(0, 0°)$, $(4,45°)$ and $(4,135°)$ are three vertices of a square and find the fourth vertex.

3. Find the polar equation of the line through $(12,120°)$ parallel to the $90°$ axis.

4. Find the polar equation of the line through $(12,180°)$ of inclination $30°$.

5. Find the center and radius of the circle $r + 8 \cos \theta - 8 \sin \theta = 0$.

6. Find the polar equation of the circle $x^2 + y^2 + 2\sqrt{3}x - 2y - 12 = 0$.

7. Find the distance between the centers of the circles $r + 12 \cos \theta = 0$ and $r + 16 \sin \theta = 0$.

8. Show that $rr_1 \sin (\theta - \theta_1) + rr_2 \sin (\theta_2 - \theta) + r_1r_2 \sin (\theta_1 - \theta_2) = 0$ is the equation of the line through (r_1, θ_1) and (r_2, θ_2).

The following curves are not lines or circles. To draw them, first assign a fixed value to a, then assign a set of values to θ, compute the corresponding values of r from the equation, plot the corresponding points and draw a smooth curve through them:

9. $r = a(1 + \cos \theta)$. *Cardioid.*   **10.** $r^2 = a^2 \sin 2\theta$. *Lemniscate.*

11. $r = a \sin 2\theta$. *Four-leaved rose.*   **12.** $r = a \tan \theta$. *Kappa curve.*

13. $r = a\theta$. *Spiral of Archimedes.*   **14.** $r = e^{a\theta}$. *Logarithmic spiral.*

The Conic Sections

6.1 Plane Sections of a Right Circular Cone. The curve of section of a right circular cone by any plane is called a **conic section** or, simply, a **conic**. If the cutting plane does not pass through the vertex of the cone, the conic belongs to one of the following three types:

(*a*) If the cutting plane cuts entirely across one nappe of the cone (Fig. 6.1a), the conic is called an **ellipse**.

(*b*) If the cutting plane is parallel to one and only one rectilinear element of the cone (Fig. 6.1b), it cuts the cone in a **parabola**.

(*c*) If the plane cuts both nappes of the cone (Fig. 6.1c), the conic is a **hyperbola**.

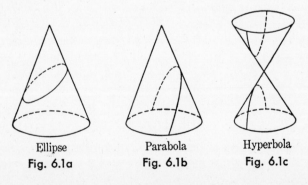

Ellipse   Parabola   Hyperbola

Fig. 6.1a   **Fig. 6.1b**   **Fig. 6.1c**

These three types of curves were named, and discussed very thoroughly, by the ancient Greek mathematicians, who studied them by the aid of methods very similar to those we now use in elementary geometry. By means of these very inefficient methods, they succeeded in proving essentially all of the properties of these curves that will be considered in this course. In particular, they found properties that will serve to define the conics as loci in their planes and which we shall use, in place of the definitions that have just been given, to derive the equations of these curves.

If the cutting plane passes through the vertex of the cone, the resulting conic section is called **degenerate.** In this case we get: (*i*) two intersecting straight lines, (*ii*) a single straight line usually counted twice since it arises when the plane is tangent to the cone, or (*iii*) a point.

6.2 Second Degree Equations and Conic Sections. It is an important and very useful fact of analytic geometry that the equation of a conic in rectangular coördinates is always of second degree, that is, it is of the form

$$Ax^2 + Bxy + Cy^2 + Dx + Ey + F = 0, \tag{1}$$

wherein A, B, C, D, E, and F are constants, of which the first three are not all zero. Equation (1) is called the **general form** of the equation of a conic.

The general form (1) of the equation of a conic is comparatively long but, for any *given* conic, it is always possible to choose the position of the coördinate axes so that several of the coefficients in its equation are zero. When the axes are so chosen that the equation of a given conic is in the simplest possible form, this simplest form is called the **standard form** of the equation of the given conic. In this chapter, we shall derive the equations of the parabola, ellipse and hyperbola, when the axes are so chosen that their equations are in the standard forms. We shall discuss these equations and determine some of the properties of these conics.

THE PARABOLA

6.3 Standard Form of the Equation of the Parabola. *A parabola is the locus of a point that moves in such a way that its undirected distances from a fixed point and from a fixed line are equal.*

The fixed point F (Fig. 6.2) is called the **focus** and the fixed line DD' the **directrix** of the parabola. The locus of the points P such

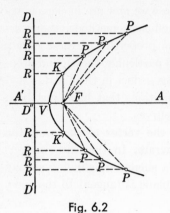

that $FP = RP$ where R is the foot of the perpendicular from P to $D'D$ is thus a parabola. The line $A'A$ through the focus perpendicular to the directrix is called the **principal axis** of the parabola. The point V on the axis midway between the focus and the directrix is the **vertex**. The chord $K'K$ of the parabola through the focus, parallel to the directrix, and terminated by the curve, is called the **latus rectum**.

To obtain the standard form of the equation of the parabola, we take the

Fig. 6.2

axis of the curve as the x-axis and the vertex as the origin. Let F be the focus and let $D'D$ (Figs. 6.3a and 6.3b) be the directrix. Let D'' be the intersection of the directrix with the axis and let the length of the directed segment $\overline{D''F} = p$. Then the coördinates of F are $(p/2, 0)$, of D'' are $(-p/2, 0)$, and the equation of the directrix is $x = -p/2$.

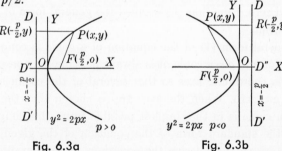

Fig. 6.3a   **Fig. 6.3b**

Let $P(x, y)$ be any point on the parabola. Draw FP and RP, where R is the foot of the perpendicular from P to the directrix. From the definition of a parabola,

$$FP = RP, \quad \text{or} \quad FP^2 = RP^2. \tag{2}$$

From the distance formula, we have

$$FP^2 = \left(x - \frac{p}{2}\right)^2 + (y - 0)^2.$$

Also, $$RP^2 = \left(x + \frac{p}{2}\right)^2.$$ (Why?)

By substituting these values of FP^2 and RP^2 in (2), we obtain

$$\left(x - \frac{p}{2}\right)^2 + y^2 = \left(x + \frac{p}{2}\right)^2.$$

On simplifying this equation, we have

$$y^2 = 2px.$$ (3)

Conversely, if the coördinates of P satisfy (3), we find, by adding $(x - p/2)^2$ to both sides of the equation, that they satisfy

$$\left(x - \frac{p}{2}\right)^2 + y^2 = \left(x + \frac{p}{2}\right)^2.$$

Hence, $$FP^2 = RP^2$$

or, since FP and RP, being undirected, are both positive,

$$FP = RP$$

so that P lies on the parabola.

Equation (3) is the equation of the parabola when the principal axis of the parabola is the x-axis and the vertex is the origin. If p is positive, the focus is to the right of the origin (Fig. 6.3*a*) and, if p is negative, the focus is to the left (Fig. 6.3*b*).

If the principal axis of the parabola is taken as the y-axis, and the vertex as the origin, we find in a similar way that the equation of the parabola is

$$x^2 = 2py$$ (4)

where the focus lies above the x-axis if p is positive, and below it if p is negative.

Equations (3) and (4) are the standard forms (Art. 6.2) of the equation of a parabola.

6.4 Discussion of the Equation. If we solve equation (3) for y, we find

$$y = \pm \sqrt{2px}.$$

To each value of x agreeing in sign with p, there correspond two values of y which are numerically equal but opposite in sign. This fact is expressed by saying that the curve is *symmetric* to the x-axis.

This symmetry could have been obtained by observing that equation (3) has only even powers of y (Art. 1.5).

As x increases numerically, the corresponding two values of y also increase numerically. It follows that the curve extends indefinitely far away from both axes.

If p and x differ in sign, then the quantity under the radical is negative and the corresponding y value is imaginary so that these values of x give no points on the curve. Thus, if p is positive (as in Fig. 6.3a) and x is negative, we say that $x < 0$ is an *excluded interval* for the curve (Art. 1.4). Similarly, if p is negative (Fig. 6.3b) then $x > 0$ is an excluded interval.

If $x = 0$, then $y = 0$, so that the vertex, which we have taken as origin, lies on the curve. The parabola does not intersect either axis in any other point since, if we put $x = 0$, the only value of y that satisfies the resulting equation is $y = 0$, and if we put $y = 0$, the only solution is $x = 0$.

Since the latus rectum (Art. 6.3) is parallel to the y-axis, its length is the sum of the numerical values of the ordinates of its end points. To find these ordinates, put $x = p/2$ (Why?) in the equation of the curve. We then have

$$y^2 = p^2 \quad \text{or} \quad y = \pm \, p.$$

Hence, *the length of the latus rectum is the numerical value of $2p$.*

Example 1. Locate the vertex, focus, principal axis, and directrix and find the length of the latus rectum of the parabola $y^2 = -6x$.

Since the equation is in the standard form (3), with $p = -3$, the coördinates of the vertex are $(0, 0)$ and of the focus are $(-\frac{3}{2}, 0)$. The equation of the principal axis of the parabola is $y = 0$ and of its directrix is $x - \frac{3}{2} = 0$. The length of the latus rectum is 6 (Fig. 6.4).

Example 2. Find the equation of a parabola, the coördinates of its focus, and the equation of its directrix, if the vertex is at the origin, the focus is on the x-axis to the right of the vertex, and the length of the latus rectum is 24.

Since the focus is to the right of the vertex, p is positive and equal to one-half of the length of the latus rectum, or 12. Since the coördinate axes are placed so that the equation of the parabola is in the standard form (3), the required equation of the curve is $y^2 = 24x$, the coördinates of the focus are $(6, 0)$, and the equation of the directrix is $x + 6 = 0$ (Fig. 6.5).

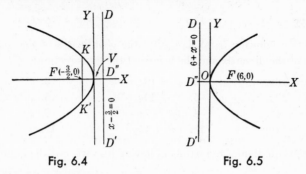

Fig. 6.4   Fig. 6.5

6.5 Applications. The parabola is frequently encountered in the applications of analytic geometry. Only a few of the best known of these applications can be mentioned here.

The path of a projectile near the surface of the earth (air resistance being neglected) is a parabola.

A cable of a suspension bridge, if the load is uniformly distributed along the bridge, assumes a parabolic form.

A parabolic mirror is one whose reflecting surface may be generated by revolving a parabola about its axis. The construction of locomotive headlights is based on the principle that, if a source of light is placed at the focus of such a mirror, the rays striking the mirror will be reflected parallel to the axis of the mirror. In the construction of reflecting telescopes, also, use is made of the fact that, if the axis of a parabolic mirror is pointed toward a star, the rays from the star that strike the mirror will all be reflected to the focus.

★ 6.6 A Continuous Construction for a Parabola. An arc of a

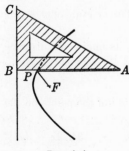

Fig. 6.6

parabola can readily be drawn in the following way: At the vertex A of a draftsman's triangle (Fig. 6.6) fasten one end of a string of length AB. Fasten the other end at the focus F of the required parabola and place the other leg BC of the triangle along the directrix. Hold the string taut by pressing it against the side of the triangle with the point of a pencil at P. If the side BC of the triangle is now made to slide along the directrix, the point P will describe an arc of the parabola.

EXERCISES

Draw the following parabolas. Find the coördinates of the focus, the equation of the directrix and the length of the latus rectum:

1. $y^2 = 16x$. **2.** $y^2 - 10x = 0$. **3.** $y^2 + 28x = 0$.
4. $x^2 = 20y$. **5.** $x^2 + 40y = 0$. **6.** $x^2 + 5y = 0$.
7. $5y^2 = 12x$. **8.** $3y^2 + 7x = 0$. **9.** $2x^2 = 7y$.
10. $3x^2 = 16y$. **11.** $7x^2 = 15y$. **12.** $y^2 = 4ax$.

Find the equation of the parabola having its vertex at the origin, given that:

13. Its focus is $(8, 0)$. **14.** Its directrix is $x + 5 = 0$.
15. Its directrix is $y - 2 = 0$. **16.** Its focus is $(0, 3)$.

17. It passes through $(5, 10)$ and the x-axis is its principal axis.

18. It passes through $(-4, -24)$ and the y-axis is its principal axis.

19. It passes through $(6, 18)$ and $(-6, 18)$.

20. Its focus lies on $3x + 5y - 15 = 0$ and the y-axis is its principal axis.

21. Its directrix passes through $(4, 7)$ and the x-axis is its principal axis.

22. Its latus rectum is of length 36 and the y-axis is its principal axis. (Two solutions.)

Find the points of intersection of the following parabolas:

23. $y^2 = 2x, x^2 = 2y$. **24.** $y^2 = 54x, x^2 = 2y$.
25. $2y^2 = 9x, 3x^2 + 4y = 0$. **26.** $3y^2 + 25x = 0, 5x^2 + 9y = 0$.

27. Find the points of intersection of the line $y = 5x - 20$ with the parabola $y^2 = 50x$.

28. Find the equation of the line through the points on the parabola $y^2 = 3x$ whose ordinates are 2 and 3.

29. Write the equation of the circle that has the latus rectum of $y^2 = 2px$ as a diameter.

30. The **focal radius** of a point on a parabola is its undirected distance from the focus. Show that the focal radius of a point $P_1(x_1, y_1)$ on the parabola $y^2 = 2px$ is numerically equal to $x_1 + p/2$.

Using the statements of Ex. 30, find the focal radii of the points on the parabola $y^2 = 12x$ for which:

31. $x = 3$. **32.** $x = \frac{4}{3}$. **33.** $y = 24$. **34.** $2x = 3y$.

35. Find the points on the parabola $y^2 + 20x = 0$ for which the focal radii are equal in length to the latus rectum.

36. Find the locus of the center of a circle that passes through $(a, 0)$ and ~~touches~~ the line $x + a = 0$.

TANGENT TO

37. Find the locus of a point whose undirected distance from $(0, 4)$ exceeds by 4 its directed distance from the x-axis.

38. The distance between the towers of a suspension bridge is 800 feet. The lowest point on the cables is 120 feet below the points of support. Assume that the form of the cables is parabolic. Take the lowest point on one of them as origin, the y-axis vertical, and find the equation of the parabola.

The equations of the following required parabolas are not in the standard form. The given point is the focus and the given line is the directrix. Using the definition of a parabola given in Art. 6.3, find the equation of the parabola:

39. $(2, 3)$, $x = 0$.   **40.** $(-3, -5)$, $x - 5 = 0$.

41. $(3, 1)$, $y + 3 = 0$.   **42.** $(0, 0)$, $4x - 3y = 10$.

43. $(-4, -2)$, $2x + y = 3$.   **44.** $(a/2, a/2)$, $x + y = 0$.

THE ELLIPSE

6.7 Standard Form of the Equation of the Ellipse. _An ellipse is the locus of a point that moves so that the sum of its undirected distances from two fixed points is equal to a constant._

The two fixed points are called the **foci,** the point midway between them is the **center** and the line through the foci is the **principal axis** of the ellipse.

To derive the standard form of the equation of the ellipse, we take the principal axis as the x-axis and the center as the origin. Let F and F'

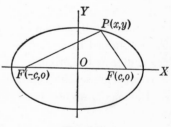

Fig. 6.7

(Fig. 6.7) be the foci and let $2c$ be the distance between them, so that the coördinates of F are $(c, 0)$ and of F' are $(-c, 0)$.

Let $P(x, y)$ be any point on the ellipse and let the sum of its distances from the foci be $2a$, so that

$$F'P + FP = 2a, \tag{5}$$

or $$\sqrt{(x + c)^2 + y^2} + \sqrt{(x - c)^2 + y^2} = 2a.$$

If we transpose the second radical, square, and solve for the radical expression, we find that

$$\sqrt{(x - c)^2 + y^2} = a - \frac{c}{a} x. \tag{6}$$

By squaring again, and simplifying, we obtain

$$\frac{a^2 - c^2}{a^2} x^2 + y^2 = a^2 - c^2 \tag{7}$$

or

$$\frac{x^2}{a^2} + \frac{y^2}{a^2 - c^2} = 1. \tag{8}$$

But $a > c$, since, in the triangle $F'PF$, the sum of the two sides $F'P + FP$, which equals $2a$ by (5), is greater than the third side $F'F$, which is equal to $2c$. Hence $a^2 - c^2$ is positive. We shall denote this positive number by b^2, that is

$$b^2 = a^2 - c^2. \tag{9}$$

If we substitute this value for $a^2 - c^2$ in (8), we have

$$\frac{x^2}{a^2} + \frac{y^2}{b^2} = 1. \tag{10}$$

It can be proved conversely that, if the coördinates of a point $P(x, y)$ satisfy (10), then $F'P + FP = 2a$, so that P lies on the ellipse. (See Ex. 31, Art. 6.9.)

Equation (10) is thus the equation of the ellipse. It is the standard form obtained by taking the line through the foci as the x-axis and the center as the origin.

If we choose the coördinate axes so that the foci are $(0, \pm c)$ on the y-axis, we obtain in a precisely similar way

$$\frac{x^2}{b^2} + \frac{y^2}{a^2} = 1 \tag{11}$$

as the standard form when the line through the foci is the y-axis and the center is the origin.

To distinguish, in numerical problems, between the cases in which the foci are on the x-axis (Eqn. 10) or on the y-axis (Eqn. 11) we notice that, because of (9), the number a, for the ellipse, cannot be less than b. It is equal to b only if $c = 0$, in which case the ellipse becomes a circle.

6.8 Discussion of the Equation. If we solve equation (10) for y and for x, we obtain

$$y = \pm \frac{b}{a} \sqrt{a^2 - x^2} \quad \text{and} \quad x = \pm \frac{a}{b} \sqrt{b^2 - y^2} \tag{12}$$

respectively.

From the first of these equations, it follows that if $x^2 > a^2$, y is imaginary and, from the second, that if $y^2 > b^2$, then x is imaginary. There are thus no points on the ellipse outside of the rectangle formed by the lines $x = \pm a$ and $y = \pm b$. Thus $x > a$ and $x < -a$ are excluded intervals for x, and $y > b$ and $y < -b$ are excluded intervals for y (Art. 1.4).

To any value of x numerically less than a, there correspond two values of y, numerically equal but opposite in sign. Hence the curve is symmetric to the x-axis. By similar reasoning, from the second of equations (12), we find that it is also symmetric to the y-axis. Both symmetries could have been obtained by observing that equation (10) has only even powers of both x and y (Art. 1.5).

If $y = 0$, we get $x = \pm a$ for the two x-intercepts. The two points $V(a, 0)$ and $V'(-a, 0)$ (Fig. 6.8) are called the **vertices** of the ellipse.

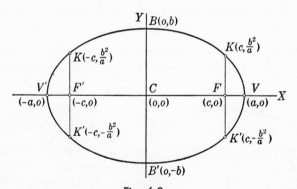

Fig. 6.8

The chord $V'V$ of length $2a$ joining them is the **major axis** of the ellipse. Similarly, the y-intercepts are $\pm b$ and the chord $B'B$ of length $2b$ joining them is the **minor axis.**

Latus Rectum. The chord $K'K$, through either focus perpendicular to the major axis, is called the **latus rectum.** Its length is obviously twice the ordinate of K. To find this ordinate, put $x = \pm c$ in (12). We find, by the aid of (9), that

$$y = \pm \frac{b}{a} \sqrt{a^2 - c^2} = \pm \frac{b^2}{a}.$$

Hence, *the length of the latus rectum is* $2b^2/a$. The ends of the two latera recta along with the ends of the major and minor axes give eight points of the ellipse which are quickly obtained and give a fairly accurate sketch of the curve.

Eccentricity. The fraction c/a is called the **eccentricity** and is denoted by the letter e. We have, by (9),

$$e = \frac{c}{a} = \frac{\sqrt{a^2 - b^2}}{a}. \tag{13}$$

Since, for an ellipse, c is always less than a, it follows that *the eccentricity of an ellipse is always less than unity.*

The shape of the ellipse (but not its size) is determined by its eccentricity. Thus, if $e = 0$, then $c = 0$, $b = a$, and the ellipse is a circle with its foci coincident at the center. As e increases from zero, the ellipse becomes more and more flattened. If we let e approach unity, holding a fixed, then c approaches a and b approaches zero so that the foci approach the vertices and the ellipse becomes very narrow.

Example 1. The vertices of an ellipse are $(\pm 4, 0)$ and its eccentricity is $e = \sqrt{3}/2$. Find its equation, locate the foci, and find the length of the latus rectum.

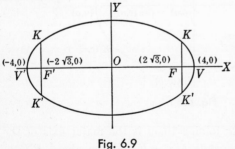

Fig. 6.9

We have $a = 4$. (Why?) Further,

$$c = ae = 4 \cdot \sqrt{3}/2 = 2\sqrt{3}.$$

The coördinates of the foci are thus $(\pm 2\sqrt{3}, 0)$. Moreover, $b^2 = a^2 - c^2 = 16 - 12 = 4$. Hence $b = 2$. The length of the latus rectum, as found from the formula $2b^2/a$, is equal to 2.

The equation of the ellipse, as found by substituting the values of a and b in equation (10), is $\dfrac{x^2}{16} + \dfrac{y^2}{4} = 1$.

Example 2. The equation of an ellipse is $25x^2 + 9y^2 = 225$. Find the coördinates of the vertices, and of the ends of the minor axis, and of the foci. Find the length of the latus rectum and sketch the curve.

If we write the given equation in the form

$$\frac{x^2}{9} + \frac{y^2}{25} = 1,$$

we find, by the last paragraph of Art. 6.7, that the foci are on the y-axis. We have

$$a = 5, \quad b = 3, \quad c = \sqrt{a^2 - b^2} = 4,$$

and

$$e = \frac{c}{a} = \frac{4}{5}.$$

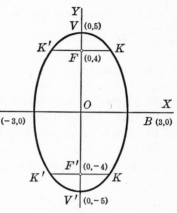

Fig. 6.10

The coördinates of the vertices are $(0, \pm 5)$, of the ends of the minor axis are $(\pm 3, 0)$, and of the foci are $(0, \pm 4)$. The length of the latus rectum is $2b^2/a = \frac{18}{5}$. This gives us the additional points $(\pm \frac{9}{5}, \pm 4)$ for sketching the curve.

6.9 Some Applications of the Ellipse. The orthogonal projection of a circle on a plane oblique to the plane of the circle is an ellipse.

Elliptic gears are used in machines, such as hay presses and power punches, where a slow, powerful motion is needed in a part, only, of each revolution.

The arches of stone and of concrete bridges are frequently constructed in the form of semi-ellipses.

The orbits in which the planets, including the earth, revolve around the sun, are ellipses.

A crescent, such as the crescent moon, is bounded by a semi-circle and a semi-ellipse.

EXERCISES

For the following equations of ellipses, find the coördinates of the vertices, of the ends of the minor axis, and of the foci. Find the length of the latus rectum and the eccentricity, and sketch the curves:

1. $16x^2 + 25y^2 = 400.$ **2.** $25x^2 + 169y^2 = 4225.$

3. $x^2 + 9y^2 = 9.$

4. $16x^2 + 9y^2 = 144.$

5. $2x^2 + y^2 = 50.$

6. $x^2 + 4y^2 = 9.$

7. $3x^2 + 4y^2 = 12.$

8. $64x^2 + 81y^2 = 64.$

Find the equation of the ellipse, given:

9. Vertices $(\pm 13, 0)$, foci $(\pm 5, 0)$. **10.** Foci $(\pm 8, 0)$, $a = 17$.

11. Foci $(0, \pm 6)$, $b = 8$. **12.** Foci $(0, \pm 3)$, $a = 4$.

13. Vertices $(\pm 5, 0)$, $e = \frac{3}{5}$. **14.** Foci $(0, \pm 6)$, $e = \frac{1}{2}$.

15. Foci $(\pm 1, 0)$, length of minor axis $2\sqrt{2}$.

16. Vertices $(0, \pm 4)$, length of latus rectum 6.

17. Ends of minor axis $(0, \pm 4)$, length of latus rectum $\frac{8}{5}$.

18. Ends of minor axis $(0, \pm 8)$, eccentricity $\frac{3}{5}$.

19. Foci $(0, \pm 2\sqrt{3})$, length of latus rectum 2.

20. Ends of minor axis, $(\pm 3, 0)$, $e = \frac{2}{7}$.

Find the equation, in one of the standard forms, of the ellipse that passes through the two given points:

21. $(3, 2)$, $(1, 4)$.   **22.** $(5, 2)$, $(4, 3)$.   **23.** $(5, 2)$, $(2, 4)$.

24. $(3, 2\sqrt{3})$, $(\sqrt{21}, 2)$.

25. Find the points of intersection of the line $x + 2y = 8$ and the ellipse $x^2 + 4y^2 = 40$.

26. Find the points of intersection of the ellipse $3x^2 + 5y^2 = 612$ and the parabola $y^2 = 3x$.

27. Show both analytically and graphically that the ellipses $2x^2 + 3y^2 = 18$ and $9x^2 + 16y^2 = 36$ do not intersect.

28. The ends of the base of a triangle are $(\pm 2, 0)$ and the sum of the lengths of the other two sides is 6. Find the equation of the locus of the vertex.

29. Find the equation of the locus of the midpoints of the ordinates of the circle $x^2 + y^2 = a^2$.

Hint. Let $p'(x', y')$ be any point on the circle. Then $x'^2 + y'^2 = a^2$. The coordinates of $P(x, y)$, the midpoint of the ordinate of P', are $x = x'$, $y = y'/2$.

30. Let $P'(x', y')$ be any point on the circle $x^2 + y^2 = a^2$ and let $P(x, y)$ be the point on the ordinate of P' such that $y = by'/a$. Find the equation of the locus of P.

31. Prove that if the coördinates of a point $P(x, y)$ satisfy equation (10), then $F'P + FP = 2a$, and thus P lies on the ellipse with foci at $F(c, 0)$ and $F'(-c, 0)$.

★ **6.10 A Second Definition of the Ellipse.** We shall prove the following theorem: *The ellipse $b^2x^2 + a^2y^2 = a^2b^2$ is the locus of a point that moves in such a way that the ratio of its undirected distance from the focus $F(ae, 0)$ to its undirected distance from the line $x - a/e = 0$ is equal to e ($e \neq 0$), the eccentricity.*

Let $P(x, y)$ be any point such that $\dfrac{FP}{RP} = e$, that is, such that

$$FP = eRP \quad \text{or} \quad FP^2 = e^2RP^2.$$

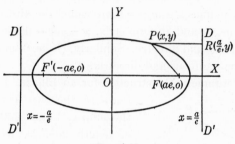

Fig. 6.11

From the distance formula, we have

$$FP^2 = (x - ae)^2 + (y - 0)^2.$$

Moreover, $\qquad\qquad RP^2 = \left(\dfrac{a}{e} - x\right)^2.$ \hfill (Why?)

If we substitute these values of FP^2 and RP^2 in the above equation, we have

$$(x - ae)^2 + (y - 0)^2 = e^2\left(\dfrac{a}{e} - x\right)^2.$$

If we simplify this equation and multiply by a^2, we obtain:

$$a^2(1 - e^2)x^2 + a^2y^2 = a^4(1 - e^2). \tag{14}$$

But, with the aid of equations (13) and (9), we find that

$$a^2(1 - e^2) = a^2 - a^2e^2 = a^2 - c^2 = b^2$$

and, on making these substitutions in (14), we have

$$b^2x^2 + a^2y^2 = a^2b^2. \tag{15}$$

Hence P lies on the given ellipse.

Conversely, if $P(x, y)$ lies on the ellipse, its coördinates satisfy (15) and, by reversing the steps in the above proof, we find that

$$\frac{FP}{RP} = e$$

that is, P satisfies the conditions of the theorem.

From the symmetry of the figure with respect to the y-axis it follows at once that the theorem of this article remains true if we replace $F(ae, 0)$ by $F'(- ae, 0)$ and the line $x - a/e = 0$ by the line $x + a/e = 0$. The lines $x \pm a/e = 0$ are called the **directrices**.

The focus $(ae, 0)$ and the directrix, $x - a/e = 0$ are said to be a *corresponding* focus and directrix. Similarly, $(- ae, 0)$ and $x + a/e = 0$ are a corresponding focus and directrix.

★ **6.11 A Continuous Construction for an Ellipse.** Fasten thumb tacks at the two foci F' and F of

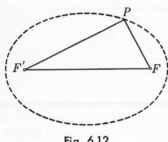

Fig. 6.12

the ellipse. Form a loop of thread of length $2a + 2c$, pass it around the thumb tacks, and draw it taut with the point of a pencil. If the pencil is now made to move around foci, holding the thread constantly taut, the pencil point will describe an ellipse.

EXERCISES

Find the equation of the following ellipses using the theorem of Art. 6.10. The given point is a focus and the given line is the corresponding directrix:

1. $(2, 0)$, $2x - 9 = 0$, $e = \frac{2}{3}$.   2. $(- 3, 0)$, $x + 12 = 0$, $e = \frac{1}{2}$.
3. $(0, - 4)$, $y + 9 = 0$, $e = \frac{2}{3}$.   4. $(0, 6)$, $3y - 32 = 0$, $e = \frac{3}{4}$.

Write the equation of the ellipse, given that its center is at the origin:

5. Focus $(2, 0)$ $e = \frac{1}{3}$.   6. Vertex $(10, 0)$, $e = \frac{3}{5}$.
7. Directrix $x + 12 = 0$, $e = \frac{1}{2}$.   8. Directrix $2y - 9 = 0$, $e = \frac{2}{3}$.
9. Focus $(0, 5)$, directrix $y - 20 = 0$.
10. Vertex $(0, - 8)$, length of latus rectum 12.
11. End of minor axis $(0, 3)$, $e = \frac{2}{5}$.
12. Directrix $3x - 20 = 0$, end of minor axis $(0, 2)$.
13. A square with sides parallel to the coördinate axes is inscribed in the ellipse $9x^2 + 16y^2 = 100$. Find the coördinates of its vertices and its area.

14. An iron bar, AB, one foot long, moves so that the end A is always on the x-axis and B is always on the y-axis. Find the locus of a point $P(x, y)$ on the bar three inches from A.

15. The arch of a bridge is a semi-ellipse with its major axis horizontal and 15 feet below the horizontal roadway. The span is 48 feet and the top of the arch is 12 feet above the major axis. Find, to three significant figures, at eight foot intervals, the vertical distance from the arch to the roadway.

16. The undirected distances of a point P on an ellipse from the foci are called the **focal radii** of P. Show that the focal radii of $P(x, y)$ on the ellipse $b^2x^2 + a^2y^2 = a^2b^2$ are $a - ex$ and $a + ex$.

Hint. Find the distances of $P(x, y)$ from the directrices and use the theorem of Art. 6.10.

Find the focal radii (Ex. 16) of the given point on the given ellipse:

17. $(5, 4)$, $9x^2 + 25y^2 = 625$.   **18.** $(2, 3)$, $3x^2 + 4y^2 = 48$.

19. $(6, -5)$, $5x^2 + 9y^2 = 405$.   **20.** $(-\sqrt{3}, 2)$, $2x^2 + 3y^2 = 18$.

21. The earth's orbit is an ellipse with the sun at one of its foci. If the major semi-axis of the ellipse is 93.0 million miles and the eccentricity is 0.0168, find, to three significant figures, the greatest and least distances of the earth from the sun.

Using the definition of Art. 6.7, find the equation of the ellipse having the given points as foci and the given length for its semi-major axis. Explain why the resulting equation is not in the standard form:

22. $(-1, 1)$, $(5, 1)$; $a = 5$.   **23.** $(-3, 2)$, $(-3, 6)$; $a = 4$.
24. $(0, 0)$, $(4, 2)$; $a = 3$.   **25.** $(-1, -3)$, $(1, 3)$; $a = 4$.

Using the definition of Art. 6.10, find the equation of the ellipse having the given point as a focus, the given line as the corresponding directrix, and the given eccentricity. Why is the resulting equation not in the standard form?

26. $(-1, 4)$, $x + 5 = 0$, $e = \frac{1}{2}$.   **27.** $(-1, -2)$, $y + 8 = 0$, $e = \frac{1}{3}$.
28. $(0, 0)$, $x + y + 2 = 0$, $e = \sqrt{2}/2$.
29. $(2, 2)$, $3x + y - 2 = 0$, $e = \frac{2}{3}$.

THE HYPERBOLA

6.12 Standard Form of the Equation of the Hyperbola. *A hyperbola is the locus of a point that moves so that the difference of its undirected distances from two fixed points is equal to a constant.*

The two fixed points are called the **foci**, the point midway between them is the **center**, and the line through the foci is the **principal axis** of the hyperbola. We shall denote the distance between the foci by $2c$ and the difference of the distances of a point on the hyperbola from the foci by $2a$. Then $a < c$, since the difference of two sides of a triangle is less than the third side.

The derivation of the standard form of the equation of the hyperbola parallels that of the ellipse (Art. 6.7). We take the principal

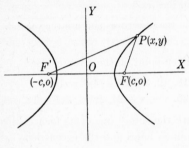

Fig. 6.13

axis as the x-axis and the center as the origin, so that the coördinates of the foci are $F(c, 0)$ and $F'(-c, 0)$ (Fig. 6.13).

Let $P(x, y)$ be any point on the curve. From the definition of the hyperbola, we have

$$F'P - FP = \pm 2a,$$

the positive sign holding for the points on the curve that lie to the right of the y-axis and the negative sign for the points to the left.

On substituting for $F'P$ and FP their values from the distance formula, we have

$$\sqrt{(x + c)^2 + y^2} - \sqrt{(x - c)^2 + y^2} = \pm 2a.$$

By transposing the second radical, squaring, and simplifying, we find that

$$cx - a^2 = \pm a\sqrt{(x - c)^2 + y^2}.$$

If we square again and collect terms, we obtain

$$(c^2 - a^2)x^2 - a^2y^2 = a^2(c^2 - a^2). \tag{16}$$

We have seen that, for the hyperbola, $a < c$, hence we may put

$$b^2 = c^2 - a^2. \tag{17}$$

If we make this substitution in (16), that equation becomes

$$b^2x^2 - a^2y^2 = a^2b^2,$$

or

$$\frac{x^2}{a^2} - \frac{y^2}{b^2} = 1. \tag{18}$$

It can be proved, conversely, that, if the coördinates of a point $P(x, y)$ satisfy (18), then P lies on the hyperbola. (See Ex. 29, Art. 6.14.)

Equation (18) is the standard form of the equation of the hyperbola when the foci are taken at $(\pm c, 0)$ on the x-axis. When the axes are taken so that the foci are at $(0, \pm c)$ on the y-axis, we obtain similarly the equation of the curve in the standard form

$$\frac{y^2}{a^2} - \frac{x^2}{b^2} = 1. \tag{19}$$

In the equation of a hyperbola a may be less than, equal to, or greater than b. To determine, in a numerical problem, whether the foci are on the x-axis or on the y-axis, we first write the equation in the form (18) or (19), then notice whether the coefficient of x^2, or of y^2, is positive.

6.13 Discussion of the Equation. Asymptotes. If we solve equation (18) for y and for x, we obtain

$$y = \pm \frac{b}{a} \sqrt{x^2 - a^2} \quad \text{and} \quad x = \pm \frac{a}{b} \sqrt{y^2 + b^2} \tag{20}$$

respectively.

From the first of these equations we find that if $x^2 < a^2$, y is imaginary; thus $-a < x < a$ is an excluded interval for x. From the second of these equations we see that every value of y gives two values of x.

Equation (18) contains only even powers for both x and y, and thus the hyperbola is symmetric to both axes.

The intercepts of the hyperbola (18) on the x-axis are found by putting $y = 0$ and solving for x. We obtain $x = \pm a$. The points $V'(-a, 0)$ and $V(a, 0)$ are the **vertices.** The segment $V'V$ of length $2a$ is the **transverse axis** of the hyperbola. Although the hyperbola does not intersect the y-axis (why?), the segment from $B'(0, -b)$ to $B(0, b)$ of length $2b$ is called the **conjugate axis.** The lines $y = \pm bx/a$, which are obtained by extending the diagonals of the rectangle whose sides are of length $2a$ and $2b$ (see Fig. 6.14), play a significant role in the discussion of the equation of the hyperbola.

We now show that if a point $P_1(x_1, y_1)$ recedes along the curve indefinitely far from the origin, its distance from one of the lines

$y = \pm\, bx/a$ becomes indefinitely small. Because of the symmetry of the curve it will be sufficient to prove this for the line $bx = ay$ in the first quadrant. Let $P_1(x_1, y_1)$ lie on the hyperbola so that

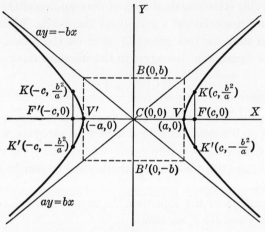

Fig. 6.14

$b^2x_1^2 - a^2y_1^2 = a^2b^2$, or therefore $(bx_1 - ay_1)(bx_1 + ay_1) = a^2b^2$. The directed distance d from the line $bx - ay = 0$ to the point (x_1, y_1) is (Art. 3.11),

$$d = \frac{bx_1 - ay_1}{-\sqrt{a^2 + b^2}} = \frac{-a^2b^2}{\sqrt{a^2 + b^2}(bx_1 + ay_1)}.$$

As x_1 increases so does y_1 (Why?). Hence as x_1 and y_1 increase indefinitely the numerical value of d decreases and becomes indefinitely small, but can never actually be zero.

The lines

$$y = \frac{bx}{a}, \quad \text{and} \quad y = -\frac{bx}{a} \tag{21}$$

are, by the proof above, good approximations to the form of the hyperbola a long way from the origin. They are called the **asymptotes** to the hyperbola (18).

An analogous discussion of the asymptotes to a hyperbola whose equation in standard from is (19) would yield that the equations of the asymptotes are

$$y = \frac{ax}{b} \quad \text{and} \quad y = -\frac{ax}{b}. \tag{22}$$

The chord $K'K$ of the hyperbola through either focus perpendicular to the transverse axis is the **latus rectum**. Its length is found, as in Art. 6.8, to be $2b^2/a$.

In drawing a hyperbola it is usually best to construct the asymptotes first and then plot the vertices and the ends of the latera recta. Additional points can be obtained by means of the equation, if needed. The hyperbola can then be drawn passing through these points and approaching the asymptotes.

The quotient c/a is denoted by e and is called the **eccentricity**. From (17), we have

$$e = \frac{c}{a} = \frac{\sqrt{a^2 + b^2}}{a}. \tag{23}$$

Since, for a hyperbola, a is always less than c, it follows that *the eccentricity of a hyperbola is always greater than unity.*

Example 1. Determine the vertices, foci, eccentricity, length of the latus rectum, and the equations of the asymptotes, and plot the hyperbola $16x^2 - 9y^2 = 144$.

If we write the given equation in the standard form $\dfrac{x^2}{9} - \dfrac{y^2}{16} = 1$, we find that $a = 3$, $b = 4$, $c = \sqrt{a^2 + b^2} = 5$, and $e = c/a = 5/3$.

Since the transverse axis is on the x-axis, the vertices are $(\pm 3, 0)$ and the foci $(\pm 5, 0)$ (Fig. 6.15).

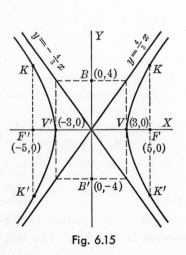

Fig. 6.15

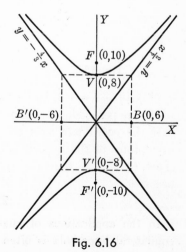

Fig. 6.16

The equations of the asymptotes are $y = \frac{4}{3}x$ and $y = -\frac{4}{3}x$. The length of the latus rectum is $2b^2/a = 32/3$. This gives us the points $(\pm\,5, \pm\,32/3)$ on the hyperbola.

Example 2. The vertices of a hyperbola are $(0, \pm\,8)$ and the equations of the asymptotes are $3y = \pm\,4x$. Find the coördinates of the foci, the eccentricity, and the equation of the curve.

Since the vertices are on the y-axis the standard equation of the hyperbola will be of the form $\dfrac{y^2}{a^2} - \dfrac{x^2}{b^2} = 1$. Thus the asymptotes will be of the form $y = \pm\,\dfrac{a}{b}x = \pm\,\dfrac{4}{3}x$. We have $a = 8$, which gives $8/b = 4/3$. Hence $b = 6$, $c = \sqrt{a^2 + b^2} = \sqrt{8^2 + 6^2} = 10$, and $e = c/a = 5/4$ (Fig. 6.16). Thus the coördinates of the foci are $(0, \pm\,10)$ and the equation of the curve is $\dfrac{y^2}{64} - \dfrac{x^2}{36} = 1$.

6.14 Equilateral Hyperbola. If we put $b = a$ in equation (18), and multiply through by a^2, that equation becomes

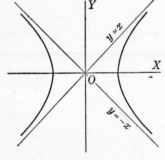

Fig. 6.17

$$x^2 - y^2 = a^2. \tag{24}$$

In this special case, the hyperbola is called an **equilateral** (or **rectangular**) **hyperbola.** Equilateral hyperbolas bear substantially the same relation to hyperbolas that circles bear to ellipses.

The eccentricity of the equilateral hyperbola is found, by putting $b = a$ in (23), to be $e = \sqrt{2}$. Its asymptotes are the lines $y = x$ and $y = -x$ which are perpendicular to each other.

If the coördinate axes are rotated through $-45°$, so that the asymptotes of the hyperbola become the coördinate axes, we shall show (Art. 7.5) that the equation of the equilateral hyperbola becomes

$$2xy = a^2. \tag{25}$$

In the applications of analytic geometry, the equation of the equilateral hyperbola is often encountered in this form. The best known of these is Boyle's Law, which states that for a gas held at constant temperature, the product of the pressure, p, and the volume, v, is a constant, k, which depends upon the gas and the temperature. Thus $pv = k$ expresses the law.

EXERCISES

Find the vertices, foci, eccentricity, length of the latus rectum, and the equations of the asymptotes and plot the following hyperbolas:

1. $25x^2 - 144y^2 = 3600$.   **2.** $x^2 - 4y^2 = 16$.

3. $16x^2 - 25y^2 = 400$.   **4.** $x^2 - 9y^2 = 36$.

5. $y^2 - x^2 = 16$.   **6.** $9y^2 - 25x^2 = 225$.

7. $9y^2 - 4x^2 = 36$.   **8.** $8y^2 - x^2 = 8$.

9. $3x^2 - y^2 = 3$.   **10.** $x^2 - 3y^2 = 9$.

Find the equations of the following hyperbolas in one of the standard forms (18) or (19):

11. Vertices $(\pm 2, 0)$, foci $(\pm 3, 0)$.

12. Foci $(\pm 10, 0)$, $e = \frac{5}{4}$.

13. Vertices $(\pm 15, 0)$, asymptotes $5y = \pm 4x$.

14. Foci $(0, \pm 6)$, length of conjugate axis $4\sqrt{5}$.

15. Ends of conjugate axes $(\pm 4, 0)$, asymptotes $2y = \pm 3x$.

16. Vertices $(0, \pm 4)$, length of latus rectum 10.

17. Foci $(\pm 5, 0)$, asymptotes $2y = \pm x$.

18. Ends of the conjugate axes $(0, \pm 3)$, $e = 2$.

19. Foci $(\pm 5, 0)$, length of the latus rectum $\frac{9}{2}$.

20. Latus rectum parallel to y-axis and of length 9, asymptotes $4y = \pm 3x$.

21. It passes through $(5, 9)$ and its asymptotes are $y = \pm x$.

22. It passes through $(4, 2)$ and its asymptotes are $3y = \pm 2x$.

23. It passes through $(-5, 2)$ and $(7, 10)$.

24. It passes through $(4, 2)$ and $(8, -6)$.

25. Find the points of intersection of the hyperbolas $3x^2 - 7y^2 = 5$ and $9y^2 - 2x^2 = 1$.

26. Find the equation of the hyperbola that has the same points for foci as the ellipse $3x^2 + 16y^2 = 48$ and has the lines $3y = \pm 2x$ as asymptotes.

27. Find the locus of the center of a circle that passes through $(6, 0)$ and is tangent to the circle $x^2 + y^2 + 12x = 0$.

Hint. If two circles are tangent externally (or internally) the distance between their centers equals the sum (or difference) of their radii.

28. Show that the distance from a focus of a hyperbola to an asymptote is numerically equal to the semi-conjugate axis.

29. Prove that if the coördinates of a point $P(x, y)$ satisfy equation (18), then P lies on the hyperbola with foci at $F(c, 0)$ and $F'(-c, 0)$.

★ **6.15 A Second Definition of the Hyperbola.** The following property of a hyperbola is also frequently used to define the curve: *The hyperbola $b^2x^2 - a^2y^2 = a^2b^2$ is the locus of a point that moves in such a way that the ratio of its undirected distance from the focus $F(ae, 0)$ to its undirected distance from the line $x - a/e = 0$ is equal to e, its eccentricity.*

The proof of this theorem, which parallels that given in Art. 6.10 for the ellipse, is left as an exercise for the student. For the hyperbola, we have $e > 1$, and

$$b^2 = c^2 - a^2 = a^2(e^2 - 1)$$

which changes the sign of b^2 from the value given in the derivation of equation (15).

From the symmetry of the figure with respect to the y-axis, it follows at once that the above theorem remains true if we replace the focus $F(ae, 0)$ by $F'(-ae, 0)$ and the line $x - a/e = 0$ by $x + a/e = 0$. The lines $x \pm a/e = 0$ are called the **directrices**.

The focus $(ae, 0)$ and the directrix $x - a/e = 0$ are called a *corresponding* focus and directrix, as are also $(-ae, 0)$ and $x + a/e = 0$.

★ **6.16 A Continuous Construction for a Hyperbola.** At one focus F' of the required hyperbola, fasten one end of a ruler of length l.

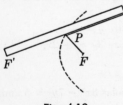

Attach one end of a string of length $l - 2a$ at the free end of the ruler and the other end at the second focus F. Hold the string taut by pressing it with the point of a pencil against the side of the ruler. If the ruler is now rotated about F', the point of the pencil will describe an arc of the hyperbola.

Fig. 6.18

Exercise. Prove that the construction just outlined yields a hyperbola.

EXERCISES

Using the definition of a hyperbola given in Art. 6.15, find the equation of the hyperbola having the given point as focus, the given line as directrix and the given eccentricity:

1. $(6, 0)$, $2x - 3 = 0$, $e = 2$.   2. $(-12, 0)$, $3x + 4 = 0$, $e = 3$.
3. $(0, -9)$, $y + 3 = 0$, $e = \sqrt{3}$.   4. $(0,9)$, $y - 4 = 0$, $e = \frac{3}{2}$.
5. $(-5, 0)$, $5x + 4 = 0$, $e = \frac{5}{2}$.   6. $(0, -5)$, $y + 4 = 0$, $e = \sqrt{5}/2$.

Find for the given hyperbola, the vertices, foci, eccentricity, and the equations of the directrices, and plot the curve:

7. $9x^2 - 16y^2 = 576$.   8. $25x^2 - 144y^2 = 14400$.
9. $3y^2 - x^2 = 12$.   10. $9y^2 - 7x^2 = 63$.
11. $4x^2 - 25y^2 = 100$.   12. $3x^2 - 2y^2 = 6$.

13. The undirected distances of a point $P(x, y)$ on a hyperbola from the foci are called the **focal radii** of P. Show that the focal radii of the point $P(x, y)$ on the hyperbola $b^2x^2 - a^2y^2 = a^2b^2$ are numerically equal to $ex - a$ and $ex + a$.

Find the focal radii (Ex. 13) of the given point on the given hyperbola:

14. $(4, 15)$, $15x^2 - y^2 = 15$.   15. $(12, 10)$, $5x^2 - 4y^2 = 320$.
16. $(9, 24)$, $8x^2 - y^2 = 72$.   17. $(2, 3)$, $3x^2 - y^2 = 3$.

18. A point moves so that the product of its directed distances from the lines $y - mx = 0$ and $y + mx = 0$ is equal to a constant k^2. Show that its locus is a hyperbola that has these lines as asymptotes.

19. The two hyperbolas $\dfrac{x^2}{a^2} - \dfrac{y^2}{b^2} = 1$ and $\dfrac{x^2}{a^2} - \dfrac{y^2}{b^2} = -1$ are called **conjugate hyperbolas.** Show that these hyperbolas have the same asymptotes, and that the transverse axis of each is the conjugate axis of the other.

The equations of the hyperbolas in Ex. 20–27 are not in the standard form.

Using the definition of Art. 6.12, find the equation of the hyperbola having the given points as foci and the given semi-transverse axis:

20. $(-2, -1)$, $(10, -1)$, $a = 4$.   21. $(3, -3)$, $(3, 7)$, $a = 3$.
22. $(-4, 2)$, $(4, -2)$, $a = 2$.   23. $(3, 4)$, $(-1, -2)$, $a = 1$.

Using the definition of Art. 6.15, find the equation of the hyperbola having the given point and line as corresponding focus and directrix and having the given eccentricity:

24. $(3, 1)$, $x + 5 = 0$, $e = 2$.   25. $(2, -1)$, $y - 2 = 0$, $e = \frac{3}{2}$.
26. $(1, 2)$, $3x + 2y - 1 = 0$, $e = \sqrt{26}$.
27. (a, a), $x + y - a = 0$, $e = \sqrt{2}$.

6.17 Standard Equation of a Conic in Polar Coördinates. Combining the definitions of Arts. 6.3, 6.10, and 6.15, we obtain the fol-

lowing single definition which holds for either the ellipse, parabola, or hyperbola: *A conic is the locus of a point that moves in such a way that the ratio of its undirected distance from a fixed point (a focus) to its undirected distance from a fixed line (the corresponding directrix) is equal to a constant e, the eccentricity.*

    The conic is

an ellipse if e < 1,

a parabola if e = 1,

a hyperbola if e > 1.

We shall derive the standard polar equations of these three conics from the above definition. We take the focus as origin,* the principal

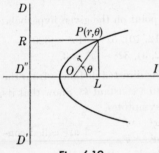

Fig. 6.19

axis as polar axis, and we shall suppose that this polar axis is directed away from the directrix (Fig. 6.19).

    Let the polar axis intersect the directrix at D'' and denote the length of the segment $D''O$ by p.

    Let $P(r, \theta)$ † be any point on the conic and let R and L (Fig. 6.19) be the feet of the perpendiculars from P to the directrix and to the polar axis, respectively. From the definition of the conic, we have

$$OP = e \cdot RP.$$

But $$\overline{OP} = r$$

and $$\overline{RP} = \overline{D''L} = \overline{D''O} + \overline{OL} = p + r \cos \theta.$$

Hence $$r = e(p + r \cos \theta) = ep + er \cos \theta.$$

If we solve the last of these equations for r, we obtain

$$r = \frac{ep}{1 - e \cos \theta}. \tag{26}$$

---

    * Since the focus is not the origin in any one of the standard rectangular equations of a conic, a transformation of the standard polar equation into rectangular coördinates will, in no case, lead to the standard rectangular equation.

    † The following proof supposes (1) that the polar coördinates of P have been chosen so that r is positive and (2) that P and the origin lie on the same side of the directrix. Supposition (1) can always be made but (2) fails for one branch of the hyperbola. In that case, however, we are led to the same final equation if we suppose the coördinates of P chosen so that r is negative.

Conversely, if the coördinates of a point P satisfy (26), we find, by reversing the steps in the above proof, that $OP = e \cdot RP$ so that P lies on the given conic.

In deriving (26), we supposed that the polar axis was directed away from the given directrix. If it is directed toward the directrix, we find in a similar way that

$$r = \frac{ep}{1 + e \cos \theta}. \tag{27}$$

Finally, if we take the directrix parallel to the polar axis, the origin remaining at the focus, we obtain, as the required equation of the conic, either

$$r = \frac{ep}{1 - e \sin \theta} \quad \text{or} \quad r = \frac{ep}{1 + e \sin \theta}, \tag{28}$$

the first equation holding if the polar axis lies *above* the given directrix and the second if it lies *below* it.

Equations (26), (27), and (28) are the standard polar equations of a conic.

One of the best known applications for the standard polar equation of a conic is in its use by astronomers in their study of the orbits of the planets.

Example 1. Reduce the equation $r = \dfrac{6}{2 - \cos \theta}$ to the standard form. Locate the vertices, the center, and the ends of the latus rectum that passes through the origin. Find the values of e, a, and b.

To reduce the equation to the standard form, we must make the first term in the denominator unity by dividing each term in the numerator and denominator by 2. We thus obtain $r = \dfrac{3}{1 - \frac{1}{2} \cos \theta}$. By comparing this equation with (26), we find that $e = \frac{1}{2}$. The curve is thus an ellipse.

The vertices of the ellipse are found, as the intersections of the principal axis with the curve, to be $(6, 0°)$ and $(2, 180°)$. Since the center lies midway between the vertices, its coördinates are $(2, 0°)$. The distance from the center to either vertex is a. Hence $a = 4$. (See Fig. 6.20.)

The ends of the latus rectum are the intersections of the 90°-axis with the curve. By putting $\theta = \pm 90°$ in the equation, we find the coördinates of these points to be $(3, 90°)$ and $(3, -90°)$. The length of the latus rectum is the distance between these points, which is 6. By Art. 6.8, the length of the latus rectum is $2b^2/a$. Since $a = 4$, we have $2b^2/a = 2b^2/4 = 6$. Hence, $b = \sqrt{12} = 2\sqrt{3}$.

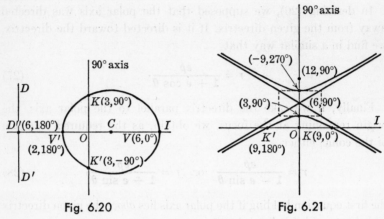

Fig. 6.20   **Fig. 6.21**

Example 2. Sketch the graph of the conic whose equation is

$$r = \frac{9}{1 + 2 \sin \theta}.$$

This is in the form of the second of equations (28) with $e = 2$ and thus is a hyperbola where the polar axis is parallel to but below the directrix. To get the vertices, substitute $\theta = 90°$ and $\theta = 270°$ in the equation. This gives the vertices as $(3, 90°)$ and $(-9, 270°)$. Thus the center is $(6, 90°)$ and $a = 3$. To get the ends of the latus rectum, put $\theta = 0°$ and $\theta = 180°$. This gives the points $(9, 0°)$ and $(9, 180°)$. Thus $2b^2/a = 18$ and therefore $b = 3\sqrt{3}$. Now by constructing the rectangle the length of whose sides are $2a$ and $2b$ as shown in Fig. 6.21, we can draw the asymptotes as the extended diagonals of the rectangle. By symmetry, we see that the other focus is $(12, 90°)$ and we can locate the ends of the other latus rectum. This gives us enough for a fairly accurate sketch of the hyperbola.

EXERCISES

Find the coördinates of the vertex or vertices, the eccentricity, the length of the latus rectum and the polar equation of the directrix corresponding to the focus at the origin, given:

1. $r = \dfrac{20}{5 - 3 \cos \theta}$.   **2.** $r = \dfrac{4}{2 - 3 \cos \theta}$.

3. $r = \dfrac{8}{1 - \sin \theta}$.

4. $r = \dfrac{10}{1 + \cos \theta}$.

5. $r = \dfrac{14}{2 + 5 \cos \theta}$.

6. $r = \dfrac{12}{4 + \cos \theta}$.

7. $r = \dfrac{66}{6 - 5 \sin \theta}$.

8. $r = \dfrac{12}{1 - \sin \theta}$.

9. $r = \dfrac{24}{3 - 5 \sin \theta}$.

10. $r = \dfrac{30}{2 + 7 \sin \theta}$.

11. $r = \dfrac{5}{1 + \sin \theta}$.

12. $r = \dfrac{28}{4 + 3 \sin \theta}$.

Find the polar equation of a conic with a focus at the origin, given:

13. Vertices $(7, 180°)$, $(3, 180°)$.   **14.** Vertex $(7, 0°)$, $e = 1$.

15. Center $(2, 0°)$, $a = 3$.   **16.** Directrix $r \sin \theta + 6 = 0$, $e = \frac{1}{2}$.

17. Center $(12, 90°)$, vertex $(30, 90°)$.

18. Vertex $(2, 90°)$, latus rectum 8.

19. Center $(6, 0°)$, directrix corresponding to the focus at the origin $3r \cos \theta - 10 = 0$.

20. Latus rectum 16, directrix corresponding to the focus at the origin $5r \sin \theta + 24 = 0$.

21. Center $(\frac{14}{3}, 0°)$, latus rectum 14 (two solutions).

22. If the conic is a parabola, show that the standard polar equations (26) and (27) may be reduced to $2r \sin^2 \theta/2 = p$ and $2r \cos^2 \theta/2 = p$.

23. Show that, if the conic (26) is an ellipse, the length of its major axis is $2ep/(1 - e^2)$ and, if it is a hyperbola, the length of its transverse axis is $2ep/(e^2 - 1)$.

24. Transform equation (26) to rectangular coördinates.

MISCELLANEOUS EXERCISES

1. Find the equation of the parabola with vertex at the origin, having the y-axis as principal axis, and passing through $(12, 6)$.

2. Find the equation of the ellipse whose foci are $(\pm 3, 0)$ and whose vertices are $(\pm 4, 0)$.

3. Find the equation in a standard form of the equilateral hyperbola through $(\pm 4, \pm 5)$.

4. Find the equation of the locus of a point, given that the product of its directed distances from the lines $3x - 4y = 0$ and $3x + 4y = 0$ is -1. Show that the locus is a hyperbola and find the coördinates of its vertices and the equations of its directrices.

5. Find the points of intersection of the parabola $y^2 - 12x = 0$ and the line $2x + 3y + 12 = 0$.

6. Find graphically the number of points of intersection of the ellipse $9x^2 + 4y^2 = 40$ and the parabola $x^2 = 4y$. Determine these points algebraically.

7. Find the equation of the hyperbola that has $(\pm 2, 0)$ for vertices and $(\pm 3, 0)$ for foci.

8. Find the equation of the hyperbola that has the vertices of $9x^2 + 25y^2 = 225$, as foci and the foci as vertices.

9. The ends of the base of a triangle are $(\pm a, 0)$ and the product of the slopes of the sides is $-b^2/a^2$. Find the equation of the locus of the vertex.

10. Find the eccentricity of an ellipse if the lines joining a focus to the ends of the minor axis are perpendicular.

11. Show that the lines joining a vertex of a hyperbola to the ends of the conjugate axis are parallel to the asymptotes.

12. Show that the eccentricity of a hyperbola is numerically equal to the secant of the angle made by an asymptote with the principal axis.

13. Show that the midpoints of all the chords of the parabola $y^2 = 2px$ that are parallel to the line $y = mx$ lie on the line $my = p$.

SELECTED EXERCISES

1. Show that the lines of the family $y = mx + \dfrac{p}{2m}$, in which m is the parameter, are tangent to the parabola $y^2 = 2px$. What is the geometrical meaning of the parameter?

Hint. Algebraically, the condition that a line is tangent to a conic is that its two intersections with the conic coincide.

2. Show that the lines of the family $y = mx \pm \sqrt{a^2m^2 + b^2}$, in which m is the parameter, are tangent to the ellipse $b^2x^2 + a^2y^2 = a^2b^2$.

3. Find the condition on k that the line $y = mx + k$ is tangent to the hyperbola $b^2x^2 - a^2y^2 = a^2b^2$. Hence find the equation of the family of lines tangent to this hyperbola.

4. Show that, if the point $P_1(x_1, y_1)$ lies on the parabola $y^2 = 2px$, then the line $y_1y = p(x + x_1)$ is tangent to the parabola at P_1.

5. Show that, if the point $P_1(x_1, y_1)$ lies on the ellipse $b^2x^2 + a^2y^2 = a^2b^2$ then the line $b^2x_1x + a^2y_1y = a^2b^2$ is tangent to the ellipse at P_1.

6. Show that, if the point $P_1(x_1, y_1)$ lies on the hyperbola $b^2x^2 - a^2y^2 = a^2b^2$, then the line $b^2x_1x - a^2y_1y = a^2b^2$ is tangent to the hyperbola at P_1.

7. If a right triangle inscribed in a conic has its right angle at a vertex of the conic, show that the point of intersection of the hypotenuse with the principal axis is independent of the angle the legs make with the principal axis.

8. Given the family of conics $\dfrac{x^2}{a^2 + k} + \dfrac{y^2}{b^2 + k} = 1$, in which k is the parameter. Show (*a*) that all the conics of this family are confocal (that is, that they have the same foci), (*b*) that through any point P_1 in the plane (not lying on a coördinate axis) there pass two conics of the family, (*c*) that the tangent lines at P_1 to the two conics that pass through P_1 are perpendicular.

Transformation of Coordinates

7.1 Changing the Coördinate Axes. It frequently happens that the solution of a problem in analytic geometry can be simplified by the use of a different pair of coördinate axes from the one employed in the statement of the problem. The process of changing from one pair of coördinate axes to another is called a **transformation of coördinates.**

If the new axes are parallel, respectively, to the old ones, and if they have the same positive directions, the transformation is

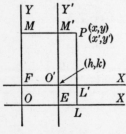

Fig. 7.1

called a **translation of axes.** If the origin remains unchanged, and the new axes are obtained by revolving the old ones about the origin through a certain angle, then the transformation is a **rotation of axes.**

7.2 Translation of Axes. Let OX and OY (Fig. 7.1) be the original axes and let $O'X'$ and $O'Y'$ be the new ones, parallel, respectively, to the old and having the same positive directions. Let the coördinates of O', referred to OX and OY, be (h, k).

Let P be any given point in the plane and let its coördinates, referred to the old axes, be (x, y) and, referred to the new ones, be (x', y'). It is required to find the values of x and y in terms of x' and y'.

Let L and L' be the feet of the perpendiculars from P on OX and $O'X'$, respectively, and M and M' the feet of the perpendiculars on OY and $O'Y'$. We have

$$x = \overline{OL} = \overline{OE} + \overline{EL} = \overline{OE} + \overline{O'L'} = h + x',$$
$$y = \overline{OM} = \overline{OF} + \overline{FM} = \overline{OF} + \overline{O'M'} = k + y'.$$

Hence *the formulas for a translation of axes are:*

$$x = x' + h \qquad y = y' + k \tag{1}$$

where (h, k) are the old coördinates of the new origin.

Equations (1) are frequently spoken of as defining a *translation of the origin to the point* (h, k).

Example 1. Find the equation of the conic $4x^2 - y^2 + 16x - 2y + 19 = 0$ when the origin is translated to the point $(-2, -1)$.

We have from (1), since $h = -2$ and $k = -1$,

$$x = x' - 2, \qquad y = y' - 1.$$

If we substitute these values of x and y in the given equation, we obtain

$$4(x' - 2)^2 - (y' - 1)^2 + 16(x' - 2) - 2(y' - 1) + 19 = 0.$$

By expanding and simplifying this equation, we find, as the equation of the given conic referred to the new axes,

$$y'^2 - 4x'^2 = 4.$$

This is the standard equation of a hyperbola with its center at the new origin and its transverse axis on the y'-axis. If we draw, with reference to the new axes, the curve defined by this last equation, the resulting locus will also be the graph of the original equation referred to the old axes (Fig. 7.2).

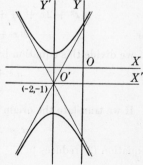

Fig. 7.2

Example 2. Find a translation of axes that will transform the equation $9x^2 + 4y^2 + 18x$

$- 24y + 9 = 0$ into one in which the coefficients of the first degree terms are zero.

First solution. If we substitute the values of x and y from (1) in the given equation and collect the coefficients of the various powers of x' and y', we have

$$9x'^2 + 4y'^2 + (18h + 18)x' + (8k - 24)y' + 9h^2 + 4k^2 + 18h - 24k + 9 = 0.$$

Equating to zero the coefficients of x' and y' gives

$$18h + 18 = 0 \quad \text{and} \quad 8k - 24 = 0$$

so that $h = -1$ and $k = 3$.

On substituting these values of h and k in the transformed equation, we obtain

$$9x'^2 + 4y'^2 - 36 = 0.$$

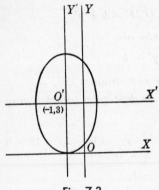

Fig. 7.3

The curve is an ellipse which has its center at the new origin, its major axis on the y'-axis, and semi-axes $a = 3$ and $b = 2$.

Second solution. By collecting the terms in x and in y, and factoring out the coefficients of x^2 and y^2, respectively, we may write the given equation in the form

$$9(x^2 + 2x \quad) + 4(y^2 - 6y \quad) = -9.$$

We can complete the square inside the first parenthesis by adding 1 and, inside the second, by adding 9. (Why?) Because of the coefficients outside these parentheses, by inserting these numbers we add 9 and 36, respectively, to the left-hand member. To preserve the equality, we must add the same numbers to the right-hand member. We then have

$$9(x^2 + 2x + 1) + 4(y^2 - 6y + 9) = -9 + 9 + 36$$

or

$$9(x + 1)^2 + 4(y - 3)^2 = 36.$$

If we divide this equation by 36, we have

$$\frac{(x + 1)^2}{4} + \frac{(y - 3)^2}{9} = 1. \tag{2}$$

If we translate the origin by putting

$$x = x' - 1, \qquad y = y' + 3,$$

equation (2) reduces to

$$\frac{x'^2}{4} + \frac{y'^2}{9} = 1.$$

This is the standard form for the equation of an ellipse with its center at the new origin. Hence, equation (2) is the equation of an ellipse with its center at $(-1, 3)$ and axes parallel to the coördinate axes.

This method of solving the given problem not only is shorter than the first one but also leads to the useful form (2) of the equation of the conic.

★ **7.3 The Quadratic Function.** The expression

$$ax^2 + bx + c \qquad (a \neq 0)$$

is called a **quadratic function** of x and the graph of the equation obtained by equating it to y is the *graph of the quadratic function.*

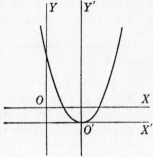

Fig. 7.4

We shall show that the graph of the quadratic function, that is, of the equation

$$y = ax^2 + bx + c \qquad (3)$$

is a parabola by reducing this equation, by a translation of axes, to one of the standard forms of the equation of the parabola.

We may write the given equation in the form

$$y = a\left(x^2 + \frac{b}{a}x + \frac{b^2}{4a^2}\right) + c - \frac{b^2}{4a}$$

or

$$y + \frac{b^2 - 4ac}{4a} = a\left(x + \frac{b}{2a}\right)^2.$$

If we now translate the coördinate axes by means of the equations

$$x = x' - \frac{b}{2a}, \quad y = y' - \frac{b^2 - 4ac}{4a}$$

the given equation reduces to

$$y' = ax'^2 \qquad (4)$$

which is the equation of a parabola with vertex at the new origin and focus on the y'-axis.

If $a > 0$, the parabola (3) opens upward and the vertex is the lowest point on it. Similarly, if $a < 0$, the vertex is the highest point on the curve. Hence we have the following useful property of the quadratic function: *The value of x for which $ax^2 + bx + c$ takes* *its least value if a > 0, and its greatest value if a < 0, is* $x = -b/2a$. *This extreme value of the function is*

$$\frac{4ac - b^2}{4a}.$$

EXERCISES

1. Find the new coördinates of the points $(5, 1)$, $(-2, 3)$, $(-4, -6)$, $(1, -2)$, $(0, 2)$, and $(5, 0)$ when the origin is translated to $(3, -1)$.

2. Find the old coördinates of the following points, given that the origin has been translated to $(2, 5)$ and that the new coördinates are $(3, 2)$, $(-1, 3)$, $(-4, -1)$, $(5, -3)$, $(2, -4)$, $(-1, 0)$, and $(0, 4)$.

Transform the following equations by translating the origin to the point indicated:

3. $2x - 3y + 7 = 0$, $(-2, 1)$.
4. $x^2 + y^2 + 6x - 8y - 11 = 0$, $(-3, 4)$.
5. $5x^2 + 9y^2 - 20x + 54y + 56 = 0$, $(2, -3)$.
6. $4x^2 - 21y^2 - 32x + 126y - 209 = 0$, $(4, 3)$.
7. $y = 2x^2 + 8x - 11$, $(-2, -19)$. Find also, from your graph, the roots of the quadratic equation $2x^2 + 8x - 11 = 0$ to one decimal place.
8. $y = -3x^2 + 6x + 5$, $(1, 8)$. Find also, from your graph, the greatest value the function $-3x^2 + 6x + 5 = 0$ can have and the value of x for which it takes this greatest value.

Remove the first degree terms from each of the following equations by a translation of axes:

9. $4x^2 + y^2 + 8x - 10y + 13 = 0$.
10. $2x^2 + 5y^2 - 12x - 20y + 8 = 0$.
11. $4x^2 - 3y^2 + 24x - 12y + 17 = 0$.
12. $7x^2 - 2y^2 + 56x + 12y + 52 = 0$.
13. $4x^2 - 5y^2 + 12x + 40y + 29 = 0$.
14. $6x^2 + 5y^2 + 24x - 40y + 74 = 0$.

Reduce the equations of the following parabolas to the standard form. State the old coördinates of the vertex and the length of the latus rectum:

15. $y^2 - 4x + 10y + 13 = 0$.   **16.** $2y^2 - 8y + 7x - 6 = 0$.
17. $x^2 - 6x - 5y + 14 = 0$.   **18.** $3x^2 + 18x + 11y + 5 = 0$.

Derive the equation of the conic from one of the definitions and reduce the resulting equation to one of the standard forms by a translation of axes:

19. Foci $(-2, 3)$, $(4, 3)$, $a = 4$.   **20.** Foci $(5, 1)$, $(5, 7)$, $a = 1$.

21. Focus $(3, -2)$, directrix $y - 1 = 0$, $e = 1$.

22. Focus $(3, 1)$, corresponding directrix $x + 5 = 0$, $e = \frac{1}{3}$.

23. Focus $(3, -2)$, corresponding directrix $2x + 3 = 0$, $e = 2$.

24. A projectile is fired from the origin with a velocity of 150 feet per second in a direction making an angle of 60° with the horizontal. If the equation of its path is $y = 1.73x - 0.00284x^2$, find, to three significant figures, how high it will rise.

25. A rectangular pasture is to be laid out alongside of a field already fenced. On each of the sides adjacent to the fenced side, there are to be two strands of wire and, on the side opposite, three strands. Find the dimensions of the largest area that can be fenced with 12,000 rods of wire.

26. Find the relation between the lengths of the adjacent sides of a rectangle if the sum of the lengths of the sides is a constant and the square of the length of a diagonal is a minimum.

7.4 Rotation of Axes. Let OX and OY be the old axes, OX' and OY', the new ones, and denote the angle XOX' by ϕ (Fig. 7.5).

Let P be any given point in the plane. Denote its coördinates, referred to the old axes, by (x, y) and, referred to the new ones, by (x', y'). It is required to find the values of x and y in terms of x' and y'.

Draw OP and let $OP = r$ and the angle $X'OP = \theta$. From the definition of the sine and cosine of an angle, we have

$$x = \overline{OL} = r \cos (\theta + \phi),$$
$$y = \overline{LP} = r \sin (\theta + \phi),$$

and

$$x' = \overline{OL'} = r \cos \theta,$$
$$y' = \overline{L'P} = r \sin \theta.$$

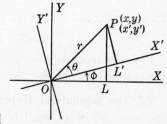

Fig. 7.5

From the formulas for the cosine and the sine of the sum of two angles, we now have

$$x = r \cos (\theta + \phi) = r \cos \theta \cos \phi - r \sin \theta \sin \phi$$
$$= x' \cos \phi - y' \sin \phi$$

and

$$y = r \sin (\theta + \phi) = r \sin \theta \cos \phi + r \cos \theta \sin \phi$$
$$= x' \sin \phi + y' \cos \phi.$$

Hence the required formulas for the *rotation of the axes through an angle ϕ* are

$$x = x' \cos \phi - y' \sin \phi$$
$$y = x' \sin \phi + y' \cos \phi. \tag{5}$$

If we solve equations (5) for x' and y', and simplify, we obtain

$$x' = x \cos \phi + y \sin \phi$$
$$y' = -x \sin \phi + y \cos \phi. \tag{6}$$

Example. Find the equation of the parabola $x^2 - 2xy + y^2 - 2ax - 2ay + a^2 = 0$ * when the axes are rotated through 45° and reduce the resulting equation by a translation of axes to the standard form.

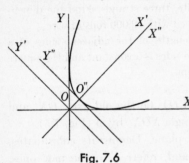

Fig. 7.6

Since $\sin 45° = \cos 45° = 1/\sqrt{2}$, equations (5) become, for this rotation,

$$x = \frac{x' - y'}{\sqrt{2}}, \quad y = \frac{x' + y'}{\sqrt{2}}.$$

On substituting these values of x and y in the given equation of the parabola, we obtain

$$\frac{(x' - y')^2}{2} - (x' - y')(x' + y') + \frac{(x' + y')^2}{2} - \sqrt{2}a(x' - y')$$
$$- \sqrt{2}a(x' + y') + a^2 = 0.$$

On expanding and simplifying this equation, we find that it reduces to

$$2y'^2 - 2\sqrt{2}ax' + a^2 = 0.$$

If we now translate the origin to the point $(\sqrt{2}a/4, 0)$, the resulting equation reduces to the standard form $y''^2 = \sqrt{2}ax''$ of the equation of a parabola.

7.5 The Equilateral Hyperbola.

We have seen (Art. 6.14) that the equation of an equilateral hyperbola with center at the origin and foci on the x-axis is

$$x^2 - y^2 = a^2.$$

------

* In the textbooks on calculus, this equation is usually given in the form $x^{\frac{1}{2}} + y^{\frac{1}{2}} = a^{\frac{1}{2}}$, wherein (contrary to the notation we have adopted) both the positive and the negative values of the square root should be taken in each case. The student should show, by removing the fractional exponents by squaring, that this equation may be reduced to the form given in the text.

The asymptotes $y = \pm x$ of this hyperbola make angles of $\pm 45°$ with the x-axis. We shall find the equation of this curve when the axes are rotated through an angle of $-45°$ so that the asymptote $y = -x$ becomes the new x'-axis and $y = x$ the new y'-axis. Since

$$\sin(-45°) = -1/\sqrt{2}, \quad \text{and} \quad \cos(-45°) = 1/\sqrt{2},$$

the equations (5) of the transformation are

$$x = \frac{x' + y'}{\sqrt{2}}, \quad y = \frac{-x' + y'}{\sqrt{2}}.$$

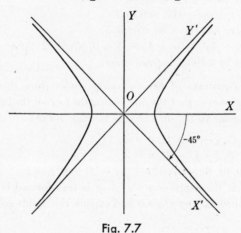

Fig. 7.7

On substituting these values of x and y in the given equation of the equilateral hyperbola, we have

$$\frac{(x' + y')^2}{2} - \frac{(-x' + y')^2}{2} = a^2,$$

which reduces, on expanding and simplifying, to

$$2x'y' = a^2. \tag{7}$$

This is the equation of the equilateral hyperbola referred to its asymptotes as coördinate axes.

EXERCISES

1. After the axes have been rotated through 45°, the new coördinates of certain points are $(5\sqrt{2}, \sqrt{2})$, $(-3\sqrt{2}, \sqrt{2})$, $(-4, -2)$, $(1, -7)$, $(-4, 0)$ and $(0, 8)$. Find the old coördinates of these points.

2. Find the new coördinates of the following points after the axes have been rotated through 60°, given that the old coördinates are $(6, 4\sqrt{3})$, $(2\sqrt{3}, -4)$, $(-1 - 3\sqrt{3}, -\sqrt{3} + 3)$, $(8, -2)$, $(6, 0)$, and $(0, -4)$.

Find the transformed equation after the axes have been rotated through the angle indicated:

3. $\sqrt{3}x + y - 10 = 0$, 30°.

4. $4x - 3y + 35 = 0$, arctan $\frac{4}{3}$.

5. $3x^2 + 10xy + 3y^2 = 12$, 45°.

6. $13x^2 - 6\sqrt{3}xy + 7y^2 = 20$, 60°.

7. $3x^2 - 6xy - 5y^2 = 12$, arctan 3.

8. $11x^2 - 4xy + 14y^2 = 30$, arctan $\frac{1}{2}$.

9. $x^2 + 4xy + 4y^2 - 3x + 4y - 5 = 0$, arctan 2. After this rotation, simplify further by a suitable translation.

Derive the equations of the following conics from their definitions. Next, rotate the axes so that the line joining the foci (or the line through the focus perpendicular to the directrix) is the new x-axis:

10. Foci $(3, 1)$, $(-3, -1)$, $a = 4$.

11. Foci $(4, 3)$, $(-4, -3)$, $a = 3$.

12. Focus $(0, 0)$, directrix $12x + 5y - 26 = 0$, $e = 1$.

13. Show that the expression $\sqrt{x^2 + y^2}$ is transformed into $\sqrt{x'^2 + y'^2}$ by a rotation through any angle ϕ and explain this result geometrically.

Conics with Equations Not in Standard Form

8.1 The General Equation of Second Degree. In Chapter 6, we studied the parabola, ellipse, and hyperbola, taking the axes, in each case, in such a position that the equation of the curve was in the standard form. Each of the equations derived in that chapter was a special case of the **general equation of second degree**; that is, of the equation

$$Ax^2 + Bxy + Cy^2 + Dx + Ey + F = 0, \tag{1}$$

where A, B, and C are not all zero.

In this chapter, we shall show that *the locus, if it exists, of any equation of second degree is a conic section;* that is, it is a parabola, ellipse, hyperbola, two straight lines,* or a point. We shall further show how, if the curve is a parabola, ellipse, or hyperbola, the equation of the curve may be reduced to its standard form. If $B = 0$, we

---

* We shall include here also the case of two parallel lines which cannot be obtained as a section of a right circular cone. They can, however, be cut from a right circular cylinder, which can be considered a limiting case of a cone.

shall see that to effect this reduction a translation of axes is sufficient. If $B \neq 0$ a rotation of axes is necessary and a translation may also be needed.

8.2 Conics with Principal Axis Parallel to a Coördinate Axis. If, in equation (1), $B = 0$, that equation takes the form

$$Ax^2 + Cy^2 + Dx + Ey + F = 0. \tag{2}$$

We first simplify this equation by the methods given in Art. 7.2. Except in certain special cases (to be stated presently) equation (2) may first be written in one of the following forms:

$$(y - k)^2 = 2p(x - h), \qquad (x - h)^2 = 2p(y - k), \tag{3}$$

$$\frac{(x-h)^2}{a^2} + \frac{(y-k)^2}{b^2} = 1, \qquad \frac{(y-k)^2}{a^2} + \frac{(x-h)^2}{b^2} = 1, \tag{4}$$

$$\frac{(x-h)^2}{a^2} - \frac{(y-k)^2}{b^2} = 1, \qquad \frac{(y-k)^2}{a^2} - \frac{(x-h)^2}{b^2} = 1. \tag{5}$$

In any one of these cases, if we translate the origin to the point (h, k) by putting

$$x = x' + h, \quad y = y' + k,$$

the equation reduces to the standard form of the equation of a parabola, ellipse, or hyperbola. It follows that: *if equation (2) reduces to one of the forms (3), the curve is a parabola; if it reduces to (4), it is an ellipse; and, if it reduces to (5), it is a hyperbola. If it is a parabola, its vertex, and if it is an ellipse or a hyperbola, its center, is at the point (h, k). In every case, its principal axis is parallel to one of the coördinate axes.*

In the following special cases, equation (2) cannot be reduced to one of the forms (3), (4), or (5). If $A = D = 0$, so that x does not appear in the equation, (2) reduces to

$$Cy^2 + Ey + F = 0 \tag{6}$$

and the locus, if it exists, reduces to the two lines parallel to the x-axis defined by solving equation (6) for y. Similarly, if $C = E = 0$, so that y does not appear, the locus, if it exists, is two lines parallel to the y-axis.

Again, equation (2) may reduce, on completing the squares, to

$$A(x - h)^2 + C(y - k)^2 = 0.$$

If A and C agree in sign, there is only one point, (h, k), on the graph and the equation is said to define a **point ellipse.** If A and C are opposite in sign, the *graph consists of two lines intersecting at* (h, k); namely,
$$\sqrt{A}(x - h) + \sqrt{-C}(y - k) = 0,$$
and
$$\sqrt{A}(x - h) - \sqrt{-C}(y - k) = 0.$$

In all of the special cases thus far enumerated, the first member of equation (2) can be factored into two (real or imaginary) linear factors and the conic is said to be a degenerate conic.

Finally, if equation (2) reduces to the form
$$A(x - h)^2 + C(y - k)^2 + F' = 0,$$

where A, C, and F' all agree in sign, there are no points on the locus and the equation is said to define an **imaginary ellipse.**

EXERCISES

Write the equations of the following parabolas in one of the forms of equations (3). Find the coördinates of the vertex and the focus. Write the equation of the directrix, and of the curve after the origin has been translated to the vertex:

1. $y^2 + 4x - 8y + 28 = 0.$ 2. $y^2 - 24x + 6y - 15 = 0.$
3. $x^2 - 4x + 8y + 36 = 0.$ 4. $5x^2 + 20x - 9y + 47 = 0.$

Write the given equation in one of the forms of equations (4) or (5). Find the coördinates of the center, vertices, and foci. Write the equation of the curve after the origin has been translated to the center:

5. $3x^2 + 4y^2 - 30x - 8y + 67 = 0.$
6. $9x^2 - 16y^2 + 90x + 64y + 17 = 0.$
7. $4x^2 - 5y^2 - 8x - 30y - 21 = 0.$
8. $9x^2 + 5y^2 + 36x + 10y - 4 = 0.$
9. $16x^2 + 7y^2 - 32x + 28y - 68 = 0.$
10. $5x^2 - 4y^2 - 10x - 24y - 51 = 0.$
11. $3x^2 - y^2 - 18x + 10y - 10 = 0.$
12. $9x^2 + 8y^2 + 54x + 80y + 209 = 0.$

Describe each of the following loci and draw the graph if it exists:

13. $9x^2 - 4y^2 - 18x - 16y - 7 = 0.$
14. $2x^2 + 3y^2 - 24x + 6y + 75 = 0.$
15. $5x^2 + 3y^2 - 20x + 6y + 40 = 0.$
16. $6x^2 + 11x - 10 = 0.$

8.3 Conics Satisfying Given Conditions. It is sometimes necessary to set up the equation of a conic having its principal axis parallel to one of the coördinate axes and satisfying a sufficient number of additional conditions to fix its position. If the curve is a parabola, we must find the coördinates of the vertex, which we take as (h, k), and the value of p, which is twice the directed distance from the vertex to the focus, and substitute these values of h, k, and p in one of equations (3). Similarly, if the curve is an ellipse or a hyperbola, we locate the center, (h, k), find the values of a and b, and substitute these values in one of equations (4) or (5).

Example 1. Find the equation of a parabola with focus $(5, 2)$ and directrix $x = 1$.

Since $p = \overline{D''F}$ (Fig. 8.1) is the directed distance from the directrix to the focus, we have $p = 4$. Further, since the vertex V is the midpoint of the segment $D''F$, its coördinates are $(3, 2)$. Since the principal axis is parallel to the x-axis, we substitute $p = 4$, $h = 3$, and $k = 2$ in the first of equations (3). The result is

$$(y - 2)^2 = 8(x - 3).$$

This is the required equation of the parabola.

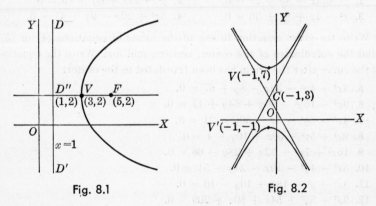

Fig. 8.1 Fig. 8.2

Example 2. Find the equation of a hyperbola given that its vertices are $(-1, -1)$ and $(-1, 7)$ and that the line $2x - y + 5 = 0$ is an asymptote.

The distance between the vertices is 8. Since this distance is $2a$, we have $a = 4$. Since the center lies midway between the vertices, its coördinates are, by Art. 2.3, equations (8), $(-1, 3)$.

Since the given asymptote passes through the center, its equation may be written in the form $2(x + 1) = (y - 3)$. But, in terms of a and b, the equation of the asymptotes are $a(x + 1) = \pm b(y - 3)$. Hence, $a/b = \frac{2}{1}$, or, since $a = 4$, $b = 2$.

The required equation is, from equations (5), after simplifying, $(y - 3)^2 - 4(x + 1)^2 = 16$.

EXERCISES

Find the equations of the following parabolas:

1. Vertex $(2, 4)$, focus $(5, 4)$.
2. Vertex $(-3, -1)$, focus $(-3, -3)$.
3. Focus $(1, 7)$, directrix $y - 3 = 0$.
4. Vertex $(-5, -2)$, directrix $x + 1 = 0$.
5. Focus $(3, -7)$, one end of latus rectum $(3, -1)$, opens to the left.
6. Ends of the latus rectum $(-4, \frac{3}{2})$ and $(10, \frac{3}{2})$, opens upward.

Find the equations of the following ellipses:

7. Vertices $(5, -1)$, $(-3, -1)$, $c = 3$.
8. Center $(-3, 2)$, vertex $(2, 2)$, $e = \frac{4}{5}$.
9. Foci $(-2, 7)$, $(-2, -1)$, $b = 2$.
10. Center $(5, 2)$, directrix $y + 4 = 0$, $c = 2$.
11. Foci $(7, -1)$, $(1, -1)$, directrix $x = 16$.
12. Vertices $(3, 2)$, $(3, -6)$, length of latus rectum 2.

Find the equations of the following hyperbolas:

13. Foci $(1, 2)$, $(-11, 2)$, $e = 3$.
14. Vertices $(-3, -1)$, $(5, -1)$, directrix $3x - 11 = 0$.
15. Vertices $(-1, -1)$, $(-1, 5)$, ends of conjugate axis $(4, 2)$, $(-6, 2)$.
16. Foci $(4, -1)$, $(4, 5)$, length of latus rectum 16.
17. Ends of conjugate axis $(3, -5)$, $(3, 7)$, length of latus rectum 8.
18. Asymptotes $3x + 4y - 11 = 0$, $3x - 4y + 5 = 0$, directrices $5x - 21 = 0$ and $5x + 11 = 0$.

8.4 Simplification by Rotation. Removal of the *xy*-term.

We shall show in this article that if, in the general equation of a conic,

$$Ax^2 + Bxy + Cy^2 + Dx + Ey + F = 0, \qquad (7)$$

the coefficient $B \neq 0$, it is always possible, by rotating the axes through a suitable angle, to reduce the equation to one in which the coefficient of the $x'y'$-term is equal to zero.

Let the coördinate axes be rotated through an angle ϕ, so that x and y are replaced by (Art. 7.4)

$$x = x' \cos \phi - y' \sin \phi, \qquad y = x' \sin \phi + y' \cos \phi.$$

After this substitution has been effected, equation (7) takes the form

$$A'x'^2 + B'x'y' + C'y'^2 + D'x' + E'y' + F' = 0, \tag{8}$$

where

$$\begin{aligned}
A' &= A \cos^2 \phi + B \sin \phi \cos \phi + C \sin^2 \phi, \\
B' &= 2(C - A) \sin \phi \cos \phi + B(\cos^2 \phi - \sin^2 \phi), \\
C' &= A \sin^2 \phi - B \sin \phi \cos \phi + C \cos^2 \phi, \\
D' &= D \cos \phi + E \sin \phi, \\
E' &= E \cos \phi - D \sin \phi, \quad \text{and} \quad F' = F.
\end{aligned} \tag{9}$$

The condition that B', the coefficient of the $x'y'$-term, becomes zero is that the angle of rotation, ϕ, is chosen so that

$$B' = 2(C - A) \sin \phi \cos \phi + B(\cos^2 \phi - \sin^2 \phi) = 0.$$

With the aid of the trigonometric formulas for the double angle (Art. 0.12), this equation may be reduced to

$$(C - A) \sin 2\phi + B \cos 2\phi = 0,$$

that is, if $C - A \neq 0$, to

$$\tan 2\phi = \frac{B}{A - C}, \tag{10}$$

and if $C - A = 0$, $B \neq 0$, to

$$\cos 2\phi = 0. \tag{10'}$$

If (10') is true, then $\phi = 45°$ is a solution. If (10) is true, it can be solved to give the required angle ϕ as illustrated in the example.

Example. Remove the xy-term from $5x^2 + 4xy + 8y^2 = 9$ by a rotation of axes.

By (10), we must rotate the axes through an angle ϕ such that

$$\tan 2\phi = \frac{4}{5 - 8} = -\frac{4}{3}.$$

By trigonometry, we have * $\cos 2\phi = -\frac{3}{5}$, and, by the half-angle formulas (Art. 0.12), we find

---

* In determining 2ϕ by means of (10), we shall suppose, throughout, that $0 \leqq 2\phi < 180°$. With this assumption, $\cos 2\phi$ will always agree in sign with $\tan 2\phi$ and, since $0 \leqq \phi < 90°$, $\sin \phi$ and $\cos \phi$ will always be positive or zero.

$$\sin \phi = \sqrt{\frac{1 - \cos 2\phi}{2}} = \sqrt{\frac{1 + \frac{3}{5}}{2}} = \frac{2}{\sqrt{5}}$$

$$\cos \phi = \sqrt{\frac{1 + \cos 2\phi}{2}} = \sqrt{\frac{1 - \frac{3}{5}}{2}} = \frac{1}{\sqrt{5}}.$$

On substituting these values of $\sin \phi$ and $\cos \phi$ in Eqns. (5), Art. 7.4, we obtain, as the formulas for the required rotation of axes,

$$x = \frac{x' - 2y'}{\sqrt{5}}, \qquad y = \frac{2x' + y'}{\sqrt{5}}.$$

If, in the given equation, we re-place x and y by these expressions, and simplify, we find, as the required equation,

$$9x'^2 + 4y'^2 = 9.$$

This is the equation of an ellipse with foci on the y'-axis and with semi-axes of lengths $\frac{3}{2}$ and 1.

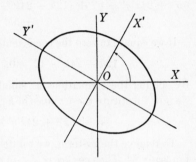

Fig. 8.3

EXERCISES

Remove the xy-term by rotation of axes. Draw both sets of axes and the curve:

1. $x^2 + 4xy - 2y^2 = 8.$ **2.** $3x^2 + 24xy - 4y^2 = 11.$
3. $4x^2 + 12xy + 9y^2 = 52.$ **4.** $4x^2 + 5xy - 8y^2 = 20.$
5. $5x^2 + 4xy + 5y^2 = 9.$ **6.** $10x^2 + 15xy + 2y^2 = 7.$
7. $11x^2 + 24xy + 4y^2 = 15.$ **8.** $5x^2 - 6xy - 3y^2 = 4.$
9. $4x^2 - 20xy + 25y^2 - 15x - 6y = 0.$

8.5 Reduction of Numerical Equations to a Standard Form. If the second degree terms in the given equation do not form a perfect square, that is if $B^2 - 4AC \neq 0$, we first translate the origin to the point (h, k), then determine h and k, as in Example 1 below, so that the coefficients of x' and y' are zero. We then rotate the axes so as to remove the xy-term.

If the second degree terms do form a perfect square, that is, if $B^2 - 4AC = 0$, it is usually not possible to make the coefficients of x' and y' both zero by a translation of axes. In this case, accordingly, we shall first remove the xy-term by a rotation of axes and then complete the simplification of the equation by a translation, as in the following Example 2.

Example 1. Simplify $6x^2 + 24xy - y^2 - 12x + 26y + 11 = 0$.

Since $B^2 - 4AC = 24^2 - 4 \cdot 6(-1) \neq 0$, we first translate the origin to the point (h, k) by putting $x = x' + h$, $y = y' + k$. We have, after collecting the coefficients,

$$6x'^2 + 24x'y' - y'^2 + (12h + 24k - 12)x' + (24h - 2k + 26)y'$$
$$+ 6h^2 + 24hk - k^2 - 12h + 26k + 11 = 0.$$

If we equate to zero the coefficients of x' and y' in this equation, we have

$$12h + 24k - 12 = 0, \qquad 24h - 2k + 26 = 0.$$

By solving these equations as simultaneous, we find $h = -1$, $k = 1$. If we now substitute these values of h and k in the above equation, we obtain

$$6x'^2 + 24x'y' - y'^2 + 30 = 0.$$

To remove the xy-term, we rotate the axes through an angle ϕ such that $\tan 2\phi = \frac{24}{7}$. Then $\cos 2\phi = \frac{7}{25}$, $\sin \phi = \frac{3}{5}$, $\cos \phi = \frac{4}{5}$, and the equations of the rotation are

$$x' = \frac{4x'' - 3y''}{5}, \qquad y' = \frac{3x'' + 4y''}{5}.$$

On making these substitutions, and simplifying, we obtain, as the required equation of the conic,

$$15x''^2 - 10y''^2 + 30 = 0, \quad \text{or} \quad \frac{y''^2}{3} - \frac{x''^2}{2} = 1.$$

The curve is a hyperbola with center at the new origin and transverse axis on the y''-axis. (See Fig. 8.4.)

Example 2. Simplify $144x^2 - 120xy + 25y^2 - 118x + 190y - 81 = 0$.

Since $B^2 - 4AC = 14400 - 14400 = 0$, we first remove the xy-term by a rotation of axes.

To determine ϕ, we put $\tan 2\phi = -\frac{120}{119}$. Hence $\cos 2\phi = -\frac{119}{169}$, $\sin \phi = \frac{12}{13}$, $\cos \phi = \frac{5}{13}$, and the equations of the required rotation are

$$x = \frac{5x' - 12y'}{13}, \qquad y = \frac{12x' + 5y'}{13}.$$

If we substitute these values of x and y in the given equation, and simplify, we obtain

$$169y'^2 + 130x' + 182y' - 81 = 0.$$

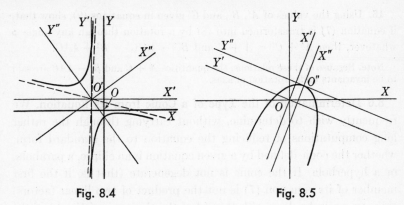

Fig. 8.4   **Fig. 8.5**

We may write this equation in the form

$$169(y' + \tfrac{7}{13})^2 + 130(x' - 1) = 0.$$

Hence, if we put $x' = x'' + 1$, $y' = y'' - \tfrac{7}{13}$, the above equation becomes

$$169y''^2 + 130x'' = 0, \quad \text{or} \quad 13y''^2 + 10x'' = 0.$$

The curve is a parabola with vertex at the new origin and axis coinciding with the x''-axis. (See Fig. 8.5.)

EXERCISES

Simplify the following equations. Draw all the coördinate axes, and draw the curve if it exists:

1. $6x^2 - 4xy + 9y^2 - 20x - 10y - 5 = 0.$
2. $2x^2 + 12xy - 3y^2 - 36x - 24y + 36 = 0.$
3. $12x^2 + 8xy - 3y^2 + 64x + 30y = 0.$
4. $9x^2 + 6xy + y^2 + 11x + 27y - 61 = 0.$
5. $2x^2 - 4xy - y^2 - 4x - 8y + 14 = 0.$
6. $11x^2 - 8xy + 11y^2 - 50x - 20y + 25 = 0.$
7. $13x^2 + 6xy + 21y^2 + 34x - 114y + 73 = 0.$
8. $11x^2 + 15xy + 3y^2 + 23x + 3y - 32 = 0.$
9. $16x^2 - 24xy + 9y^2 - 85x - 30y + 175 = 0.$
10. $2x^2 + 40xy - 7y^2 - 92x - 92y + 200 = 0.$
11. $2x^2 - 12xy + 7y^2 + 8x + 20y - 14 = 0.$
12. $5x^2 - 15xy + 13y^2 - 5x - 3y - 18 = 0.$
13. $7x^2 + 6xy - y^2 - 2x - 10y - 9 = 0.$
14. $36x^2 + 24xy + 29y^2 - 48x + 34y + 41 = 0.$
15. $25x^2 + 20xy + 4y^2 + 30x + 12y - 20 = 0.$

16. Using the values of A', B', and C' given in equations (9), show that, if equation (7) is transformed into (8) by a rotation through any angle ϕ whatever, then $A' + C' = A + C$ and $B'^2 - 4A'C' = B^2 - 4AC$.

Note. Because of these relations, the quantities $A + C$ and $B^2 - 4AC$ are said to be **invariants** under rotation of axes.

8.6 Determination of the Type of a Conic from Its Equation. We frequently wish to determine, without carrying through the rather long computations of reducing the equation to the standard form, whether the conic defined by a given equation is an ellipse, a parabola, or a hyperbola. If the conic is not degenerate (that is, if the first member of its equation (7) is not the product of two linear factors) this can easily be done with the aid of the theorems of Ex. 16 of the preceding article.

Suppose the axes have been rotated through such an angle ϕ that $B' = 0$. From Ex. 16, we now have, since $B' = 0$,

$$- 4A'C' = B^2 - 4AC \tag{11}$$

and the equation of the conic is

$$A'x'^2 + C'y'^2 + D'x' + E'y' + F' = 0. \tag{12}$$

By completing the squares of the terms in x' and in y', we see that the conic is an ellipse if A' and C' agree in sign (so that $- 4A'C'$ is negative); a parabola if either A' or C' is zero (giving $- 4A'C' = 0$); and a hyperbola if A' and C' are opposite in sign ($- 4A'C'$ positive). But, from (11), $- 4A'C' = B^2 - 4AC$. Hence, the conic (7) is:

                an ellipse if $B^2 - 4AC$ is negative,

                a parabola if $B^2 - 4AC = 0$,

and   *a hyperbola if $B^2 - 4AC$ is positive.*

EXERCISES

1 to 12. In Ex. 1 to 12 of Art. 8.5, find, without simplifying the equation or drawing the curve, whether the conic is an ellipse, a parabola, or a hyperbola.

MISCELLANEOUS EXERCISES

The ends of the base of a triangle are $A(- a, 0)$ and $B(a, 0)$. Find the locus of the vertex C, given that:

1. The sum of the slopes of the sides is $\frac{8}{3}$.

2. The product of the slopes of the sides is $\frac{2}{7}$.

3. The angle from the line AC to the line BC is arctan $\frac{2}{3}$.

4. The base angle of the triangle at A is twice the base angle at B.

5. The base angle of the triangle at A exceeds the base angle at B by 45°.

6. Taking A and B as in the preceding exercises, let C describe the line $y = b$ and find the locus of the point of intersection of the altitudes of the triangle.

7. Find the equation of the locus of a point, given that the square of its distance from the origin equals the sum of the squares of its distances from the lines $ax + by - ab = 0$ and $bx + ay - ab = 0$.

Find the equation of the conic that passes through the five given points:

Hint. Denote the equations of the lines through P_1 and P_2, P_3 and P_4, P_1 and P_3, and P_2 and P_4 by $l_1 = 0$, $l_2 = 0$, $l_3 = 0$, and $l_4 = 0$ respectively. Verify that, for all values of k, the conic $l_1l_2 + kl_3l_4 = 0$ passes through these four points. Determine k so that this conic also passes through P_5.

8. $P_1(0, 0)$, $P_2(0, 3)$, $P_3(1, 0)$, $P_4(-1, 1)$, $P_5(3, 2)$.

9. $P_1(3, 0)$, $P_2(0, 2)$, $P_3(2, -1)$, $P_4(-2, 1)$, $P_5(2, 1)$.

10. $P_1(1, 1)$, $P_2(2, -1)$, $P_3(2, 1)$, $P_4(-1, 3)$, $P_5(1, -1)$.

11. $P_1(2, 1)$, $P_2(4, -1)$, $P_3(-1, 3)$, $P_4(1, -1)$, $P_5(2, 2)$.

SELECTED EXERCISES

1. If the axes are rotated so that $B' = 0$, show that A' and C' are the roots of the following quadratic equation in t:

$$t^2 - (A + C)t + AC - B^2/4 = 0.$$

2. Show that, if $B^2 - 4AC \neq 0$, the general equation of second degree becomes, after a translation to remove the first degree terms,

$$Ax'^2 + Bx'y' + Cy'^2 = \frac{\Delta}{2(B^2 - 4AC)}, \text{ where } \Delta = \begin{vmatrix} 2A & B & D \\ B & 2C & E \\ D & E & 2F \end{vmatrix}$$

Note. The determinant Δ is called the *discriminant* of the given equation.

Hint. First show that the new constant term can be written in the form $\frac{1}{2}[(2Ah + Bk + D)h + (Bh + 2Ck + E)k + (Dh + Ek + 2F)]$ and hence that, if h and k are chosen so that the coefficients of x' and y' are zero, this expression reduces to $\frac{1}{2}(Dh + Ek + 2F)$.

3. Show that, if $B^2 - 4AC = 0$, the general equation of second degree may be reduced, after a rotation of axes to remove the xy-term, to

$$(A + C)x'^2 + \frac{D\sqrt{A} \pm E\sqrt{C}}{\sqrt{A + C}}\, x' + \frac{E\sqrt{A} \mp D\sqrt{C}}{\sqrt{A + C}}\, y' + F = 0 \quad \text{where the}$$

indeterminate sign in the coefficient of x' agrees with, and that in the coefficient of y' is opposite to, the sign of B.

4. Using the results of Ex. 2 and 3, show that the condition that a conic is degenerate, that is, that the left-hand member of its equation can be factored into real or imaginary linear factors, is that $\Delta = 0$.

Hint. In the case in which $B^2 - 4AC = 0$, show that

$$\Delta = -2(E\sqrt{A} \mp D\sqrt{C})^2.$$

Algebraic Curves

9.1 Introduction. We have seen that, if the equation of a curve is of first degree in x and y,

$$Ax + By + C = 0,$$

the curve is a line and, if its equation is of the second degree,

$$Ax^2 + Bxy + Cy^2 + Dx + Ey + F = 0,$$

the locus of the equation (if it exists) is a conic section. If the given equation cannot be reduced to either of the above forms, its locus is said to be a **higher plane curve.**

A plane curve is **algebraic** if it can be defined by equating to zero a polynomial in which x and y appear only with positive integral exponents; otherwise, it is **transcendental.** Lines and conics, for example, are algebraic curves, as are also the loci defined by such equations as $x^3 + y^3 + 1 = 0$ or $3xy + x^5 - y^5 = 0$. The curves defined by such equations as $y = \tan x$, $y = e^x$, and $x^2 + y \log x = 0$ are transcendental and will be discussed in the next chapter.

In this chapter we shall point out some of the properties of certain algebraic curves and discuss some of the methods that may be used to assist in drawing their graphs. Frequently in advanced mathematics and applications one does not need an extremely accurate plot of a curve, but rather needs to get a sketch of the curve which shows its general properties and approximate position. This can usually be made fairly quickly from the information obtained by a discussion of symmetries (Art. 1.5 and Art. 6.4), intercepts (Art. 1.4), excluded intervals (Art. 1.4 and Art. 6.4), asymptotes (Art. 6.13), and tangents to the curve at the origin. This chapter will be devoted primarily to developing this discussion. If a very accurate plot of a curve is needed then one must also plot many points on the curve.

9.2 Symmetries. A curve is symmetric with respect to a given line or to a given point if, when $P(x, y)$ is any point on the curve, then its symmetric point with respect to the given line or the given point also lies on the curve.

The point symmetric to $P(x, y)$ with respect to:

(1) the x-axis is $(x, -y)$,   (2) the y-axis is $(-x, y)$,
(3) the line $y = x$ is (y, x),   (4) the origin is $(-x, -y)$.

Hence, an algebraic curve is symmetric to:

(1) the x-axis if y enters its equation only to even powers,
(2) the y-axis if x enters its equation only to even powers,
(3) the line $y = x$, if its equation remains unchanged when x and y are interchanged in it,
(4) the origin, if the equation remains unchanged when x and y are replaced by $-x$ and $-y$, respectively.

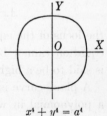

$x^4 + y^4 = a^4$

Lamé's Special Quartic

Fig. 9.1

The curve $x^4 + y^4 = a^4$ (Fig. 9.1) exhibits all of the above-mentioned symmetries. The student will find it interesting to plot this curve and the circle $x^2 + y^2 = a^2$ carefully on one set of axes. Are there any points on the curve that lie inside the circle?

The curve $xy^2 + x - 2y = 0$ is symmetric to the origin. The curve $xy - x - y = 0$ is symmetric to the line $y = x$. What kind of curve is it?

EXERCISES

Test the following curves for the above symmetries:

1. $x^2y = 4$.   **2.** $x^2 + y^2 + x + y = 0$.

3. $x^3 + xy^2 + y^2 + x = 0$.   **4.** $y^3 + x^2 + y - 4 = 0$.

5. $x^2 + xy + y^2 = 7$.   **6.** $x^4 - x^2y^2 + x^2 + 4y^2 = 0$.

7. $x^2y^2 - x^2 - y^2 = 0$.   **8.** $xy^4 - 2y^4 - y^2 + x^2 = 0$.

9. $x^3 - xy - x - y = 0$.   **10.** $x^4 - x^2y^2 + y^4 + xy^2 = 2yx^2$.

11. Determine a test for symmetry with respect to the line $y = -x$. Are any of the above curves symmetric with respect to this line?

9.3 Intersection with the Coördinate Axes. Polynomial Functions.

The x-intercepts are found by setting $y = 0$ in the equation of the curve and solving for x (Art. 1.4). Similarly, the y-intercepts are found by setting $x = 0$ and solving for y. The curve must pass through every point determined in this way and it does not meet either axis in any other point. Thus the curve $x^4 + y^4 = a^4$, shown in Fig. 9.1, meets the x-axis at $(\pm a, 0)$ and the y-axis at $(0, \pm a)$.

The expression

$$a_0x^n + a_1x^{n-1} + \cdots + a_n \qquad (a_0 \neq 0)$$

where the a's are real numbers and n is a positive integer is called a **polynomial function** of x (see Art. 3.8 and Art. 7.3). The graph of the equation obtained by equating it to y is the *graph of the polynomial function*. In sketching the graph of the polynomial function, that is of the equation

$$y = a_0x^n + a_1x^{n-1} + \cdots + a_n,$$

the intercepts are particularly useful.* This is certainly true if the polynomial $a_0x^n + a_1x^{n-1} + \cdots + a_n$ can be factored into n real factors. Otherwise, a large number of points may have to be obtained by assigning values to x and determining the corresponding values of y, either by direct substitution in the equation, or by synthetic division and the remainder theorem.

---

* To find the x-intercepts, we must find the real roots of the equation

$$a_0x^n + a_1x^{n-1} + \cdots + a_n = 0.$$

If these cannot be found by inspection or by a formula, they can be found, at least approximately, by Horner's method or by some other method of approximating the roots of a polynomial equation.

Example 1. Discuss and sketch the curve $y = x^3 - 9x$.

The curve is symmetric to the origin. We see that by assigning any value to x we get only one value for y. By putting $x = 0$ we get $y = 0$ for the only

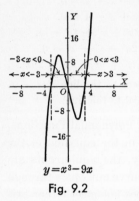

$y = x^3 - 9x$

Fig. 9.2

y-intercept. By putting $y = 0$ we get $x^3 - 9x = 0$ which gives $x = 0$, and $x = \pm 3$ for the x-intercepts.

Now let us see what happens to the curve for, x-values, other than the intercepts. This means, that we have to consider the intervals $x > 3$, $0 < x < 3$, $-3 < x < 0$, and $x < -3$ (Fig. 9.2). By writing the equation of the curve in the form $y = x(x + 3)(x - 3)$, we see that for all values of $x > 3$ we get positive values of y which increase indefinitely as x increases. Similarly, for $x < -3$, or by the symmetry of this curve with respect to the origin, we get negative values of y which decrease indefinitely as x decreases. For the interval $0 < x < 3$, we see that the first two factors of $x(x + 3)(x - 3)$ are positive, while the third is negative. Thus in this interval the y-values are negative, i.e. the curve lies below the x-axis. The symmetry with respect to the origin tells us what happens for the interval $-3 < x < 0$. This gives us a rough idea of what the curve looks like. A more careful plot is obtained by assigning several values to x in each interval.

Example 2. Discuss and sketch the curve $y = x^5 - 4x^4 + 4x^3$.

This curve has none of the symmetries mentioned in the last article. By factoring the right member, we find that the equation can be written $y = x^3(x - 2)^2$. By putting $x = 0$, we get $y = 0$ for the only y-intercept. By putting $y = 0$, we get $x = 0$ three times, and $x = 2$ twice for the x-intercepts.

We need now to see what kind of y-values we get in the intervals $x > 2$, $0 < x < 2$, and $x < 0$ (Fig. 9.3). For $x > 2$ we get positive values of y which increase indefinitely as x increases. We also get positive values of y for $0 < x < 2$. But $y = 0$ for $x = 2$. Thus the curve comes down and is tangent to the x-axis at $x = 2$. In fact, whenever a polynomial function in x has a

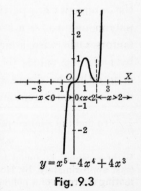

$y = x^5 - 4x^4 + 4x^3$

Fig. 9.3

factor to an even power, one always gets a tangency to one side or the other of the x-axis. This is because as x varies from values just a little bit less than the x-value which makes that repeated factor vanish, to values just a little larger, the polynomial function always has the same sign (except, of course, where it is 0). For $x < 0$ we get negative values for y which decrease as x decreases. Notice here that x is a triple factor. For x-values just a little larger than zero y has one sign and for x-values just a little smaller than zero y has the other sign. This happens whenever we have a factor raised to an odd power. The student will observe in this example and in working others that the higher the power, the flatter the curve in the area where it cuts across the x-axis.

Another point which it is useful to observe in plotting polynomial functions is that the sign of the y-values for x sufficiently large in numerical value is determined by the sign of the highest degree term in the polynomial. Thus in this example the sign of the y-values when x is large in numerical value takes the sign of the term x^5. Hence this curve comes into view from the upper right and goes out of view on the lower left.

EXERCISES

Discuss and sketch the following curves:

1. $y = x^3 - 3x^2 + 2x$.
2. $y = x^4 - 4x^3 + 4x^2$.
3. $y = x^3 - 3x^2 + 3x - 1$.
4. $y = x^3 + 6x^2 + 9x$.
5. $y = x^4 - 3x^3$.
6. $y = 3x^2 + 2x^3 - x^4$.
7. $y = -x^3 - 2x^2 + 4x + 8$.
8. $y = 2 - x + 2x^2 - x^3$.

9.4 Horizontal and Vertical Asymptotes. Rational Functions.

When we were studying in Art. 6.13 the graph of the equation $b^2x^2 - a^2y^2 = a^2b^2$ of a hyperbola, we noticed that the curve recedes toward infinity, in any one of the quadrants, in such a way that it approaches a fixed line which we called an asymptote to the hyperbola.

Since many other curves extend out indefinitely far in a similar way, we make the following definition: *If a branch of a curve extends toward infinity in such a way that it approaches indefinitely near to a fixed line, this line is called an asymptote to the curve.*

If an algebraic curve has vertical or horizontal asymptotes, these lines can be determined from the equation of the curve as in the following example.

Example 1. Find the vertical and the horizontal asymptotes to the curve $xy^2 - a^2y - b^2x = 0$.

In this equation, if we assign to x a fixed value $x_1 \neq 0$, the resulting quadratic equation in y has two roots,

$$y_1 = \frac{a^2 + \sqrt{a^4 + 4b^2x_1^2}}{2x_1}, \quad \text{and} \quad y_2 = \frac{a^2 - \sqrt{a^4 + 4b^2x_1^2}}{2x_1},$$

which are the ordinates of the two intersections of the vertical line $x = x_1$ with the curve.

If we now let x_1 approach indefinitely near to zero, the first of these values of y increases indefinitely in numerical value and the corresponding

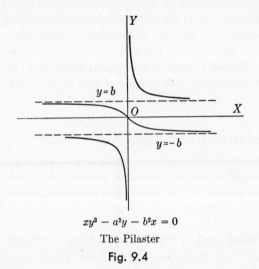

$$xy^2 - a^2y - b^2x = 0$$

The Pilaster

Fig. 9.4

point on the curve recedes toward infinity in such a way that it approaches indefinitely near to the line $x = 0$, that is, to the y-axis (Fig. 9.4). This line is, accordingly, an asymptote.

Similarly, if we arrange the given equation in powers of x,

$$(y^2 - b^2)x - a^2y = 0,$$

and assign to y any value $y_1 \neq \pm b$, the root of the resulting equation in x is the abscissa of the single intersection of the line $y = y_1$ with the curve. If y_1 is now made to approach $+b$ or $-b$, the numerical value of x will increase indefinitely and the corresponding point on the curve will approach the asymptote $y = b$ or $y = -b$.

By applying reasoning similar to the foregoing to any given algebraic curve, it is possible to deduce the following general rule for finding the vertical and horizontal asymptotes: *To find the vertical asymptotes to an algebraic curve, equate to zero the real, linear factors of the coefficient of the highest power of y in the equation. To find the horizontal asymptotes, equate to zero the real, linear factors of the coefficient of the highest power of x in the equation.*

If the coefficient of the highest power of y (or of x) in the given equation is a constant, or if its linear factors are all imaginary, there are no vertical (or no horizontal) asymptotes. Thus, the curve $y^4 + x^2y^2 + x^2 - 1 = 0$ has no vertical asymptotes since the coefficient of the highest power of y is unity. It has no horizontal asymptotes since the factors of $y^2 + 1$, the coefficient of the highest power of x, are imaginary.

Exercise. Show that the polynomial curves do not have horizontal or vertical asymptotes.

The expression $\dfrac{P(x)}{Q(x)}$ where $P(x)$ and $Q(x)$ are any two polynomials in x (Art. 9.3) is called a **rational function** of x. The graph of the equation

$$y = \frac{P(x)}{Q(x)}$$

is called the *graph of the rational function.* A knowledge of the vertical and horizontal asymptotes is particularly useful in obtaining this graph.

Example 2. Sketch the curve $y = \dfrac{x^2 + 2x}{x^2 - 1}$.

The x-intercepts are $x = 0$, and $x = -2$. The only y-intercept is $y = 0$. By writing the equation of the curve in the form $y(x^2 - 1) = x^2 + 2x$ we see that the coefficient of the highest power in y is $x^2 - 1$. Thus, applying the rule for vertical asymptotes, we obtain $x = \pm 1$. By substituting $x = \pm 1$ in the equation $y(x^2 - 1) = x^2 + 2x$, we see that the curve does not cut the vertical asymptotes. By writing the equation in the form $x^2(y - 1) - 2x - y = 0$ we see that $y = 1$ is the only horizontal asymptote. By putting $y = 1$ in this equation we see that the curve does cut this asymptote at the point where $x = -\frac{1}{2}$ (Fig. 9.5).

For values of x just slightly larger than 1, the numerator of the y-value is slightly larger than 3 while the denominator is a very small positive number. This gives us very large positive values for y. Thus the curve lies along the upper right side of the asymptote $x = 1$. The curve does not cut the asymptote $x = 1$ or the asymptote $y = 1$ for $x > 1$. Thus the curve must go out along the upper side of the asymptote $y = 1$. Similarly, by taking values of x just slightly less than 1, we see that the curve comes up along the lower left side of the asymptote $x = 1$. A study of the x-values near -1 shows that the curve lies on the upper right and lower left of the asymptote

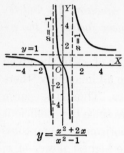

$$y = \frac{x^2 + 2x}{x^2 - 1}$$

Fig. 9.5

$x = -1$. As the curve comes up on the left of $x = -1$ it must intersect the x-axis at $x = -2$. Again, however, it cannot cut across either $x = -1$ or $y = 1$ for $x < -1$ so it must go out along the lower left of the asymptote $y = 1$. The above clues give us an adequate sketch of the curve, except for the branch to the right of the line $x = 1$. To fix the position of this branch we determine a few points with x-coördinates greater than 1.

9.5 Excluded Intervals. If, when the given equation of a curve is solved for y, square roots occur in the right-hand member, the values of x throughout certain intervals may cause the quantity under the radical sign to be negative and thus make y imaginary. Since no point can be plotted if either of its coördinates is imaginary, any such interval should be excluded from consideration in drawing the graph and is called an excluded interval (Art. 1.4 and Art. 6.4).

In the same way, when we solve for x, certain intervals may be found on the y-axis for which the values of x are imaginary. These intervals must also be excluded when we draw the graph.

Example. Discuss and sketch the curve $x^2y^2 - a^2x^2 - a^2y^2 = 0$.

This curve is symmetric to the x-axis, y-axis, the origin, and the line $y = x$. The only x-intercept is $x = 0$ counted twice and the only y-intercept is $y = 0$ counted twice. If we solve the equation for y, we find that

$$y = \frac{\pm\, ax}{\sqrt{x^2 - a^2}},$$ which shows that, for all values of x between $x = -a$ and

$x = a$, except $x = 0$, y is imaginary. There are, accordingly, no points on the curve, except the point $(0, 0)$, obtained from values of x within this interval (Fig. 9.6). The vertical asymptotes are $x = \pm a$.

If we now solve the above equation for x, we obtain $x = \dfrac{\pm\, ay}{\sqrt{y^2 - a^2}}$. It follows that, for all values of y between $-a$ and a, except $y = 0$, x is imaginary. Hence this interval on the y-axis is excluded except for $y = 0$. The horizontal asymptotes are $y = \pm a$.

A point, such as the origin in this example, that lies on the curve, but which has no other points on the curve in its neighborhood, is called a *conjugate* (or *isolated*) *point* on the curve.

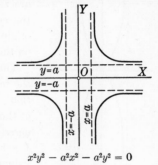

$$x^2y^2 - a^2x^2 - a^2y^2 = 0$$

Cruciform Curve

Fig. 9.6

EXERCISES

Discuss and sketch the following curves:

1. $y = \dfrac{x}{x^2 - 1}$.

2. $y^2 = \dfrac{x}{x^2 - 1}$.

3. $y^2 = \dfrac{x}{x - 2}$.

4. $y = \dfrac{2x - x^2}{x^2 + x - 2}$.

5. $y^2 = \dfrac{x^2}{4 - x^2}$.

6. $y = \dfrac{x^3}{2 - x - x^2}$.

7. $(x - 1)^2 y = x^2 + x^3$.

8. $(x^2 - 9)y^2 = 2x + x^2$.

9.6 Multiplicity of the Origin. Tangent Lines at the Origin.

If the coördinates of the origin satisfy the equation, we can find the multiplicity of the origin, as a point on the curve, and the equations of the tangent lines at the origin by the method developed in the following example.

Example 1. Find the multiplicity of the origin and the tangent lines at the origin for the curve $x^2y^2 + a^2x^2 - a^2y^2 = 0$ (Fig. 9.7).

The equation of the family of lines through the origin is

$$y = mx. \tag{1}$$

If we substitute this value of y in the equation of the curve, we obtain

$$m^2x^4 + a^2(1 - m^2)x^2 = 0. \tag{2}$$

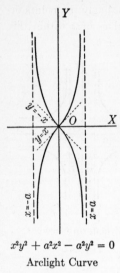

$$x^2y^2 + a^2x^2 - a^2y^2 = 0$$

Arclight Curve

Fig. 9.7

The roots of this equation in x are the abscissas of the points of intersection of the line (1) with the curve. Since, for all values of m, two roots of (2) are zero, two intersections of every line (1) with the curve lie at the origin and we say that the origin is a *double point* or (*point of multiplicity two*) on the curve.

The tangent lines at the origin are the lines of the family (1) that have more than two intersections with the curve at $(0, 0)$. To find the slopes of these lines, equate to zero the coefficient of the *lowest* power of x in (2) and solve for m. We have $1 - m^2 = 0$ or $m = \pm 1$. On substituting these values of m in (1) we find, as the equations of the tangent lines at the origin,

$$y = x \quad \text{and} \quad y = -x.$$

Since the y-axis has no slope, this computation does not decide whether the y-axis is tangent at the origin. Under (*b*), however, we find that just two intersections of the curve with the y-axis coincide at the origin (Why?). Since the origin is a double point, it follows that the y-axis is not tangent at the origin.

The actual process of finding the multiplicity of the origin and the equations of the tangents to the curve at the origin can be shortened in the following way. In example 1, write the sum of the terms of *the lowest degree* * in x and y in the given equation, thus:

$$a^2x^2 - a^2y^2 = a^2(x - y)(x + y).$$

Since this expression is of degree two in x and y, the origin is a double point on the curve. Further, by equating to zero its factors linear in x and y, we obtain $x - y = 0$ and $x + y = 0$. These, as we have seen, are the tangents to the curve at the origin.

By precisely the same reasoning, we find, for any algebraic curve, the following rule for finding the multiplicity at the origin and the equations of the tangents at the origin. *Write down the sum of all of the terms of the given curve that are of the lowest degree in x and y. The*

---

* The degree of a term in x and y is the sum of the exponents of x and y in that term.

degree of this expression is the multiplicity of the origin on the curve and its real factors linear in x and y, equated to zero, are the equations of the tangents to the curve at the origin. This rule can be seen intuitively by observing that the coördinates of points on the curve very near the origin are very small. Thus the higher degree terms of the equation are so much smaller in comparison with the lowest degree terms that they can be ignored. If the lowest degree term in an equation is a constant $\neq 0$, then, of course, the curve does not go through the origin. Hence, no discussion of the tangents at the origin is necessary.

Example 2. Find the multiplicity of the origin and the tangent lines at the origin for the curve $x^4 + x^2y^2 - y^3 + xy = 0$.

The lowest degree term here is of the second degree and hence the origin is a double point. Setting $xy = 0$, we get as tangent lines at the origin $x = 0$ and $y = 0$.

Example 3. Find the multiplicity at the origin and show that there are no tangents at the origin for the curve $x^4 + y^4 - a^2x^2 - a^2y^2 = 0$.

The sum of the lowest degree terms is $-a^2x^2 - a^2y^2 = -a^2(x^2 + y^2)$. Since this is of the second degree in x and y the origin is a double point. Since the factors of $x^2 + y^2$ are imaginary, there are no tangents at the origin. The origin is an isolated point (Art. 9.5) on this curve.

Exercise. Show by the method of Example 1 that the origin is a simple point on $xy^2 - a^2y - b^2x = 0$ (Fig. 9.4) and that the line $a^2y + b^2x = 0$ is the tangent at the origin.

9.7 Graphs of Equations. In the previous articles we have been discussing some properties of curves and developing methods for sketching them. To summarize, whenever it is required to sketch the graph of a given equation we first write up a discussion of (a) the symmetries, (b) the intercepts, (c) the excluded intervals, (d) the asymptotes and (e) the tangents to the curve at the origin. We then record this information on the graph. Study of this information along with knowledge of the way each variable varies with respect to the other and a few actual points will usually give an adequate sketch of the curve. If a more accurate plot is required, additional points will have to be plotted, being careful to include numerous points at the places where the curve is rapidly changing direction.

The methods thus far presented will be supplemented in the next two chapters and later by courses in calculus. In some cases, the information obtained from a discussion of all of the properties mentioned so far is found to be too limited to give an adequate sketch. For example, the polynomial curve $y = x^4 + x^2 + 2$ is symmetric with respect to the y-axis and its only intercept is a y-intercept of 2. It has no horizontal or vertical asymptotes and no tangents at the origin, since it does not go through the origin. Hence, to obtain an adequate sketch of the curve it is necessary to plot many points.

We shall further illustrate the process of discussing and sketching a curve by three examples which are of general interest.

Example 1. Discuss and sketch the *trisectrix of Maclaurin* whose equation is $x^3 + xy^2 + ay^2 - 3ax^2 = 0$.

(a) The equation of the curve has only even powers of y and thus the curve is symmetric to the x-axis.

(b) Setting $x = 0$ gives $y = 0$ twice for the y-intercepts. Setting $y = 0$ gives $x = 0$ twice and also $x = 3a$ for the x-intercepts.

(c) Solving the equation for y in terms of x we get $y = \pm x \sqrt{\dfrac{3a - x}{x + a}}$.

From this we see that $x < -a$ and $x > 3a$ are excluded intervals for x since they give imaginary values for y. Since the equation is of the third degree in x we cannot solve it algebraically for x in terms of y. Since it is of the third degree in x, however, we know that for every value of y there is at least one real value for x since complex roots must appear in pairs. Hence no y is excluded.

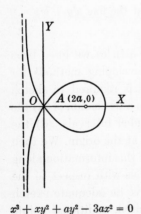

$x^3 + xy^2 + ay^2 - 3ax^2 = 0$

The Trisectrix

Fig. 9.8

(d) The coefficient of the highest power in x is one so there are no horizontal asymptotes. The coefficient of the highest power in y is $x + a$. Hence $x = -a$ is a vertical asymptote.

(e) The lowest degree terms in x and y are $ay^2 - 3ax^2$. Hence $y = \pm \sqrt{3}x$ are the tangents to the curve at the origin. The origin is a double point.

Combining this information on the graph we get the sketch shown in Fig. 9.8.

This curve is of interest in connection with the problem of trisecting a given angle,* as may be seen from the following exercise.

Exercise. Through the origin, draw any line and denote its inclination by α. Through the point $A(2a, 0)$ draw the line having an angle of inclination 3α. Show that the locus of the point of intersection of these lines is composed of the x-axis and a trisectrix of Maclaurin. Hence, show how, given a trisectrix of Maclaurin, any given angle may be trisected.

Example 2. Discuss and sketch the *cissoid of Diocles*, whose equation is $x^3 + xy^2 - 2ay^2 = 0$.

(*a*) The curve is symmetric to the x-axis.

(*b*) Setting $x = 0$ gives $y = 0$ twice. Setting $y = 0$ gives $x = 0$ three times.

(*c*) There are no excluded y-values (Why?). Solving for y in terms of x we get

$$y = \pm\, x \sqrt{\frac{-x}{x - 2a}}.$$

Hence $x > 2a$ and $x < 0$ are excluded intervals for x.

(*d*) The only horizontal or vertical asymptote is the vertical one $x = 2a$.

(*e*) Setting $-2ay^2 = 0$ we get $y = 0$ twice for the tangents at the origin. A point, such as the origin on this curve (Fig. 9.9), at which the curve abruptly reverses its direction, is said to be a *cusp* on the given curve.

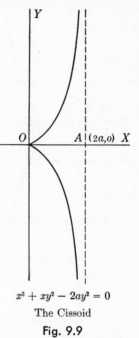

$x^3 + xy^2 - 2ay^2 = 0$

The Cissoid

Fig. 9.9

---

* The following problems became famous in antiquity because of the unsuccessful efforts of the Greek geometers to solve them by the methods of elementary geometry:

To trisect a given angle.

To construct a square equal in area to a given circle.

To construct the edge of a cube whose volume is equal to twice the volume of a given cube.

In elementary geometry, it is customary to assume that the only construction instruments that are permitted to be used are: the straightedge to draw lines that pass through two known points and compasses to draw circles of known centers and known radii. It has been proved in modern times that, *under these limitations*, the above constructions are all impossible. They are, however, all possible, and were all actually effected by the Greeks, with the aid of other instruments.

Exercise. On the segment joining $O(0,0)$ to $A(2a,0)$ (Fig. 9.9) as a diameter, draw a circle. Through O draw any line meeting the circle at a point B and the line $x - 2a = 0$ at C. On OC, lay off $\overline{OP} = \overline{BC}$ and show that the locus of P is the cissoid.

Example 3. Discuss and sketch the locus of the equation

$$y^2 = x(x - a)(x - b) \qquad 0 < a < b.$$

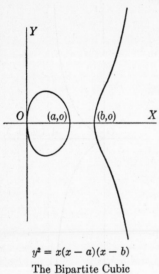

$y^2 = x(x - a)(x - b)$

The Bipartite Cubic

Fig. 9.10

(a) The curve is symmetric to the x-axis.

(b) Setting $x = 0$ gives $y = 0$ twice. Setting $y = 0$ gives $x = 0$, $x = a$, and $x = b$.

(c) Every y-value gives at least one x-value. The excluded intervals for x are $x < 0$ and $a < x < b$.

(d) There are no horizontal or vertical asymptotes.

(e) There is only one lowest degree term, namely abx. Hence the origin is a simple point on the curve and the curve is tangent to the y-axis.

By plotting points carefully on this locus, we find that the branch between $x = 0$ and $x = a$ is an oval, slightly more pointed to the right than to the left, and that the branch for $x \geq b$ extends to infinity in the first and fourth quadrants without approaching any rectilinear asymptote. This curve is called a *bipartite cubic*.

Exercise. Draw the bipartite cubic curve $y^2 = x^3 - 10x^2 + 21x$ from $x = 0$ to $x = 10$.

EXERCISES

Discuss the given equation; plot enough points to determine its form, and sketch the curve:

1. $xy - 2x - 2y = 0$.
2. $4x^2 - y^2 = 8x + 8y$.
3. $(x - y)^2 = 6x + 6y$.
4. $9x^2 - 25y^2 = 225$.
5. $y = x - x^3$.
6. $y^2 = x - x^3$.
7. $a^2y = x^3$. *The Cubical Parabola.*

8. $ay^2 = x^3$. *The Semi-cubical Parabola.*

9. $y = x^n$. Plot on one set of axes for $n = -2$, -1, $\frac{1}{2}$, and 4.

10. $y^2 = x^2 - x^3$.   **11.** $y = (x^2 - 1)^2$.

12. $y^3 - ay^2 + ax^2 = 0$.   **13.** $x^2y - ay^2 + ax^2 = 0$.

14. $x^2y^2 - 4y^2 + x = 0$.   **15.** $(x - 1)^2y = x^2 + x$.

16. $xy^2 - 9x^2 + 8 = 0$.   **17.** $xy^2 - y^2 - x - 1 = 0$.

18. $y^4 + x^2y^2 - a^2x^2 = 0$.   **19.** $a^2y^2 + x^4 - a^2x^2 = 0$.

20. $x^2y - a^2y = ax^2 + 2a^2x$.   **21.** $a^4x^2 - 4a^2y^4 + y^6 = 0$.

22. $x^3 + y^3 = a^3$.   **23.** $x^6 + y^6 = a^6$.

24. $x^2y + a^2y - a^3 = 0$. *The Witch.*

25. $x^3 + xy^2 + ax^2 - ay^2 = 0$. *The Strophoid.*

26. $x^2y + b^2y - a^2x = 0$. *The Serpentine.*

27. $x^3 + 3xy^2 = ax^2 - ay^2$. *The Folium.*

28. $(x^2 + y^2)^2 = a^2xy$. *The Lemniscate.*

29. $y^4 - 2ay^3 + a^2x^2 = 0$. *The Top.*

30. $(x^2 + y^2)^2 = ax^2y$. *The Bifolium.*

31. The locus of a point that moves so that the product of its distances from two fixed points, $(-a, 0)$ and $(a, 0)$, is equal to a constant b^2 is called an *oval of Cassini.* Find the equation of the curve and draw it for $a = b/2$, $a = b$, and $a = 2b$.

32. The locus of a point that moves so that its distances from $O(0, 0)$ and $A(a, 0)$ satisfy the relation $AP = \pm bOP \pm c$ is called a *Cartesian oval.* Find the equation and draw the curve.

33. If a is the length of the edge of a given cube, show that the parabolas $y^2 = 2ax$ and $x^2 = ay$ intersect in a point whose abscissa is the edge of a cube of twice the volume of the given cube.

34. The force F of gravitational attraction between two bodies is expressed as a function of the distance r between them by the equation $F = k/r^2$. Show this relation graphically.

35. The squares of the periods of revolution of the planets about the sun are proportional to the cubes of the major semi-axes of their orbits. Express this relation by an equation, and draw the graph.

36. Equal squares of side x are cut from the corners of a square piece of tin of side a and the edges are then folded up so as to form a box with an open top. Express the volume of the box as a function of x, and draw the graph.

Transcendental Curves

10.1 Introduction. The higher plane curves which are not algebraic are called *transcendental curves* (Art. 9.1). Some transcendental curves involving the trigonometric, logarithmic, and exponential functions will be discussed in this chapter. Some of the common applications of these curves will be cited.

10.2 The Sine and Cosine Curves. The sine function, $\sin x$, and the cosine function, $\cos x$, are examples of periodic functions. *A function $f(x)$ is said to be periodic if there is a number $p \neq 0$ such that $f(x + p) = f(x)$ for all values of x.* If there is a smallest positive number p satisfying this definition it is called *the period of the function.* Thus since $\sin (x + 2\pi) = \sin x$, $\sin x$ is periodic. It has the period 2π, since this is the smallest number for which this is true. Similarly, $\cos x$ is periodic with period 2π.

The sine curve is defined by the equation

$$y = \sin x \tag{1}$$

It may be plotted by laying off, on the x-axis, the radian measure of the angle (Art. 0.7) and, in the y direction, the value of the sine. For angles in the interval $0 \leqq x \leqq 90°$, these values of x and y may be found from the table on page 271. For angles outside of this interval, we add to, or subtract from, the given angle integral multiples of 90° ($\pi/2$ radians) and determine the value of the sine with the aid of the trigonometric reduction formulas (Art. 0.10).

Since the sine function has the period 2π the sine curve repeats the same set of y-values for every consecutive interval on x of length 2π. (See Fig. 10.1). Since replacing x by $-x$ and y by $-y$ in (1) gives

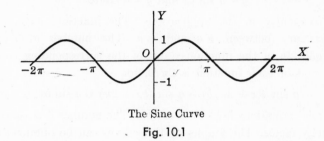

The Sine Curve

Fig. 10.1

$-y = \sin(-x)$ or $-y = -\sin x$, which gives the same locus as (1), the curve is symmetric to the origin. From the fact that $\sin n\pi = 0$ for n any integer, the x-intercepts are $x = 0, \pm\pi, \pm 2\pi, \cdots$. The only y-intercept is $y = 0$. Since $-1 \leqq \sin x \leqq 1$, $y > 1$ and $y < -1$ are excluded intervals on y for the sine curve. The maximum points, where $y = 1$, are obtained when $x = \pi/2 + n(2\pi)$. The minimum points, where $y = -1$, are obtained when $x = 3\pi/2 + n(2\pi)$.

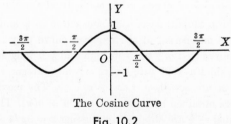

The Cosine Curve

Fig. 10.2

The cosine curve. By means of the reduction formula $\sin(\pi/2 + x) = \cos x$ we find that Fig. 10.1 may also be used to represent the cosine curve

$$y = \cos x, \tag{2}$$

provided that the origin is moved $\pi/2$ *units to the right* (Fig. 10.2). In other words, the sine curve and the cosine curve are identical in size and form. They differ only in their position with respect to the y-axis.

Since $\cos(-x) = \cos x$, the cosine curve is symmetric with respect to the y-axis.

The curves

$$y = a \sin bx \text{ and } y = a \cos bx \tag{3}$$

occur frequently in the applications. The functions $a \sin bx$ and $a \cos bx$ vary between $+a$ and $-a$. The number a is called the **amplitude** of the functions (and of the corresponding curves). The period of each function is $2\pi/b$, for

$$a \sin b(x + 2\pi/b) = a \sin (bx + 2\pi) = a \sin bx,$$

and similar equations hold for $a \cos bx$. The number b is called the **periodicity factor**. The graphs of the curves can be obtained from the sine and cosine curves respectively by multiplying the ordinates by the amplitude a and dividing the abscissas by the periodicity factor b.

A well-known application of the functions $a \sin bx$ and $a \cos bx$ is in the study of simple harmonic motion. For example, the function $a \cos kt$ frequently occurs in the form $s = a \cos kt$ where s represents the displacement of a particle along a fixed line from some fixed position and t represents the time.

Example 1. Sketch the curve $y = (\frac{3}{2}) \sin 2x$ from $x = 0$ to $x = 2\pi$.

We see that the amplitude of this sine curve is $\frac{3}{2}$ and the period is $2\pi/2 = \pi$. Hence one period of the required curve may be obtained by drawing a sine curve that is $\frac{3}{2}$ times as high and $\frac{1}{2}$ as long as one period of $y = \sin x$. Since $\sin 2(n \cdot \pi/2) = 0$, where n is any integer, the x-intercepts for $y = (\frac{3}{2}) \sin 2x$ are $x = 0, \pm \pi/2, \pm \pi, \cdots$. The maximum y-values which equal $\frac{3}{2}$ are obtained by putting $x = \pi/4 + n(\pi)$. The minimum y-values which equal $-\frac{3}{2}$ are obtained by putting $x = 3\pi/4 + n\pi$.

We draw $y = (\frac{3}{2}) \sin 2x$ for two periods since we want it from 0 to 2π. The graphs of $y = \sin x$ and $y = (\frac{3}{2}) \sin x$ are also shown for comparison.

The student should always be careful to indicate the units used on each axis since it is seldom convenient to use the same units on both axes.

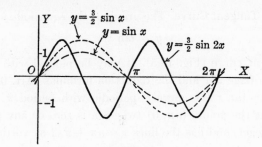

Fig. 10.3

The following example illustrates some terms frequently used, particularly in physics and electrical engineering.

Example 2. Discuss and sketch the graph of $y = 4 \cos (3x + \pi)$.

By writing this equation in the form $y = 4 \cos 3(x + \pi/3)$ and performing the translation $x = x' - \pi/3$, and $y = y'$, we get $y' = 4 \cos 3x'$. Thus after a translation this equation has the form of the second of equations

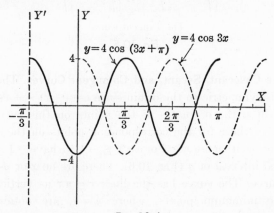

Fig. 10.4

(3). The sketch of $y = 4 \cos 3(x + \pi/3)$ together with the sketch of $y = 4 \cos 3x$ is shown in Fig. 10.4. To borrow a term commonly used in applications, we see that the first curve *lags* behind the second curve with an *angle of lag* of $\pi/3$.

Exercise. Sketch the curve $y = 2 \sin (4x - \pi/2)$ and show that it leads the curve $y = 2 \sin 4x$ with an *angle of lead* of $\pi/8$.

10.3 The Tangent Curve. The graph of the equation

$$y = \tan x \tag{4}$$

is the tangent curve (Fig. 10.5). It may be plotted with the aid of the table on page 271 and the reduction formulas (Art. 0.10). Since $\tan (x + \pi) = \tan x$ the curve is periodic with period π. It crosses the x-axis at the points $(n\pi, 0)$ (where n is zero or any positive or negative integer) and has the lines $x = n\pi + \pi/2$ as vertical asymptotes. Since $- \tan (- x) = \tan x$, the curve is symmetric with respect to the origin.

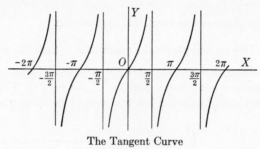

The Tangent Curve

Fig. 10.5

10.4 The Cosecant, Secant, and Cotangent Curves. The graph of $y = \csc x$ is symmetric to the origin since $\csc (- x) = - \csc x$. Since $\csc x = 1/\sin x$, the ordinates of the points on this curve are the reciprocals of those for the corresponding points on the sine curve $y = \sin x$. Since either $\csc x \geqq 1$ or $\csc x \leqq - 1$, we have $- 1 < y < 1$ as an excluded interval of y (Fig. 10.6). There are no x-or y-intercepts for this curve. The curve has the lines $x = n\pi$ as vertical asymptotes. The minimum points, where $y = 1$, are obtained when $x = \pi/2 + n(2\pi)$. The maximum points, where $y = - 1$, are obtained when $x = 3\pi/2 + n(2\pi)$. By using table III, page 271, enough additional points can be obtained to give a satisfactory sketch of the curve. The discussion of the secant curve is similar to that of the cosecant curve and is left as an exercise. The discussion of the cotangent curve is similar to that of the tangent curve given in Art. 10.3 and is also left as an exercise. In drawing the graphs of the six trigonometric functions, an adequate sketch may be made by using the points obtained by the use of table III, page 271, together with the information obtained in the discussion of the properties of the curves.

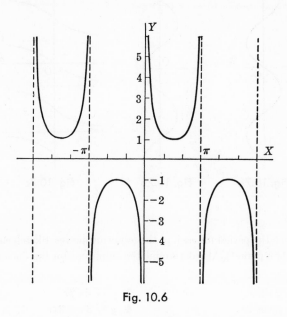

Fig. 10.6

10.5 The Inverse Trigonometric Functions. If we solve the inverse trigonometric equations

$$y = \text{arc sin } x, \; y = \text{arc cos } x, \quad \text{and} \quad y = \text{arc tan } x \qquad (5)$$

for * x, we have respectively,

$$x = \sin y, \quad x = \cos y, \quad \text{and} \quad x = \tan y.$$

It follows that the curves defined by equations (5) are identical in form with the ordinary sine, cosine, and tangent curves and differ from them only in that they are placed on the figure in such a way that their positions with respect to the x- and y-axes are interchanged.

___

* The notation $y = \sin^{-1} x$ is also used. This notation has the disadvantage that the -1 is sometimes misinterpreted as an exponent.

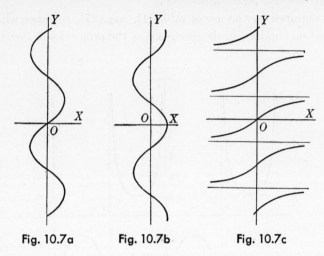

Fig. 10.7a   Fig. 10.7b   Fig. 10.7c

EXERCISES

Determine the period for each of the following curves. Sketch each of the curves for two periods. Also determine the amplitude for the sine and cosine curves:

1. $y = 2 \sin x$.
2. $y = \sin 2x$.
3. $y = 2 \cos 2x$.
4. $y = 3 \cos 3x$.
5. $y = (\frac{1}{2}) \sin 2x$.
6. $y = 2 \tan x/3$.
7. $y = \tan 2x$.
8. $y = 2 \tan \pi x$.
9. $y = \sin \pi x$.
10. $y = \csc \pi x$.
11. $y = \sec x$.
12. $y = \cot x$.
13. $y = 1 + \cos (x - 1)$.
14. $y = 1 + \sin 2(x - 1)$.

Hint. In Ex. 13 and 14, first move the origin to (1, 1).

In the following problems determine also the angle of lag or lead with respect to a similar curve whose equation lacks the constant term in the parenthesis:

15. $y = 3 \sin (2x - \pi/3)$.
16. $y = 2 \cos (4x - 2\pi)$.
17. $y = 4 \cos (\pi x + \pi/2)$.
18. $y = 3 \sin (2\pi x - \pi/3)$.

Sketch the following curves:

19. $y = \text{arc sec } x$.
20. $y = \text{arc tan } x$.
21. $y = \text{arc cot } 2x$.
22. $2y = \text{arc cos } 3x$.
23. $y = 1 + \text{arc sin } (x + 2)$.
24. $y = 2 + \text{arc cos } (x - 2)$.

10.6 The Logarithmic Curves. The graph of the equation

$$y = \log_a x, \qquad\qquad a > 1 \qquad\qquad (6)$$

is called a *logarithmic curve.*

The number a is the **base.** Two bases are in common use: the base 10, which is the one usually employed in numerical computations, and the base $e = 2.71828^+$, which is the one almost invariably used in advanced mathematics. Logarithms to the base e are called *natural,* or *Naperian,* logarithms.

To draw the graph of

$$y = \log_{10} x,$$

we assign to x a series of values and determine the corresponding values of y with the aid of the table of logarithms on pages 268–269.

Since the logarithms of negative numbers are imaginary, the graph does not extend to the left of the y-axis. The curve intersects the x-axis at $(1, 0)$, since $\log 1 = 0$. If $x > 1$, $\log_{10} x$ is positive and

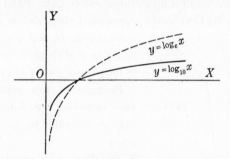

Fig. 10.8

the curve lies in the first quadrant. The points on the curve in the interval $0 < x < 1$ are found by using the relation $\log (1/M)$ $= - \log M$ (Art. 0.4). The graph approaches the negative end of the y-axis as an asymptote (Fig. 10.8).

The logarithmic curve $y = \log_a x$, where $a \neq 10$, can be plotted by means of the table on pages 268–269, provided that we also make use of the formula $\log_a x = \dfrac{\log_{10} x}{\log_{10} a}$ (Art. 0.4).

For example, since $\log_{10} e = \log_{10} 2.71828 = 0.4343^- = \dfrac{1}{2.303^-}$, we may draw the graph of $y = \log_e x$ by putting

$$y = \log_e x = \frac{\log_{10} x}{\log_{10} e} = 2.303 \log_{10} x.$$

The graph of the equation $y = \log_e x$ may thus be obtained from that of $y = \log_{10} x$ by multiplying all the ordinates of the latter curve by 2.303. Tables for the values of $\log_e x$ exist and can be used, if available, thus eliminating this multiplication. The resulting graph is shown by the dotted curve in Fig. 10.8.

10.7 The Exponential Curves. The graph of the equation

$$y = a^x, \qquad\qquad a > 1 \qquad\qquad (7)$$

is called an *exponential curve*.

If we solve equation (7) for x, we have, from the definition of a logarithm (Art. 0.4)

$$x = \log_a y. \qquad\qquad (8)$$

This is the equation of a logarithmic curve (Art. 10.6) with x and y interchanged in it; that is, *the exponential curve differs from the logarithmic only in that it is placed on the figure so that its position with reference to the x- and y-axes is interchanged.*

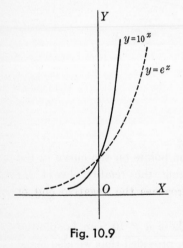

Fig. 10.9

Because of this relation between their graphs, the functions a^x and $\log_a x$ are said to be *inverse functions.*

To draw the graph of equation (7), where a is different from 10 or $e = 2.71828^+$, one usually takes the logarithms to the base 10 of both sides of the equation. One thus obtains

$$\log_{10} y = x \log_{10} a.$$

Values may then be assigned to y and the corresponding values of x determined with the aid of a table of logarithms.

If $a = 10$, (7) is sketched directly. If $a = e$, (7) is graphed by means of tables of values for e^x. (See page 272.)

In the applications, the exponential equation usually appears in the form

$$y = ae^{bx}$$

where a and b are constants the values of which are assigned in the given problem. The graph of this equation is usually found by assigning values to x and then looking up the values of e^{bx} in tables and then multiplying by a.

Example 1. Draw the graph of the exponential equation $y = 1.8e^{0.6x}$.

To facilitate determining the y-value from the given x-values, we set up the table shown below.

x	-4	-3	-2	-1	0	1	2	3	4
$.6x$	-2.4	-1.8	-1.2	$-.6$	0	$.6$	1.2	1.8	2.4
$e^{.6x}$	.091	.165	.301	.549	1	1.82	3.32	6.05	11.0
y	.164	.297	.542	.988	1.8	3.28	5.98	10.9	19.8

If we plot these points and draw a smooth curve through them, we obtain Fig. 10.10.

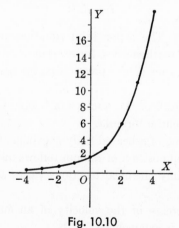

Fig. 10.10

Example 2. Draw the graph of the logarithmic equation $y = \log_{10} 2(x+1)^3$.

Write the equation in the equivalent form

$$y = 3 \log_{10} (x + 1) + \log_{10} 2.$$

By assigning to x values greater than -1 and computing the corresponding values of y, we obtain the following table.

x	-0.9	-0.75	-0.5	-0.25	0	0.5	1	2
y	-2.70	-1.51	-0.602	-0.074	0.301	0.829	1.20	1.73

Fig. 10.11 is obtained by plotting these points and drawing a smooth curve through them.

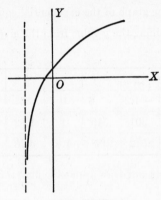

Fig. 10.11

10.8 Applications. The exponential equation appears in many of the applications of mathematics, for example:

The law of variation of the pressure of the atmosphere with the height is exponential.

The rate of increase of the number of bacteria in a culture tends to follow an exponential formula.

The law of cooling of a heated body is exponential.

The rate of decomposition of radium follows an exponential law.

The speed of many chemical reactions varies according to an exponential law.

The rate of decrease of the velocity of an automobile, coasting along a level road, is exponential.

The strength of a physiological stimulus tends to vary as an exponential function of the reaction it produces.

The amount A of a sum of money P, at compound interest at a rate r for n years, is given by the exponential equation $A = P(1 + r)^n$.

For this reason, the exponential equation is often called "the compound interest law."

★ **10.9 Damped Vibrations.** If a vibrating body, such as a tuning fork or a swing, is allowed to oscillate subject only to the action of gravity and frictional forces, the motion tends to die out in such a way that the displacement, d, of a point of the body from the position of rest varies with the time, t, approximately, according to the law

$$d = ae^{-kt} \cos (\alpha t + \beta). \qquad (9)$$

This equation is said to define a *damped vibration*.

Example. Draw the graph of $d = 2e^{-\frac{t}{4}} \cos \pi t$.

We first draw the curves $d = 2e^{-\frac{t}{4}}$ and $d = - 2e^{-\frac{t}{4}}$ which bound the amplitudes of the vibrations, since $- 1 \leqq \cos \pi t \leqq 1$ for all values of t. We next draw the curve $d = \cos \pi t$ and observe that the ordinates for the required curve are the product of the ordinates for the two curves $d = 2e^{-\frac{t}{4}}$ and $d = \cos \pi t$.

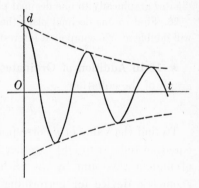

Fig. 10.12

When $t = 0$, $d = 2$ and the required curve touches the upper boundary curve $d = 2e^{-\frac{t}{4}}$. As t increases to unity, the value of d decreases. The graph crosses the t-axis when $t = \frac{1}{2}$ and touches the lower boundary curve when $t = 1$. The value of d now increases, the graph crosses the t-axis at $t = \frac{3}{2}$, and touches the upper boundary curve again at $t = 2$ (Fig. 10.12).

EXERCISES

Sketch the graphs of the following equations, using tables if necessary:

1. $y = \log_{10} (- x)$.
2. $y = - \log_{10} x$.
3. $y = \log_{10} 3x$.
4. $y = \log_{10} x^3$.
5. $y = \log_{10} 1/x$.
6. $y = \log_{10} (x + 1)$.
7. $y = \log_{10} (1 + x^2)$.
8. $y^2 = \log_{10} x$.
9. $y = \log_e (x - 2)$.
10. $y = \log_{10} \sqrt{x + 1}$.
11. $y = \log_e \sqrt{x - 2}$.
12. $y^2 = \log_2 4x$.
13. $y = 2^x$.
14. $y = e^{-x}$.

15. $y = e^{-x+2}$.   **16.** $2y = e^{2x}$.

17. $5y = e^{x/2}$.   **18.** $y = (1.05)^x$.

19. $y = 3.1e^{-1.4x}$.   **20.** $y = xe^x$.

21. $y = e^x/x^2$.   **22.** $y = e^{-x^2}$. *Probability Curve.*

23. Compare the graphs of $y = (\frac{1}{2})^x$ and $y = 2^{-x}$.

24. Compare the graphs of $y = 2\log_{10} x$ and $y = \log_{10} x^2$.

25. Using the formula $A = P(1 + r)^n$ of Art. 10.8, draw on one set of axes the graphs expressing the amount of one dollar at interest for n years (*a*) at 6% compounded annually, and (*b*) at 8% simple interest. State the meaning of the points of intersection of these curves and find their coördinates graphically to one decimal place.

26. Find to one decimal place the number of years in which one dollar will double at 5% compound interest.

★ **10.10 Addition of Ordinates.** Let it be required to sketch the graph of the equation

$$y = x + \sin x.$$

To find the value of y corresponding to a given value x_1, of x, the equation tells us to add together the numbers x_1 and $\sin x_1$. Instead of finding this sum by an arithmetic computation, the following geometric device for performing the addition will often be found easier and more satisfactory.

We first draw the curves

$$y = x \quad \text{and} \quad y = \sin x.$$

The values of y for the points on these two curves, when $x = x_1$, are obviously $y = x_1$ and $y = \sin x_1$. Hence, *the algebraic sum of the ordinates of the points on the two curves, for $x = x_1$, is the ordinate of the point on the required curve for $x = x_1$.* We may locate as many points as we please on the required curve, accordingly, by adding graphically the ordinates of the corresponding points on the component curves; that is, by laying off, in a vertical direction from any point on the line $y = x$, a directed distance equal to the ordinate of the point directly above or below it on the curve $y = \sin x$ (Fig. 10.13).

For a second example of the method of addition of ordinates we will sketch the curve

$$y = 3 \cos x + 2 \sin (x/2).$$

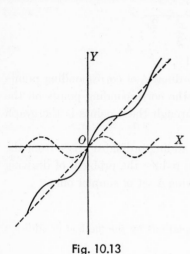

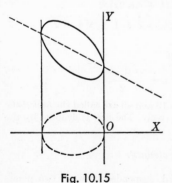

Fig. 10.13   Fig. 10.14

We first sketch the curves

$$y = 3 \cos x \quad \text{and} \quad y = 2 \sin (x/2).$$

The period of the first curve is 2π and of the second is 4π. We thus sketch each curve as x varies from 0 to 4π (Fig. 10.14). By adding graphically the ordinates of corresponding points on these two curves we get the corresponding points on the required curve.

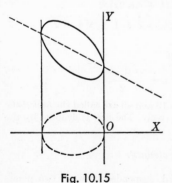

Fig. 10.15

This type of example has wide use in the applications, such as in the analysis of sound waves.

As a third example of the method of addition of ordinates, consider the ellipse

$$x^2 + 2xy + 2y^2 - 3x - 8y + 8 = 0.$$

If we solve this equation for y, we have

$$y = \tfrac{1}{2}(-x + 4 \pm \sqrt{-x^2 - 2x}).$$

To draw the graph of this equation, we shall first draw the line

$$y = \frac{-x + 4}{2},$$

and the ellipse

$$y = \pm \frac{\sqrt{-x^2 - 2x}}{2};$$

that is, the ellipse $(x + 1)^2 + 4y^2 = 1$.

If we now add, graphically, the ordinates of corresponding points on these two curves, we determine the corresponding points on the required curve. An ellipse drawn through these points is the graph of the given equation (Fig. 10.15).

The importance of this device of adding ordinates arises from the fact that it sometimes enables us to reduce the problem of drawing a complicated graph to that of drawing a set of simpler ones.

EXERCISES

Draw the graphs of the following equations by the method of addition of ordinates:

1. $y = \sin x + \cos x$.

2. $y = 2 \sin x + \sin 2x$.

3. $y = 3 \cos x + \cos 2x$.

4. $y = 2 \cos 2x + 3 \sin 3x$.

5. $y = 3 \sin x - \cos (x/2)$.

6. $y = 4 \sin 2x - 3 \cos (x/3)$.

7. $y = \frac{x}{2} + \cos 2x$.

8. $y = -x - \sin (x/2)$.

9. $y = x + (1/x)$.

10. $y = x + \log_{10} x$.

11. $y = e^x + \cos x$.

12. $y = x^2 + \sin x$.

13. $y = \sin^2 x$.

14. $y = \cos^2 x$.

Hint. $\sin^2 x = (1 - \cos 2x)/2$ and $\cos^2 x = (1 + \cos 2x)/2$.

15. $y = x - 2 \pm \sqrt{x}$.

16. $y = x + 1 \pm \sqrt{4 - x}$.

17. $x^2 - 2xy + y^2 - 2x + 4y - 6 = 0$.

18. $3x^2 - 2xy + y^2 + 2x - 2y - 4 = 0$.

19. $y = \frac{e^x - e^{-x}}{2}$.

20. $y = \frac{e^x + e^{-x}}{2}$.

Note. The right-hand members of Exercises 19 and 20 are called the *hyperbolic sine of x* and the *hyperbolic cosine of x*, respectively. The first is denoted by the symbol sinh x and the second by cosh x.

21. $y = \frac{a}{2}\left(e^{\frac{x}{a}} + e^{\frac{-x}{a}}\right) = a \cosh \frac{x}{a}$. *The Catenary.*

Note. A perfectly flexible, inextensible cord, suspended between two points on it, hangs in the form of a catenary.

22. Using the definition above, prove the following identities:

(*a*) $\cosh^2 x - \sinh^2 x = 1$

(*b*) $\sinh (-x) = -\sinh x$.

(*c*) $\sinh 2x = 2 \sinh x \cosh x$.

(*d*) $\cosh 2x = \cosh^2 x + \sinh^2 x$.

Parametric Equations

11.1 Introduction. Instead of representing a curve by a single equation connecting x and y, it is sometimes preferable to use two equations which express the coördinates of the points on the curve in terms of a third variable. This third variable is called the **parameter** and the two equations which express x and y in terms of this parameter are the **parametric equations** of the curve.

In the following articles, we shall discuss the parametric equations of a number of curves and indicate a few of the uses of such equations.

11.2 Parametric Equations of the Circle. Let there be given a circle with center at the origin and radius a (Fig. 11.1). Let $P(x, y)$ be any point on this circle and denote the angle XOP by ϕ. From the figure, we obtain

$$x = a \cos \phi, \qquad y = a \sin \phi. \qquad (1)$$

These two equations, which express the coördinates of any point P on the circle in terms of the parameter ϕ, are *parametric equations of the given circle.*

If the parametric equations of a curve

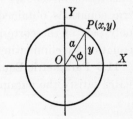

Fig. 11.1

are given, the rectangular equation may be found by eliminating the parameter between the two given equations. Thus, from (1), if we square both members of each equation, add, and simplify the result, we have

$$x^2 + y^2 = a^2, \tag{2}$$

which is the rectangular equation of the given circle.

If the rectangular equation of the curve is given, however, various parametric equations can be found for it, depending on the choice of the parameter. For the circle (2), for example, we may choose as the parameter the slope m of the line through any point P on the circle and the fixed point $(-a, 0)$. The equation of this line is $y = m(x + a)$. Since the coördinates of P satisfy the equation of this line and also the equation (2) of the circle, we find, on solving these two equations for x and y,

$$x = a \frac{1 - m^2}{1 + m^2}, \qquad y = a \frac{2m}{1 + m^2}. \tag{3}$$

These two equations, also, constitute a pair of parametric equations of the circle (2).

If we start with the pair of parametric equations

$$x = t^2, \; y = \pm \sqrt{a^2 - t^4},$$

assign real values to t and plot the resulting points, we obtain only the semicircle to the right of the y-axis, since x can only be positive. If, however, we eliminate the parameter between the two parametric equations to get the corresponding rectangular equation, we get $y = \pm \sqrt{a^2 - x^2}$. The graph of this is the entire circle. This is an illustration of the fact that frequently the graph of a pair of parametric equations obtained by using real values for the parameter is only part of the corresponding curve obtained from the rectangular equation by eliminating the parameter.

11.3 Parametric Equations of the Ellipse. Any point whose coördinates satisfy the parametric equations,

$$\begin{aligned} x &= a \cos \phi, \\ y &= b \sin \phi, \end{aligned} \tag{4}$$

wherein ϕ is the parameter, lie on an ellipse. For, if we divide the first equation by a, the second by b, square both members, add, and simplify, we find, as the rectangular equation of the curve,

$$\frac{x^2}{a^2} + \frac{y^2}{b^2} = 1,$$

which is the equation of an ellipse.

From equations (4) one readily derives a point by point construction for the ellipse. With the origin as center and radii

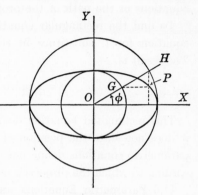

Fig. 11.2

b and a ($b < a$) draw two circles (Fig. 11.2). Draw any half line from the origin intersecting the smaller circle at G and the larger at H. Draw through G a line parallel to OX and through H a line perpendicular to it. Then the point $P(x, y)$ of intersection of these two lines lies on the ellipse for,

$$x = OH \cos \phi = a \cos \phi, \quad \text{and} \quad y = OG \sin \phi = b \sin \phi.$$

11.4 Path of a Projectile. If a projectile is fired from the origin with an initial velocity v_0, in a direction making an angle α with

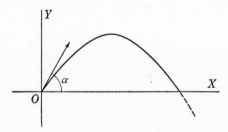

Fig. 11.3

OX, and if it moves subject only to the attraction of gravitation, it is shown in the textbooks on physics that its position at the end of t seconds is given by the equations

$$x = tv_0 \cos \alpha, \qquad y = tv_0 \sin \alpha - \tfrac{1}{2}gt^2,$$

where g is a constant. These two equations constitute the parametric equations of the path of the projectile in terms of the parameter t.

To find the rectangular equation of the path, we solve the first equation for t, substitute in the second equation, and simplify. The result is

$$y = x \tan \alpha - \frac{gx^2}{2v_0{}^2} \sec^2 \alpha.$$

This rectangular equation defines the path of the projectile, but it does not state the position of the body at any given time. The parametric equations define not only the path but also the law according to which the projectile traverses its path.

11.5 Parametric Equations and Curve Plotting. The folium of Descartes, which is defined by the equation

$$x^3 + y^3 - 3axy = 0,$$

is a good example of a curve whose parametric equations can be used to advantage in plotting the curve. We find, by discussing the equation as in Chapter 9, that the curve is symmetric with respect to the line $y = x$, that it touches both axes at the origin, and that it has no other points in common with either axis. This does not give us much information about the curve, so we try to get some points on the curve by assigning values to either x or y. We find, however, that any time this is done we have to solve a cubic equation either in y or x. Instead of doing this, it is more convenient to determine a pair of parametric equations of the curve and to plot points on the curve from these parametric equations.

To find the required parametric equations, we notice that any line $y = mx$ through the origin intersects the folium at the origin and at the point whose coördinates are

$$x = \frac{3am}{1 + m^3}, \qquad y = \frac{3am^2}{1 + m^3}. \tag{5}$$

These equations constitute a pair of parametric equations of the curve in terms of the parameter m. However, it is not always possible to obtain a convenient parametric representation for a curve as we did here.

By assigning to m real values (other than -1) we can now determine as many points as we please on the curve. By drawing a smooth curve through these points (that joins them in the order of the corresponding values of m), we obtain the required graph of the folium (Fig. 11.4).

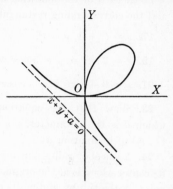

Fig. 11.4

If we assign to m the value $m = -1$, we do not obtain a corresponding point on the curve. (Why?) By assigning to m a number of values very near to -1, however, we find that the corresponding points are far from the origin but very close to the line $x + y + a = 0$. This line is thus an asymptote.

Frequently it is advantageous to give a curve parametrically rather than by its rectangular equation. This occurs, for example, in applications where the position of some object is given as a function of time, as in Art. 11.4. When a curve is given parametrically, then we can, by assigning a succession of values to the parameter, get a succession of points on the curve and thus plot it, even when it is not feasible to plot from the corresponding rectangular equation.

EXERCISES

Find the rectangular equation for each of the following curves. Draw the curve either from the parametric equations or from the rectangular equation:

1. $x = 2 + 3t, y = 5 - 2t.$
2. $x = 2pt^2, y = 2pt.$
3. $x = a \sec \phi, y = b \tan \phi.$
4. $x = 1 + 3 \cos \phi, y = 2 + 4 \sin \phi.$
5. $x = at, y = a/t.$
6. $x = t + 1/t, y = t - 1/t.$
7. $x = at^3, y = at.$
8. $x = at^3, y = at^2.$
9. $x = a \cos^3 \phi, y = a \sin^3 \phi.$
10. $x = a \cos^4 \phi, y = a \sin^4 \phi.$
11. $x = 4 \sin \phi + 3 \cos \phi, y = 4 \cos \phi - 3 \sin \phi.$
12. $x = \sin \phi - \cos \phi, y = \cos \phi.$

13. $x = t^2 + t, y = t - 1.$ **14.** $x = t^2 - t, y = t^2 + t.$

15. $x = t^2 - 4, y = t(t^2 - 4).$ **16.** $x = t^2(1 + t), y = t(1 + t).$

Draw each of the following curves both from the parametric equations and the corresponding rectangular equation:

17. $x = t^2 + 1, y = t^2.$ **18.** $x = 1 - t^2, y = -t^2.$

19. $x = 2 \sin^2 \phi, y = 3 \cos^2 \phi.$ **20.** $x = \dfrac{1}{t^2} + t^2, y = \dfrac{1}{t^2} - t^2.$

21. $x = 9 \sin^2 \pi t, y = 3 \cos \pi t.$ **22.** $x = \sqrt{t}, y = t^2 - t.$

23. Show that the equations $x = x_1 + d \cos \alpha, \; y = y_1 + d \sin \alpha,$ in which d is the parameter, are parametric equations of the line through (x_1, y_1) of inclination α.

24. A wheel of radius 6 inches turns through 5 radians per second around its center which is at the origin. Find parametric equations of the path of a point on the rim by finding its coördinates at the end of t seconds.

Find parametric equations of the following curves by finding their intersections with the lines of the given family.

25. The circle $x^2 + y^2 + Dx + Ey = 0$, using the family $y = mx$.
26. The parabola $y^2 = 2px$, using $y = mx$.
27. The ellipse $b^2x^2 + a^2y^2 = a^2b^2$, using $y = m(x + a)$.
28. The hyperbola $b^2x^2 - a^2y^2 = a^2b^2$, using $y = m(x + a)$.
29. The strophoid (Ex. 25, Art. 9.7) $x^3 + xy^2 + ax^2 - ay^2 = 0$, using $y = mx$.
30. The trisectrix (Art. 9.7) $x^3 + xy^2 + ay^2 - 3ax^2 = 0$, using $y = mx$.
31. The cissoid (Art. 9.7) $x^3 + xy^2 - 2ay^2 = 0$, using $y = mx$.
32. A line through the point $P_1(4, 6)$ intersects the coördinate axes at A and B. Find the locus of the midpoint of the segment AB as the line rotates around P_1.
33. A crank OA, 2 feet long, rotates about the origin, O. A rod AB, 6 feet long, has one end attached at A while the other end B slides along the x-axis. Find the path of a point P on AB at a distance k from A.

11.6 The Cycloid. The path of a point fixed on the circumference of a circle that rolls along a fixed line is called a **cycloid**.

We shall find the parametric equations of the cycloid when the fixed line on which the circle rolls is taken as the x-axis and any one of the positions at which the tracing point comes in contact with this line is taken as origin.

Let a be the radius of the rolling circle, $P(x, y)$ be any position of the tracing point, and let ϕ be the number of *radians* in the angle through which the circle has rolled from its position when the tracing point was at the origin.

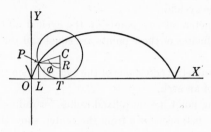

Fig. 11.5

From the figure

$$x = \overline{OL} = \overline{OT} - \overline{LT}, \tag{6}$$

and $$y = \overline{LP} = \overline{TR} = \overline{TC} - \overline{RC}. \tag{7}$$

Since the circle has rolled from O to T, $\overline{OT} = $ arc TP, and, since ϕ is measured in radians, we have (Art. 0.7) arc $TP = a\phi$. Hence

$$\overline{OT} = \text{arc } TP = a\phi.$$

Also $\overline{LT} = \overline{PR} = a \sin \phi$, $\overline{RC} = a \cos \phi$, and $\overline{TC} = a$.

If we make these substitutions in (6) and (7), we have as the required parametric equations of the cycloid in terms of ϕ as the parameter:

$$\begin{aligned} x &= a(\phi - \sin \phi) \\ y &= a(1 - \cos \phi) \end{aligned} \tag{8}$$

To find the rectangular equations of the cycloid, we first solve the second of equations (8) for $\cos \phi$, giving $\cos \phi = (a - y)/a$. From this equation, we find the values of ϕ and $\sin \phi$ and substitute in the first of equations (8). The result is

$$x = a \text{ arc } \cos \frac{a - y}{a} \pm \sqrt{2ay - y^2}.$$

For most practical purposes, this equation is less convenient than the parametric equations (8).

EXERCISES

1. Taking values of ϕ at intervals of $\pi/6$ radians, sketch one arch of the cycloid.

2. Find the length of the base and the coördinates of the highest point on one arch of the cycloid.

3. If the parameters of two points on the cycloid differ by 2π radians, show that the ordinates of these points are equal and their abscissas differ by $2\pi a$.

4. Find the parametric equations of the cycloid when the origin is translated to the top of an arch.

5. If the tracing point lies on a fixed radius (or radius produced) of the rolling circle, at a distance $b \neq a$ from the center, show that the equations of its path are,

$$x = a\phi - b \sin \phi, \qquad y = a - b \cos \phi.$$

This curve is called a *prolate cycloid* if $b > a$ and a *curtate cycloid* if $b < a$. In either case, it is also called a *trochoid*.

6. Draw the graph of a prolate cycloid for which $b = 2a$.

7. Draw the graph of a curtate cycloid for which $2b = a$.

8. A circle of radius a feet rolls along a line at the rate of b radians per second. At the instant that a certain radius extends vertically downward, a particle starts from the center along that radius at the rate of c feet per second. Find the path of the particle.

★ **11.7 The Epicycloid.** The path of a point fixed on the circumference of a circle that rolls tangent externally to a fixed circle is called an **epicycloid.**

Denote the radius of the fixed circle by a and of the rolling circle

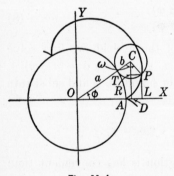

by b. Take the center, O, of the fixed circle as origin and the x-axis through a point A where the tracing point is in contact with the fixed circle (Fig. 11.6).

Let ϕ be the number of radians in the angle XOC which the line of centers makes with the x-axis and let ω be the number of radians in the angle OCP through which the radius CP has turned from the line of centers.

Fig. 11.6

From the figure,

$$\text{angle } DCO = \frac{\pi}{2} - \phi,$$

and

$$\text{angle } DCP = \omega - \text{angle } DCO = \omega - \left(\frac{\pi}{2} - \phi\right) = \phi + \omega - \frac{\pi}{2}.$$

Also

$$x = \overline{OL} = \overline{OD} + \overline{DL} = \overline{OD} + \overline{RP},$$

and

$$y = \overline{LP} = \overline{DR} = \overline{DC} - \overline{RC}. \tag{9}$$

Since $OC = a + b$ (Why?), we have, from the definitions of the sine and cosine of an angle,

$$\overline{OD} = (a + b) \cos \phi, \quad \overline{RP} = b \sin (DCP) = - b \cos (\phi + \omega).$$

$$\overline{DC} = (a + b) \sin \phi, \quad \overline{RC} = b \cos (DCP) = b \sin (\phi + \omega).$$

On making these substitutions in equations (9), we have

$$\begin{aligned} x &= (a + b) \cos \phi - b \cos (\phi + \omega), \\ y &= (a + b) \sin \phi - b \sin (\phi + \omega). \end{aligned} \tag{10}$$

Since the outside circle rolls on the fixed one, arc AT = arc PT, that is, $a\phi = b\omega$, or $\omega = a\phi/b$.

On substituting this value of ω in equations (10), we have

$$\begin{aligned} x &= (a + b) \cos \phi - b \cos \frac{a + b}{b} \phi, \\ y &= (a + b) \sin \phi - b \sin \frac{a + b}{b} \phi. \end{aligned} \tag{11}$$

These are the parametric equations of the epicycloid.

★ **11.8 The Hypocycloid.** *The path of a point fixed on the circumference of a circle that rolls tangent internally to a fixed circle is an* **hypocycloid.**

The derivation of the equations of the hypocycloid, which parallels that of the epicycloid, is left as an exercise for the student. The resulting equations are

$$\begin{aligned} x &= (a - b) \cos \phi + b \cos \frac{a - b}{b} \phi, \\ y &= (a - b) \sin \phi - b \sin \frac{a - b}{b} \phi. \end{aligned} \tag{12}$$

It should be observed that these equations differ from those of the epicloid only in that b is replaced by $-b$.

In Fig. 11.7, we have taken $b = a/4$. This curve is of special interest and is called the **four-cusped hypocycloid.**

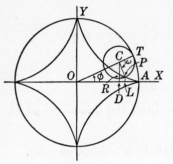

Fig. 11.7

If we put $b = a/4$ in equations (12) and simplify by means of the trigonometric identities

$$\cos 3\phi = 4 \cos^6 \phi - 3 \cos \phi,$$
$$\sin 3\phi = 3 \sin \phi - 4 \sin^3 \phi,$$

we obtain

$$x = a \cos^3 \phi, \qquad y = a \sin^3 \phi,$$

as the parametric equations of the curve.

By eliminating ϕ between these equations, we obtain

$$x^{\frac{2}{3}} + y^{\frac{2}{3}} = a^{\frac{2}{3}},$$

as the rectangular equation of the four-cusped hypocycloid.

EXERCISES

Sketch the epicycloid, given:

1. $a = 4b.$ **2.** $a = 2b.$ **3.** $a = b.$ **4.** $2a = b.$

Sketch the hypocycloid, given:

5. $a = 8b.$ **6.** $a = 6b.$ **7.** $a = 3b.$ **8.** $2a = 5b.$

9. Discuss the degenerate cycloid that arises when $a = 2b.$

10. If a thread is unwound from around a fixed circle, and is held taut in the plane of the circle, any point fixed on the thread will describe a curve called an *involute of the circle.* Show that the parametric equations of this curve are

$$x = a(\cos \phi + \phi \sin \phi) \quad y = a(\sin \phi - \phi \cos \phi).$$

Hint. Show that the angle OTP (Fig. 11.8) is a right angle.

11. Plot the involute of the circle from $\phi = 0$ to $\phi = 2\pi.$

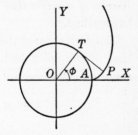

Fig. 11.8

Curves in Polar Coördinates

12.1 Polar Equations. In preceding chapters, we have discussed the polar equations of lines, of circles, and of the conic sections. We shall now consider the problem of drawing a higher plane curve when its equation is given to us in polar coördinates.

The problem of drawing the graph of an equation in polar coördinates is complicated by the fact that, for a given point $P(r, \theta)$, there are infinitely many equivalent pairs of polar coördinates (Art. 5.2), namely $(r, \theta + 2n\pi)$ and $(-r, \theta + \pi + 2n\pi)$. It is further complicated by the fact that frequently there are two or more different equations that define the same curve. For example, the equations $r = 1$ and $-r = 1$ define the same circle. Two equations that define the same curve are said to be **equivalent equations.** Equivalent equations are obtained from a given equation in r and θ by replacing the pair (r, θ) by any one of the equivalent pairs $(r, \theta + 2n\pi)$ or $(-r, \theta + \pi + 2n\pi)$. To further illustrate, consider the parabola $r = \dfrac{1}{1 - \sin \theta}$. Replacing the pair (r, θ) by the equivalent pair $(-r, \theta + \pi)$ we get

$$-r = \frac{1}{1 - \sin (\theta + \pi)} \quad \text{or} \quad r = \frac{-1}{1 + \sin \theta}$$

as an equivalent equation of the same parabola. This is verified by graphing both equations. (Fig. 12.1.)

By consideration of the possible equivalent pairs for (r, θ), we see that

$$r = \frac{1}{1 - \sin \theta} \quad \text{and} \quad r = \frac{-1}{1 + \sin \theta} \tag{1}$$

are the only two *distinct equivalent equations* for the parabola. We are using the word distinct in the sense that we reject equations which reduce to equations (1) by the use of trigonometric identities. For example, we reject all equations $r = \dfrac{1}{1 - \sin (\theta + 2n\pi)}$, with $n \neq 0$, since they reduce to $r = \dfrac{1}{1 - \sin \theta}$ by a standard reduction formula. Equations (1) are distinct as is shown by equating the right-hand sides and proving that the resulting equation is not an identity. Many of the curves commonly studied by the use of polar coördinates have only two distinct equivalent equations.

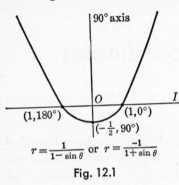

$$r = \frac{1}{1 - \sin \theta} \text{ or } r = \frac{-1}{1 + \sin \theta}$$

Fig. 12.1

If any one of the infinitely many pairs of equivalent polar coördinates of a point P satisfy the given equation, then the point P lies on the curve. In many instances all the pairs of equivalent polar coördinates satisfy the given equation, as in the case of the line $r \cos \theta = 1$. Here is an instance in which there is only one distinct equation representing the curve. Sometimes only one pair of equivalent polar coördinates may satisfy the given equation, as in the case of the curve $r = \theta$. In this case however, it can be shown that equivalent pairs of coördinates for a point will satisfy an equivalent equation for the curve. Thus the equations $r = \theta$ and $r = \theta + 2\pi$ are equivalent equations. If the point (r, θ) satisfies the first of these, then the equivalent pair $(r, \theta - 2\pi)$ satisfies the second of these equations. Here is an example of a curve which has infinitely many distinct equivalent equations representing it.

12.2 Discussion of the Equation. When it is required to plot the curve defined by a given equation in polar coördinates, time will usually be saved, and better results obtained, if, before plotting points on the curve, one tests the curve with respect to the following properties.

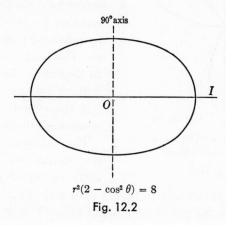

$$r^2(2 - \cos^2 \theta) = 8$$

Fig. 12.2

(*a*) *Symmetries.* If the equation of a curve remains unchanged, or is changed to an equivalent equation, when

(1) θ is replaced by $-\theta$, or if r and θ are replaced by $-r$ and $\pi - \theta$, it is symmetric with respect to the initial line.

(2) θ is replaced by $\pi - \theta$, or if r and θ are replaced by $-r$ and $-\theta$, it is symmetric with respect to the 90°-axis,

(3) θ is replaced by $\pi + \theta$, or when r is replaced by $-r$, the curve is symmetric with respect to the origin.

The curve $r^2(2 - \cos^2 \theta) = 8$, for example, exhibits all of the above symmetries. This curve is an ellipse, as may be seen at once by writing its equation, $x^2 + 2y^2 = 8$, in rectangular coördinates.

The curve $r = \dfrac{1}{1 - \sin \theta}$ (Fig. 12.1) is symmetric with respect to the 90°-axis, as is seen by replacing θ by $\pi - \theta$. If a test for symmetry with respect to the 90°-axis is made by replacing r and θ by $-r$ and $-\theta$, we get

$$-r = \frac{1}{1 - \sin(-\theta)} \quad \text{or} \quad r = \frac{-1}{1 + \sin \theta}$$

This is an equivalent equation for the curve as shown in Art. 12.1, and thus again we have symmetry.

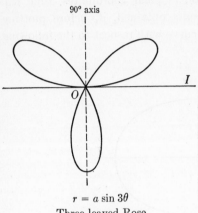

90° axis

$r = a \sin 3\theta$

Three-leaved Rose

Fig. 12.3

(b) *Intercepts.* To find the intercepts on the initial line, one puts $\theta = 0$, $\pm \pi$, $\pm 2\pi$, etc., and solves for r. Similarly, the intercepts on the 90°-axis are found by putting $\theta = \pm \pi/2$, $\pm 3\pi/2$, etc. This method frequently fails to determine the intersections, if there are any, at the origin, but these intersections will be determined under (c).

For example, the points of intersection of the ellipse $r^2(2 - \cos^2 \theta) = 8$ with the initial line are found in this way to be $(2\sqrt{2}, 0)$ and $(2\sqrt{2}, \pi)$ and its intersections with the 90°-axis are found to be $(2, \pm \pi/2)$.

(c) *Tangents at the origin.* If the curve passes through the origin, the angles made by its tangent line, or lines, with the initial line are found by putting $r = 0$ in the equation and solving for θ.

Thus, in the equation

$$r = a \sin 3\theta,$$

if we put $r = 0$, we have $\sin 3\theta = 0$, so that $3\theta = 0$, $\pm \pi$, $\pm 2\pi$, etc. Hence, $\theta = 0$, $\pm \pi/3$, $\pm 2\pi/3$, etc. There are thus three tangent lines to this curve at the origin, of inclinations 0, $\pi/3$, and $2\pi/3$, respectively. This curve is called a *three-leaved rose* curve. It belongs to a type we shall discuss in Art. 12.7.

(d) *Directions in which the curve extends to infinity.* To determine the directions in which the curve

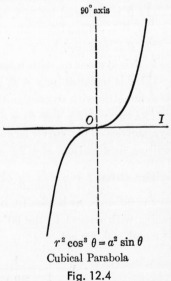

90° axis

$r^2 \cos^3 \theta = a^2 \sin \theta$

Cubical Parabola

Fig. 12.4

extends to infinity, we equate to zero the coefficient of the highest power of r in the given equation and solve for θ.

For example, to determine the directions in which the curve

$$r^2 \cos^3 \theta = a^2 \sin \theta$$

(Fig. 12.4) recedes to infinity, we equate to zero the coefficient of r^2. This gives $\cos^3 \theta = 0$, so that $\theta = \pm \pi/2, \pm 3\pi/2$, etc. This curve (see also Art. 9.7, Ex. 7) thus extends to infinity in the $\pm 90°$ directions, but the $90°$-axis is not an asymptote. Since this frequently occurs the student must be very careful in deciding just how a curve extends to infinity.

(*e*) *Intervals in which one coördinate is imaginary.* It is frequently possible, by using the fact that neither $\sin \theta$ nor $\cos \theta$ is ever numerically greater than unity, to assign limits between which the numerical values of r must lie.

Thus, for the three-leaved rose (Fig. 12.3), the largest numerical value that r can have is a. This numerical value is attained when $\sin 3\theta = \pm 1$, that is, when $\theta = \pm \pi/6, \pm \pi/2, \pm 5\pi/6$, etc.

Similarly, for the line $r \cos \theta = 5$, the smallest numerical value that r can have is 5. This value is reached when $\cos \theta = \pm 1$, that is, when $\theta = 0, \pm \pi, \pm 2\pi$, etc.

For the ellipse $r^2(2 - \cos^2 \theta) = 8$ (Fig. 12.2), we find in a similar way that the largest numerical value that r can have is $2\sqrt{2}$, and the smallest is 2.

Again, if the given equation can be solved for r^2, it may be possible to find values of θ for which r is imaginary. These values of θ must be excluded in drawing the graph. In the case of the cubical parabola, $r^2 \cos^3 \theta = a^3 \sin \theta$ (Fig. 12.4), for example, r is imaginary if $\sin \theta$ and $\cos \theta$ have opposite signs, that is, if θ is in the second or fourth quadrants. There are thus no points on the curve corresponding to these values of θ.

(*f*) *Transformation to rectangular coördinates.* It frequently happens that the equation of the curve in rectangular coördinates is one with which the student is already familiar, or from which it is easier to determine the properties of the equation than it is from its polar equation. We found that the locus of the equation $r^2(2 - \cos^2 \theta) = 8$, for example, was an ellipse by finding its rectangular equation.

Similarly, it is usually easier to recognize that the locus of the equation $r \cos \theta = 5$ (or $r = 5 \sec \theta$) is a line from its rectangular equation $x = 5$ than it is from either of the polar forms.

In any event, any information about the curve that is obtained from the discussion of its equation in rectangular coördinates, or by plotting points on it from its rectangular equation, must hold for the required graph.

Equally, if the equation is given to us in rectangular coördinates, it may be possible to simplify the problem of drawing the curve by finding its equation in polar coördinates. It is thus good practice, when the equation of a curve is given to us either in rectangular or in polar coördinates, to discuss its equation in the system which gives us the most information. In some cases it may be necessary to discuss it in both systems of coördinates before attempting to draw the graph.

(*g*) *Use of the laws of variation of the trigonometric functions.* If the given equation defines r as equal to a simple expression in terms of the trigonometric functions of θ, a fairly accurate preliminary sketch of the curve can often be obtained quickly by observing how these functions change as θ increases. For this purpose, the graphs of the trigonometric curves in Arts. 10.2, 10.3, and 10.4 will be found quite helpful. The preliminary sketch obtained in this way may then be corrected by discussing the equation and plotting points on the curve.

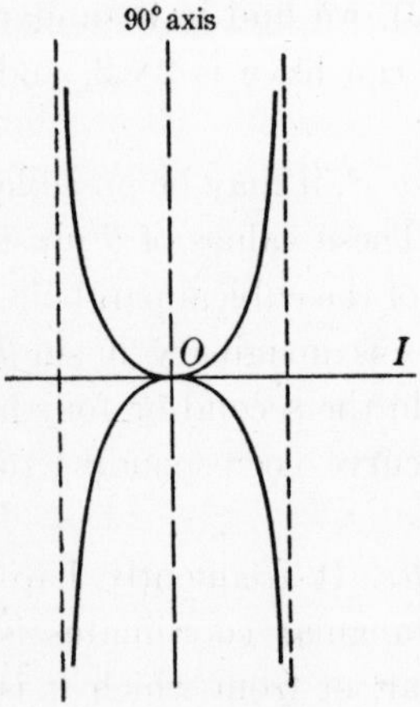

Thus, if the given equation is

$$r = a \tan \theta,$$

it is obvious that $r = 0$ when $\theta = 0$, that r increases to a as θ increases to $\pi/4$ and that it then increases indefinitely as θ increases to $\pi/2$. By following the variation of $\tan \theta$ through the four quadrants, a figure somewhat resembling Fig. 12.5 will thus be obtained. By discussing the given polar equation, and the rectangular equation $x^4 + x^2 y^2 = a^2 y^2$, of this curve, and plot-

90° axis

O

I

$r = a \tan \theta$

Kappa Curve

Fig. 12.5

ting a number of points on it, we obtain Fig. 12.5. The lines
$x = \pm a$ are asymptotes.

This curve is called the *kappa curve*, from its supposed resemblance
to the Greek letter kappa.

In the following articles, we shall discuss the equations and draw
the graphs of a number of curves the equations of which are frequently encountered in polar coördinates.

12.3 The Lemniscate. The locus of the equation $r^2 = a^2 \cos 2\theta$ is
called a *lemniscate of Bernoulli*
(or, usually, simply a *lemniscate*)
(Fig. 12.6).

This curve is symmetric with
respect to both axes and the
origin. It intersects the initial
line at $(\pm a, 0)$ and these are
the points on the curve farthest
from the origin. It also passes

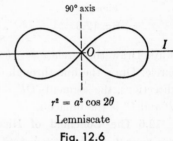

90° axis

I

$r^2 = a^2 \cos 2\theta$

Lemniscate

Fig. 12.6

through the origin and touches, at that point, the lines making
angles of $\pm \pi/4$ and $\pm 3\pi/4$ with the initial line. The radius vector r
is imaginary if $\cos 2\theta$ is negative, that is, if θ lies in the intervals
$\pi/4 < \theta < 3\pi/4$, or $5\pi/4 < \theta < 7\pi/4$, etc.

12.4 The Cardioid. The locus of the equation $r = a(1 - \cos \theta)$ is
a *cardioid*.

This locus is symmetric with respect to the initial line. It touches
the initial line at the origin and intersects it at $(2a, \pi)$. The latter
point is the point of the curve that is
farthest from the origin. It crosses the
90°-axis at $(a, \pm \pi/2)$. The radius vector
increases from 0 at $\theta = 0$ to $2a$ at $\theta = \pi$,
then decreases to 0 again at $\theta = 2\pi$.

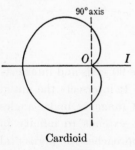

90° axis

O   *I*

Cardioid

Fig. 12.7

12.5 The Limaçon. The polar equation
$r = a - b \cos \theta$ defines a curve called the
limaçon of Pascal (or *limaçon*).

If $a = b$, the limaçon becomes a cardioid.
In Fig. 12.8, we have taken $a < b$. The
construction of the figure for $a > b$ is left as an exercise for the
student.

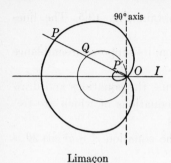

90° axis

Limaçon

Fig. 12.8

If we replace the pair (r, θ) by the equivalent pair $(-r, \theta - \pi)$ in $r = a - b \cos \theta$ we get the equivalent equation

$$-r = a - b \cos (\theta - \pi) \quad \text{or}$$
$$-r = a + b \cos \theta$$

for the limaçon. These two are the only distinct equivalent equations in this case.

The limaçon is frequently constructed by points in the following way: Draw the circle $r = -b \cos \theta$ and let Q be any point on this circle. Draw the line through O and Q and on it lay off, in opposite directions, the segments $QP = QP' = a$. Then the locus of the points P and P' is the limaçon.

12.6 The Conchoid of Nicomedes. The locus of the equation $r = a \csc \theta \pm b$ is the *conchoid of Nicomedes*.

There are three cases according as $a \lesseqgtr b$. In the following discussion, and in the figure, we have taken $a < b$. The discussion of the other two cases is left as an exercise for the student.

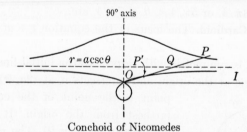

90° axis

$r = a \csc \theta$

Conchoid of Nicomedes

Fig. 12.9

The curve is symmetric with respect to the 90°-axis and intersects it at the origin and at the points $r = a \pm b$. It intersects the initial line only at the origin, at which point its tangents make angles $\theta = \text{arc csc } (\pm b/a)$ with the initial line. It extends to infinity in such a way that each of its two branches approaches the horizontal line $r = a \csc \theta$ as an asymptote.

This curve may be constructed by points in the following way: Draw the line $r = a \csc \theta$ and let Q be any point on it. Draw the line through O and Q and on it lay off, in opposite directions, the segments $QP = QP' = b$. Then the locus of the points P and P' is the conchoid.

12.7 The Rose Curves. The loci of the equations,

$$r = a \cos n\theta \quad \text{and} \quad r = a \sin n\theta, \tag{1}$$

wherein n is an integer, are called *rose curves*. Each loop extending out from the origin is called a "leaf" of the rose.

The three-leaved rose, $r = a \sin 3\theta$, was shown in Fig. 12.3.

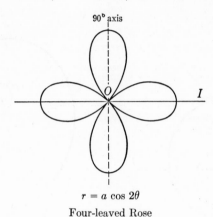

90° axis

I

$r = a \cos 2\theta$

Four-leaved Rose

Fig. 12.10

The four-leaved rose, $r = a \cos 2\theta$, appears in Fig. 12.10. It is symmetric with respect to the origin and to both axes and it intersects the axes at the points $(a, 0)$, $(- a, \pi/2)$, (a, π), and $(- a, 3\pi/2)$. Its tangent lines at the origin are defined by $\theta = \pm \pi/4$, $\pm 3\pi/4$, etc.

Exercise. Show that the one-leaved rose, $r = a \cos \theta$, is a circle.

12.8 The Spirals. If a curve, or one of its branches, winds infinitely many times about the origin in such a way that r increases (or decreases) continuously as θ increases or decreases continuously, then the curve is called a *spiral*.

The equation $r = a\theta$ defines a **spiral of Archimedes.**

This curve is symmetric with respect to the 90°-axis since, if a point (r, θ) lies on the curve, so also does $(- r, - \theta)$ and any two such points are symmetric with respect to the 90°-axis. It touches the initial line at the origin and the rate of increase of the numerical value of r is proportional to that of θ (Fig. 12.11).

Exercise. Show that the lengths of the successive segments OA, OB, OC, etc. from the origin to the successive intersections of the curve with the axes, as θ increases through positive values, form an arithmetic progression.

The locus of the equation $\log_e r = a\theta$, where $e = 2.71828^+$ (Art. 10.6) is called a **logarithmic spiral.** The equation of this curve is also often written in the equivalent form $r = e^{a\theta}$.

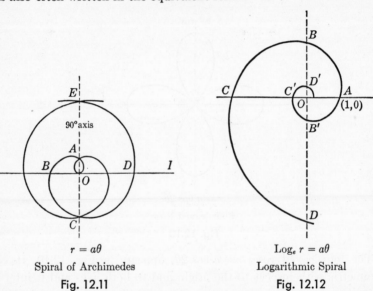

$r = a\theta$

Spiral of Archimedes

Fig. 12.11

$\text{Log}_e\, r = a\theta$

Logarithmic Spiral

Fig. 12.12

For $\theta = 0$, we have $r = 1$. As θ increases from zero, the value of r increases more and more rapidly and becomes very large as θ approaches $+\infty$. If θ decreases from zero, the value of r decreases slowly and approaches zero as θ approaches $-\infty$.

To plot points on this curve, we assign values to θ and determine the corresponding values for r by using the table of exponential functions.

Exercise. Show (*a*) that the length of the segments OC', OB', OA, OB, etc. from the origin to successive intersections of the curve with the axes form a geometric progression, (*b*) that the angles $C'B'A$, $B'AB$, ABC, etc. are right angles.

EXERCISES

Discuss the given equation and draw the curve. If just one literal coefficient appears, assign to it any convenient value. If two such constants, a and b appear, consider three cases, $a > b$, $a = b$, and $a < b$. State the name of the curve if you know it:

1. $r \sin \theta = a$.
2. $r = a \sin \theta$.
3. $r^2(5 - 3 \sin^2 \theta) = a^2$.
4. $r^2(3 - 5 \sin^2 \theta) = a^2$.
5. $r^2 \cos 2\theta = a^2$.
6. $r^2 = a^2 \sin 2\theta$.
7. $r(1 - \cos \theta) = a$.
8. $r = a(1 - \sin \theta)$.
9. $r \sin^3 \theta = a \cos^2 \theta$.
10. $r \cos^2 \theta = a \sin \theta$.
11. $r = a - b \sin \theta$.
12. $r = a + b \cos \theta$.
13. $r = a \cos 4\theta$.
14. $r = a \cos 5\theta$.
15. $r^2 = a^2 \cos \theta$.
16. $r^2 \cos \theta = a^2$.
17. $r = a \sin \theta/2$.
18. $r = a \sec \theta \pm b$.
19. $r^2\theta = a^2$. *The Lituus.*
20. $r^2 = a^2\theta$. *The Parabolic Spiral.*
21. $r\theta = a$. *The Hyperbolic or Reciprocal Spiral.*
22. Find the polar equations of the curves in Ex. 24 to 28 of Art. 9.7.
23. Find the rectangular equations of the curves in Arts. 12.3 to 12.6.
24. Determine the distinct equivalent equations for the curve $r = a \cos 2\theta$ and $r = a \cos (\theta/2)$.
25. Determine the distinct equivalent equations for the curves $r = a \cos 3\theta$ and $r = a \cos (\theta/3)$.
26. Determine the distinct equivalent equations for the curves $r = a \sin m\theta$ and $r = a \sin (\theta/m)$ where m is a positive integer.

★ **12.9 Intersections of Curves in Polar Coördinates.** We have seen (Art. 5.2) that any given point in the plane has infinitely many pairs of polar coördinates and it has been pointed out (in Art. 12.1) that not all of these pairs need to satisfy the given polar equation of the curve. This fact introduces difficulties into the problem of finding the coördinates of the intersections of two curves whose polar equations are given. For, at a given intersection P, the pair of coördinates of P that satisfy the first equation may not be the pair that satisfy the second one. They may, instead, satisfy only an equation that is equivalent (Art. 12.1) to the given second equation.

Again, at the origin, $r = 0$ but θ may have any value whatever. The origin may therefore lie on both curves although the values of θ that make $r = 0$ may be entirely different for the two equations.

It is, accordingly, usually best, when one wishes to find the intersections of two curves from their polar equations, to plot both curves on one set of axes, and then to determine the intersections indicated on the figure by considering, if necessary, not only the given equations but also the equations equivalent to them.

The following examples will illustrate how the above-mentioned difficulties may arise, and how they may be met.

Example 1. Find the points of intersection of the curves $r = 3\theta$ and $r = \pi$.

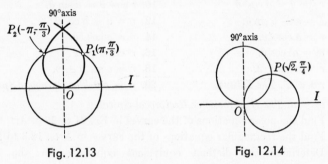

Fig. 12.13   Fig. 12.14

From the figure, it is seen that these curves intersect in two points, one in the first quadrant and one in the second. The solution of the two given equations, however, determines only the intersection $P_1(\pi, \pi/3)$. To find the second intersection P_2, we replace the second equation by the equivalent equation $r = -\pi$. This, with $r = 3\theta$, determines $P_2(-\pi, -\pi/3)$.

Example 2. Find the points of intersection of the circles

$$r = 2 \sin \theta \quad \text{and} \quad r = 2 \cos \theta.$$

If we eliminate r between these equations, we have

$$2 \sin \theta = 2 \cos \theta, \quad \text{or} \quad \tan \theta = 1,$$

so that $\theta = \pi/4, 5\pi/4$, etc. On substituting back in both given equations, we find that $P_1(\sqrt{2}, \pi/4)$ is one of the required intersections.

The two circles also intersect at the origin since $(0, 0)$ satisfies one of the given equations and $(0, \pi/2)$ satisfies the other. Hence, the origin is the second required intersection of the two circles.

Example 3. Find the points of intersection of the curves $r = \cos 2\theta$ and $r = 1 + \sin \theta$.

If we eliminate r between these equations, we have, after replacing $\cos 2\theta$ by its equal $1 - 2\sin^2\theta$, $1 - 2\sin^2\theta = 1 + \sin\theta$, or $2\sin^2\theta + \sin\theta = 0$, so that $\sin\theta = 0$ and $\sin\theta = -\frac{1}{2}$. Thus $\theta = 0$, π, etc. and $\theta = 7\pi/6$, $11\pi/6$, etc. Upon substituting these in the original equations, we obtain

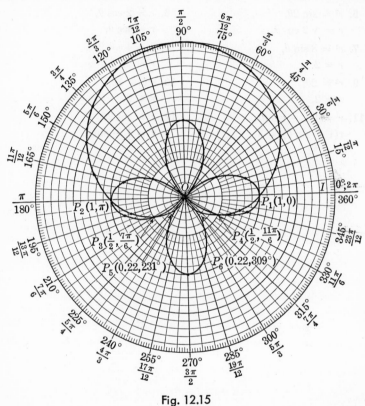

Fig. 12.15

$P_1(1, 0)$, $P_2(1, \pi)$, $P_3(\frac{1}{2}, 7\pi/6)$, $P_4(\frac{1}{2}, 11\pi/6)$ for four of the intersections. To obtain P_5 and P_6, replace the second equation by the equivalent equation $-r = 1 - \sin\theta$. This together with $r = \cos 2\theta$ gives approximately $P_5(0.22, 231°)$ and $P_6(0.22, 309°)$. The two curves also intersect at the origin. Thus there are seven points of intersection as shown in Fig. 12.15.

EXERCISES

Draw the following pairs of curves on one set of axes and find polar coördinates for their points of intersection:

1. $r \cos \theta = 2$,
   $r = 4$.

2. $r = 10 \sin \theta$,
   $r = 5$.

3. $r = 2 \cos \theta$,
   $r = 2 \cos 2\theta$.

4. $r \sin \theta = 2 \cos^2 \theta$,
   $r = 2 \sin \theta$.

5. $r^2 = \sin 2\theta$,
   $r = \sqrt{2} \cos \theta$.

6. $r = 2 \cos \theta$,
   $r = \sec \theta$.

7. $r^2 = 8 \sin \theta$,
   $r = 2$.

8. $r = 4 \cos 2\theta$,
   $r = 2$.

9. $r^2 = 2\theta$,
   $r = 2$.

10. $r^2\theta = 12$,
    $r = 2$.

11. $r = 4(1 - \sin \theta)$,
    $r(1 + \sin \theta) = 3$.

12. $r = \cos 2\theta$,
    $r = 1 - \sin \theta$.

Empirical Equations

13.1 Equations Derived from Experimental Data. The student is familiar with many pairs of variables whose values are known to be connected by an equation. The relation between the distance traversed by a freely falling body and the time, between the radius of a circle and its area, or between the length of a pendulum and its period, are examples of such equations. In scientific work it is often necessary to determine equations of this sort by finding experimentally a number of pairs of values of the two variables and then setting up a law connecting the variation of the two quantities as shown by this experimental data. An equation connecting two variables, determined in this way, it is called an **empirical equation.**

In this chapter we shall show how empirical equations of certain types can be set up to fit given sets of data. Among the types of such equations that are most frequently used in scientific work are the following:

(1) $y = mx + b$ Linear type

(2) $y = ax^n$ Parabolic type if $n > 0$; hyperbolic, if $n < 0$

(3) $y = a10^{kx}$ Exponential type

(4) $y = a + bx + cx^2 + \cdots + lx^n$ Polynomial type

We shall limit our discussion to these four types, but the methods we shall use can readily be extended to equations of various other kinds.

13.2 Selecting the Type of Equation. The general form of the required equation may be known from theoretical considerations, or it may be prescribed for us for reasons outside of the given data. If not, we first consider the given pairs of values of the variables as coördinates of points and plot them on a diagram. If the points so plotted tend definitely to lie along a line, we use an equation of type (1). If they do not, we may try plotting them on logarithmic paper (Art. 13.6). If, when plotted in this way, the points tend to lie on a line, an equation of type (2) may be used. Similarly, if the points tend to lie on a line when they are plotted on semi-logarithmic paper (Art. 13.7), an equation of type (3) is suggested. If none of these types seems to fit the data satisfactorily, we shall seek an equation of type (4), of as low a degree n as possible, that will fit the data with sufficient accuracy.

Since data determined by measurement is always subject to experimental errors, the required curve is not expected actually to pass through all of the given points. It may not, and in fact usually does not, pass through any of them, but it should not depart from them by an amount greater than the experimental error, and it should show clearly the *trend* of the given data.

When we have settled on the type of equation to be used, we must next determine the values of the coefficients. We shall discuss this problem for each of the various types of curves separately.

13.3 Linear Type by the Method of Averages. The determination of the coefficients in an empirical equation by the method of averages, which we shall illustrate in this article, while not as accurate as by the method of least squares which will be discussed in Art. 13.4, is shorter than that method and easier to carry out. The method of averages consists, essentially, in dividing the given points into two groups and determining the line which passes through an average point for each group, as in the following example.

Example. The maximum osmotic pressure P, in meters, of a sugar solution was found by experiment to vary with the concentration C, in per cent, according to the following table. Express P in terms of C.

C	1	2	3	4	5	6	7
P	0.4	1.1	1.5	2.2	2.6	3.1	3.8

If we plot the pairs of values of C and P on a diagram, we obtain the points shown in Fig. 13.1. Since these points tend clearly to lie along a line, a linear type equation is suggested. As a check on the accuracy of the computations, the line defined by the answer to the problem should be drawn on the figure and compared with the trend of the plotted points.

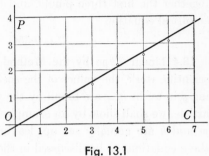

Fig. 13.1

If we substitute the pairs of values of P and C from the table in the assumed equation of linear type

$$P = mC + b \qquad (1)$$

and group together the first four and the last three of the resulting equations, we have the following two sets of equations:

$$0.4 = m + b \qquad\qquad 2.6 = 5m + b$$
$$1.1 = 2m + b \qquad\qquad 3.1 = 6m + b$$
$$1.5 = 3m + b \qquad\qquad 3.8 = 7m + b$$
$$2.2 = 4m + b$$

These seven equations are called the **observational equations** for the given data. They are not consistent with one another since the given points do not all lie on a line. If, however, we add together the members of the equations in each group, we obtain the following two equations:

$$5.2 = 10m + 4b \qquad\qquad 9.5 = 18m + 3b. \qquad (2)$$

These two equations are the conditions that the required line (1) passes through the points $(10/4, 5.2/4)$ and $(18/3, 9.5/3)$. The first of these points $(10/4, 5.2/4)$ is the *average point* for the first four of the given points. It is determined by adding together the abscissas, and the ordinates, of these four points and dividing each sum by the number of points. Similarly, $(18/3, 9.5/3)$ is the average point for the last three of the given points.

The values of m and b found by solving equations (2) are taken as the required coefficients in the empirical equation (1). These values are found to be, approximately,

$$m = 0.53 \qquad b = -0.03.$$

Hence, the required empirical equation is

$$P = 0.53C - 0.03.$$

The values of the coefficients obtained for the empirical equation by the method of averages depend on the way the given points are grouped together. In the above problem, for example, if we group together the first three points, and the last four, we obtain, as the empirical equation

$$P = 0.55C - 0.10.$$

13.4 Linear Type by the Method of Least Squares. In accurate scientific work, the values of the coefficients in the formula expressing y in terms of x are found by the method of least squares. In this article, we shall show by an example how the equations to determine m and b are actually set up, leaving the theoretical derivation of these equations to be discussed in the next article (Art. 13.5).

Example. Find by the method of least squares, for the data given in Art. 13.3, an equation expressing P in terms of C.

We write down two sets of equations. The equations of the first set are the seven observational equations formed, just as in Art. 13.3 by substituting the pairs of values of P and C from the table into the assumed equation

$$P = mC + b.$$

The equations of the second set are formed by multiplying each equation of the first set by the coefficient of m in it; thus

$0.4 = m + b$	$0.4 = m + b$
$1.1 = 2m + b$	$2.2 = 4m + 2b$
$1.5 = 3m + b$	$4.5 = 9m + 3b$
$2.2 = 4m + b$	$8.8 = 16m + 4b$
$2.6 = 5m + b$	$13.0 = 25m + 5b$
$3.1 = 6m + b$	$18.6 = 36m + 6b$
$3.8 = 7m + b$	$26.6 = 49m + 7b$

If we add the members of the equations in each of these two sets, we obtain the following two equations

$$14.7 = 28m + 7b \qquad 74.1 = 140m + 28b.$$

The values of m and b are found by solving these equations as simultaneous. The results are, approximately,

$$m = 0.55 \qquad b = -0.09.$$

The required formula is, accordingly, by this method,

$$P = 0.55C - 0.09.$$

When, as in this example, the points representing the given data lie nearly on a line, the results obtained by the method of averages and by the method of least squares usually differ but little. When the plotted points are rather widely scattered, the results obtained by the two methods may differ considerably.

In practice, in determining empirical equations, labor can be saved, and more accurate results can usually be obtained, by moving the origin to some convenient point near the middle of the diagram. Thus, in the above example, the computations could have been shortened by putting $C = C' + 4$, $P = P' + 2$, finding the equation expressing P' in terms of C', and then replacing P' and C' by their values in terms of P and C.

★ **13.5 Derivation of the Formulas for the Method of Least Squares.** Let (x_1, y_1), (x_2, y_2), (x_3, y_3), . . . (x_n, y_n) be the tabulated pairs of values of the variables. It is required to find, by the method of least squares, two equations from which to determine the values of m and b in a linear type equation

$$y = mx + b \tag{3}$$

which expresses the value of y in terms of that of x.

Let x_k be any one of the values of x in the given table. Then the value of y corresponding to this value of x, as computed from equation (3), is $mx_k + b$, whereas the corresponding value of y, as given by the table, is y_k. The difference between these two values of y is denoted by r_k, that is

$$r_k = y_k - (mx_k + b). \tag{4}$$

The number r_k is called the **residual** of the point (x_k, y_k) with respect to equation (3). There are n residuals; one for each of the n points (x_1, y_1), (x_2, y_2), . . . (x_n, y_n). The values of these residuals depend on the values assigned to m and b.

Let us form the sum of the squares of the n residuals. We shall denote this sum by Σr^2.* The method of least squares depends essentially on the following **Principle**: *The values of m and b determined by the method of least squares are those that make the sum of the squares of the residuals, Σr^2, as small as possible.*

If we write out the n equations (4) obtained by giving k the successive values $1, 2, 3, \ldots n$, and square both sides of each equation, we obtain

$$r_1{}^2 = y_1{}^2 - 2my_1x_1 - 2y_1b + m^2x_1{}^2 + 2mx_1b + b^2$$
$$r_2{}^2 = y_2{}^2 - 2my_2x_2 - 2y_2b + m^2x_2{}^2 + 2mx_2b + b^2$$
$$\cdot \quad \cdot \quad \cdot \quad \cdot \quad \cdot \quad \cdot \quad \cdot \quad \cdot \quad \cdot \quad \cdot \quad \cdot \quad \cdot \quad \cdot \quad \cdot \quad \cdot \quad \cdot \quad \cdot$$
$$\cdot \quad \cdot \quad \cdot \quad \cdot \quad \cdot \quad \cdot \quad \cdot \quad \cdot \quad \cdot \quad \cdot \quad \cdot \quad \cdot \quad \cdot \quad \cdot \quad \cdot \quad \cdot \quad \cdot$$
$$\cdot \quad \cdot \quad \cdot \quad \cdot \quad \cdot \quad \cdot \quad \cdot \quad \cdot \quad \cdot \quad \cdot \quad \cdot \quad \cdot \quad \cdot \quad \cdot \quad \cdot \quad \cdot \quad \cdot$$
$$r_n{}^2 = y_n{}^2 - 2mx_ny_n - 2y_nb + m^2x_n{}^2 + 2mx_nb + b^2.$$

If we add the members of these equations and arrange the right-hand member of the sum in powers of b, we have

$$\Sigma r^2 = nb^2 + 2b(m\Sigma x - \Sigma y) + m^2\Sigma x^2 - 2m\Sigma xy + \Sigma y^2. \qquad (5)$$

The right-hand member of (5) is a quadratic function of b, and the coefficient of b^2 is positive. Hence, by Art. 7.3, the value that must be assigned to b in order to make the value of this function as small as possible must satisfy the equation

$$b = \frac{-(m\Sigma x - \Sigma y)}{n} \qquad (6)$$

If we rearrange the right-hand member of (5) in powers of m, we obtain

$$\Sigma r^2 = m^2\Sigma x^2 + 2m(b\Sigma x - \Sigma xy) + \Sigma y^2 - 2b\Sigma y + nb^2.$$

Since the right-hand member is a quadratic in m, and the coefficient of m^2 is positive, it follows once more from Art. 7.3 that the value of

---

* The symbol Σr^2 is read "sigma r square." By definition

$$\Sigma r^2 = r_1{}^2 + r_2{}^2 + r_3{}^2 + \cdots \cdots + r_n{}^2.$$

Similarly, we shall put

$$\Sigma x = x_1 + x_2 + x_3 \cdots \cdots + x_n, \text{ etc.}$$

m that makes the right-hand member as small as possible must satisfy the equation

$$m = \frac{-(b\Sigma x - \Sigma xy)}{\Sigma x^2} \qquad (7)$$

The values of m and b that make Σr^2 as small as possible must satisfy equations (6) and (7). If we solve these two equations for m and b and substitute in equation (3), we obtain the required linear type equation by the method of least squares.

To determine equations (6) and (7) for a given problem, we first write out the two sets of equations called for in Art. 13.4, that is,

$$y_1 = mx_1 + b \qquad\qquad x_1y_1 = mx_1{}^2 + bx_1$$
$$y_2 = mx_2 + b \qquad\qquad x_2y_2 = mx_2{}^2 + bx_2$$
$$\cdot\ \cdot\ \cdot\ \cdot\ \cdot\ \cdot \qquad\qquad \cdot\ \cdot\ \cdot\ \cdot\ \cdot\ \cdot\ \cdot$$
$$\cdot\ \cdot\ \cdot\ \cdot\ \cdot\ \cdot \qquad\qquad \cdot\ \cdot\ \cdot\ \cdot\ \cdot\ \cdot\ \cdot$$
$$\cdot\ \cdot\ \cdot\ \cdot\ \cdot \qquad\qquad \cdot\ \cdot\ \cdot\ \cdot\ \cdot\ \cdot\ \cdot$$
$$y_n = mx_n + b \qquad\qquad x_ny_n = mx_n{}^2 + bx_n.$$

If we add the members of each of these two sets of n equations we obtain, respectively,

$$\Sigma y = m\Sigma x + bn \qquad\qquad \Sigma xy = m\Sigma x^2 + b\Sigma x.$$

The first of these equations is equivalent to equation (6) and the second to (7). Hence the required values of m and b, which are to be substituted in the empirical equation

$$y = mx + b$$

as determined by the method of least squares, are the values determined by these two equations.

EXERCISES

Plot the points determined by the given data and find a linear equation connecting the variables (a) by the method of averages and (b) by the method of least squares. Under (a), if the number of observational equations is even, put the first half of them in one group; if the number is odd, group the middle one with those that precede it:

1. Express y in terms of x.

x	-3	-2	-1	0	1	2	3
y	-7	-2	1	5	7	10	13

2. Express y in terms of x.

x	0	1	2	3	4	5
y	3	4	6	8	9	11

3. Express y in terms of x.

x	-1	0	1	2	3	4	5
y	8	7	4	2	0	-1	-3

4. Express y in terms of x.

x	1	3	7	8	12	15
y	8	7	5	4	1	0

5. Express the length l, in inches, of a spring in terms of the weight W, in pounds, suspended from it, given:

W	3	6	9	12	15	18	21
l	11.1	11.7	12.4	13.0	13.7	14.4	15.2

6. Express the length l, in meters, of an iron bar in terms of the Centigrade temperature C, from the following data:

C	0	50	100	150	200	250	300
l	1.0000	1.0011	1.0023	1.0036	1.0046	1.0058	1.0069

7. Express W, the number of grams of a certain salt that will dissolve in 100 grams of water at a Centigrade temperature C, given:

C	10	18	30	34	44	52
W	20	27	43	46	55	66

8. Find the latent heat of vaporization of water L, in calories, in terms of the Centigrade temperature C, given:

C	50	75	100	125	150	175	200
L	555	539	525	509	490	470	458

9. The force f, in pounds, that will just lift a weight of w pounds by a certain lifting device is given by the following table. Express f in terms of w.

w	200	500	700	1100	1400	1500
f	21	40	53	79	98	106

10. The number of years N, at the end of which half of the people now living of various ages A will be dead, is given by the following table. Express N in terms of A.

A	20	25	30	35	40	45	50
N	46.5	42.3	38.2	34.0	29.8	25.6	21.5

11. The number N of billions of cigarettes sold in t years in the United States during a six-year period is given by the following table. Express N terms of t.

t	1	2	3	4	5	6
N	66.7	79.7	82.3	92.1	93.0	100

12. Find the net yearly sales s, in thousands of dollars, of a certain firm, in terms of the time t, in years, given:

t	1	2	3	4	5	6	7
s	105	132	168	193	226	245	265

13.6 Parabolic and Hyperbolic Types. If we wish to determine, for a given set of data, an empirical equation of the form

$$y = ax^n \tag{8}$$

we first take the logarithms (to the base 10) of both sides of the equation. We thus obtain

$$\log y = n \log x + \log a.$$

Let u and v be two new variables, such that

$$u = \log x \qquad v = \log y.$$

If we substitute these values for $\log x$ and $\log y$ in the preceding equation, we have

$$v = nu + \log a.$$

This is an equation of linear type connecting u and v. Hence, if we make a new table, formed by taking the logarithms of the entries in the given table, and if we denote the entries for $\log x$ by u, and for $\log y$ by v, our problem reduces to the determination of a linear relation connecting u and v and may be solved by the method of Art. 13.3 or of Art. 13.4.

It follows that, to determine whether an equation of the type of equation (8) is applicable to a given set of data, we may plot, on ordinary coördinate paper, the logarithms, u and v, of the numbers in the given table. If the points so plotted tend to lie on a line, an equation of this type may be used to express y in terms of x.

We may, however, when we are trying to decide whether an equation (8) is applicable to a given set of data, save the inconvenience of looking up the logarithms of all the numbers in the given table by plotting the given values of x and y directly on **logarithmic paper**. This paper (Fig. 13.2) has rulings, both horizontal and vertical, which are spaced at distances equal to the logarithms of the numbers 1, 2, 3, . . . 10, 20, 30, . . . In order that an equation of the type of equation (8) may be applicable to the data, its points must tend to lie on a line when they are plotted on logarithmic paper.

Example. Derive a formula for the air resistance R, in pounds per square foot of projecting area, against an automobile traveling V miles per hour, given

V	10	20	30	40	50	60
R	0.32	1.26	3.06	5.42	8.34	11.6

When we plot this data on logarithmic paper, as in Fig. 13.2, we find that the points tend to lie on a line. Hence, an equation of the type $R = aV^n$ may be used to express the required formula. We shall determine the values of a and n by the method of least squares.

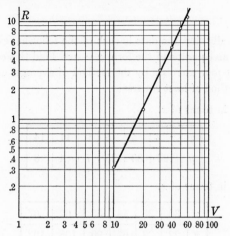

Fig. 13.2

From the table of logarithms on pages 268–269, we have

$u = \log V$	1.0000	1.3010	1.4771	1.6021	1.6990	1.7782
$v = \log R$	− 0.4949	0.1004	0.4857	0.7340	0.9212	1.0645

To simplify the computations, we put $u' = u - 1.5$ and $v' = v - 0.5$ and determine the empirical equation $v' = mu' + b$, where $b = \log a$. We have

$$
\begin{aligned}
-.9949 &= -.5000m + b & .4975 &= .2500m - .5000b \\
-.3996 &= -.1990m + b & .0795 &= .0396m - .1990b \\
-.0143 &= -.0229m + b & .0003 &= .0005m - .0229b \\
.2340 &= .1021m + b & .0239 &= .0104m + .1021b \\
.4212 &= .1990m + b & .0838 &= .0396m + .1990b \\
.5645 &= .2782m + b & .1570 &= .0774m + .2782b.
\end{aligned}
$$

If we add the members of the equations of each of these two sets, we obtain

$$-.1891 = -.1426m + 6b \quad \text{and} \quad .8420 = .4175m - .1426b.$$

Hence, $m = 2.02$, $b = 0.0165$, so that $v' = 2.02u' + 0.0165$, that is,

$$\log R - 0.5 = 2.02(\log V - 1.5) + 0.0165$$

or

$$\log R = 2.02 \log V - 2.5135.$$

Since $-2.5135 = 7.4865 - 10 = \log 0.00307$, our required equation is

$$R = 0.00307 V^{2.02}.$$

EXERCISES

Show graphically that the data in each of the following exercises may be represented by an equation of the form $y = ax^n$. Find this equation for the data of the first four exercises by the method of averages and, for the last four, by the method of least squares:

1. Express y in terms of x.

x	1	4	5	9	11	14
y	123	33	25	7	4	3

2. Express y in terms of x.

x	30	35	46	53	62	67
y	22	33	67	90	138	163

3. Express the coal consumption C of a locomotive, in tons per hour, in terms of the velocity v, in miles per hour, from the following data:

v	35	40	45	50	55	60
C	3.3	4.4	5.5	6.8	8.2	9.8

4. Find the distance of the sea horizon d, in miles, from a point h feet above the water, given:

h	5	12	20	50	90	150
d	2.7	4.2	5.5	8.7	12	15

5. Find the period of revolution T, in days, of the moons of Jupiter in terms of the distance of the moon from Jupiter, d, in thousands of miles, from the following data for the five inner moons.

d	11	26	42	66	117
T	0.5	1.8	3.6	7.1	16.7

6. Find the pressure p, in millimeters of mercury, of a gas expanding adiabatically, in terms of the volume V, in cubic centimeters, given:

V	1.3	1.7	2.0	3.2	4.1	5.8
p	23	16	13	6.5	4.6	2.8

7. Find the horsepower *H*, generated by a certain water wheel, in terms of the head of water, *h*, in feet, from the following data:

h	1.5	2.0	2.5	3.0	3.5	4.0
H	12	19	27	35	44	54

8. Find the horsepower *H*, that a shaft can safely transmit under given conditions in terms of the diameter of the shaft *d*, in inches, given:

d	1.1	1.3	1.5	1.7	1.9	2.1
H	112	180	282	411	563	779

13.7 Exponential Type. If we wish to express the required formula by an exponential equation

$$y = a10^{kx},$$

we again take the logarithms of both sides of the equation. This gives

$$\log y = kx + \log a.$$

If we now put $\log y = v$, this equation becomes a linear relation

$$v = kx + \log a$$

between *x* and *v* and may be solved by the methods of the preceding articles.

To determine the suitability of an equation of the exponential type for expressing a given set of data, we may either plot on ordinary coördinate paper the values of *x* and log *y*, or we may plot the given data on **semi-logarithmic paper,** that is, on paper that is ruled with equal spaces in one direction and like logarithmic paper in the other (Fig. 13.3). An exponential equation may be used to represent the required relationship if the points, when plotted in this way, tend to lie on a line.

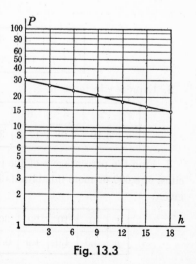

Fig. 13.3

Example. Find the atmospheric pressure p, in inches of mercury, in terms of the height above sea level h, in thousands of feet, from the following data:

h	0	3	6	9	12	15	18
p	29.9	26.7	23.5	21.2	18.6	16.8	14.7

By plotting the pairs of values of h and p on semi-logarithmic paper (Fig. 13.3), we find that, within the limits of experimental error, the points lie on a line so that we may represent p in terms of h by an exponential equation. By the method of least squares, we find that

$$\log p = -0.017h + 1.4762,$$

or $$p = 29.9(10^{-.017h}).$$

It is often preferable to write an exponential equation in the form $y = ae^{kx}$, where $e = 2.71828^+$ is the base of the natural system of logarithms (Art. 10.6). Since $10 = e^{2.303}$ approximately, we have, in this example,

$$p = 29.9(e^{2.303})^{-.017h} = 29.9e^{-.039h}.$$

EXERCISES

Show graphically that the data of each of the following exercises can be represented by an equation of the form $y = a10^{bx}$ and also by one of the form $y = ae^{kx}$. Find these equations for exercises 1 to 4 by the method of averages and, for the others, by the method of least squares:

1. Express y in terms of x.

x	2	3	4	5	6	7
y	7	15	26	60	112	216

2. Express y in terms of x.

x	2	3	6	8	11	14	18	19
y	5.19	7.08	17.4	31.2	78.1	189	637	851

3. Find the percentage p of the people in the United States who lived in cities of 8,000 or more inhabitants in terms of the time in years $t + 1790$, given:

t	0	10	20	30	40	50	60	70
p	3.3	4.0	4.9	6.7	8.5	12.5	16.1	20.9

4. A vessel of water was allowed to cool. Find the Fahrenheit temperature F, in terms of the time t, in minutes, given:

t	0	4	8	12	16	20	24
F	130	116	106	93	86	76	69

5. Find the vapor pressure of water p, in centimeters of mercury, in terms of the Centigrade temperature C, from the following data:

C	0	20	40	60	80	100
p	0.5	1.7	5.4	15	35	76

6. The electric power P, in billions of kilowatt hours, produced in the United States during a series of years is given in the following table. Find p in terms of t.

t	0	1	2	3	4	5	6
p	4.6	4.9	5.5	6.1	6.7	7.2	8.1

7. The number N, in thousands, of bacteria per unit of volume found in a culture at the end of t hours is given by the following table. Find N in terms of t.

t	1	2	3	4	5	6	7
N	24	39	63	103	167	272	442

8. The fire losses L, in millions of dollars, in the United States during a series of years is given in the following table. Express L in terms of t.

t	1	2	3	4	5	6
L	172	290	321	495	535	570

13.8 Polynomial Type. If none of the preceding types of equations adequately express the trend of the data, an equation of the polynomial type,

$$y = a + bx + cx^2 + \cdots + lx^n,$$

is frequently used.

The value of n should first be determined graphically in such a way that an equation of the given degree will satisfactorily express the behavior of the data. The values of the coefficients may then be determined as in the following example.

Example. Find a formula of the polynomial type, with $n = 2$,

$$y = a + bx + cx^2 \tag{9}$$

to represent the relation between the variables as given in the following table:

x	-3	-2	-1	0	1	2	3	4	5
y	10	4	1	-1	-3	-4	-2	1	3

a. Solution by the method of averages. We divide the tabulated data into three groups, each of which we shall take, in this example, to consist of three consecutive pairs of values of x and y, and form the observational equations for each group by substituting these pairs of values in equation (9). The resulting equations are

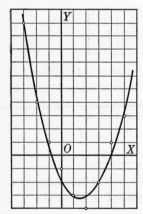

Fig. 13.4

$$10 = a - 3b + 9c$$
$$4 = a - 2b + 4c$$
$$1 = a - b + c$$

$$-1 = a + 0b + 0c$$
$$-3 = a + b + c$$
$$-4 = a + 2b + 4c$$

$$-2 = a + 3b + 9c$$
$$1 = a + 4b + 16c$$
$$3 = a + 5b + 25c.$$

By adding the members of the equations in each of these groups, we obtain the following three equations from which to determine a, b, and c:

$$15 = 3a - 6b + 14c$$
$$-8 = 3a + 3b + 5c$$
$$2 = 3a + 12b + 50c.$$

On solving these equations, we find that

$$a = -1.74 \qquad b = -1.94 \qquad c = 0.611$$

The required equation, by the method of averages is, accordingly,

$$y = -1.74 - 1.94x + 0.611x^2.$$

As in Art. 13.3, the result obtained by the method of averages depends on the way the points are grouped together.

   b. Solution by the method of least squares. We form the following three sets of equations: (1) the nine observational equations formed by substituting the pairs of values of x and y from the table in (9), (2) the equations formed by multiplying each observational equation by the coefficient of b in it, and (3) the equations formed by multiplying each observational equation by the coefficient of c in it. We obtain in this way the following sets of equations:

$$
\begin{aligned}
10 &= a - 3b + 9c & -30 &= -3a + 9b - 27c \\
4 &= a - 2b + 4c & -8 &= -2a + 4b - 8c \\
1 &= a - b + c & -1 &= -a + b - c \\
-1 &= a + 0b + 0c & 0 &= 0a + 0b + 0c \\
-3 &= a + b + c & -3 &= a + b + c \\
-4 &= a + 2b + 4c & -8 &= 2a + 4b + 8c \\
-2 &= a + 3b + 9c & -6 &= 3a + 9b + 27c \\
1 &= a + 4b + 16c & 4 &= 4a + 16b + 64c \\
3 &= a + 5b + 25c & 15 &= 5a + 25b + 125c
\end{aligned}
$$

$$
\begin{aligned}
90 &= 9a - 27b + 81c \\
16 &= 4a - 8b + 16c \\
1 &= a - b + c \\
0 &= 0a + 0b + 0c \\
-3 &= a + b + c \\
-16 &= 4a + 8b + 16c \\
-18 &= 9a + 27b + 81c \\
16 &= 16a + 64b + 256c \\
75 &= 25a + 125b + 625c.
\end{aligned}
$$

If we add the members of each of these three sets of equations, we have

$$
\begin{aligned}
9 &= 9a + 9b + 69c \\
-37 &= 9a + 69b + 189c \\
161 &= 69a + 189b + 1077c.
\end{aligned}
$$

Hence, $a = -1.62$ $b = -1.96$ $c = 0.60$

and the required equation, by the method of least squares, is

$$ y = -1.62 - 1.96x + 0.60x^2. $$

EXERCISES

In exercises 1 to 6, express y in terms of x by an equation of the form $y = a + bx + cx^2$. Use the method of averages in exercises 1 to 3 and the method of least squares in exercises 4 to 6:

1. Express y in terms of x.

x	-2	-1	0	1	2	3	4	5	6
y	6	-4	-9	-7	-3	4	15	31	42

2. Express y in terms of x.

x	-2	1	5	7	8	11
y	2	12	20	17	16	7

3. Express the percentage p of the married population who are divorced after n years of married life, given:

n	1	2	3	4	5	6	7	8	9
p	0.70	1.20	1.32	1.32	1.27	1.10	1.00	0.97	.84

4. Express the efficiency E, in percent, of a certain twelve horsepower motor when it is run to generate H horsepower, given:

H	3	6	9	12	15	18	21
E	40	56	62	70	67	59	32

5. Express the melting point C, on the Centigrade scale, of an alloy of lead and zinc, in terms of the percentage p, of zinc, given:

p	15	25	35	45	55	65
C	289	263	237	215	195	177

6. The following table gives approximately the decrease d from 212°, on the Fahrenheit scale, of the temperature of boiling water in terms of the height h, in hundreds of feet, above sea level. Express h in terms of d.

d	4	6	8	10	12	14	16
h	22.3	33.5	44.9	56.2	67.7	79.2	90.7

7. The number N of customers who entered a store during the successive business hours on a certain day is given by the following table. Find an expression for N in terms of h of the form $N = a + bh + ch^2 + dh^3$. Use the method of averages.

h	1	2	3	4	5	6	7	8
N	39	62	68	53	57	79	84	81

8. Fit an equation of the form $y = a + b/x^2$ to the following data by putting $u = 1/x^2$ and expressing y as a linear function of u. Use the method of averages.

x	1	2	3	4	5	6
y	66	22	14	11	9.4	8.6

9. Fit an equation of the form $x = axy + by$ to the following data by putting $u = 1/x$ and $v = 1/y$ and expressing v linearly in terms of u. Use the method of averages.

x	2	3	4	5	6	7
y	2.9	3.7	4.4	5.0	5.5	5.9

SOLID
ANALYTIC
GEOMETRY

Definitions and Theorems

In plane analytic geometry, we saw that the position of a point in the plane could be fixed by means of directed distances measured on two mutually perpendicular lines. We shall now show how a similar method may be used to fix the position of any point in space.

14.1 Rectangular Coördinates. Through a fixed point O, the **origin,** in space, let there be given three directed lines, the **x-axis,** the **y-axis,** and the **z-axis,** each perpendicular to both of the others. The three planes, each of which contains two of the axes, are the **coördinate planes.** They are named, from the two axes that they contain, the **xy-plane,** the **yz-plane,** and the **zx-plane,** respectively.

Let P be any given point in space. To define the coördinates of P, we pass planes through P parallel to the three coördinate planes and denote the points of intersection of these planes with the x-, y-, and z-axes by

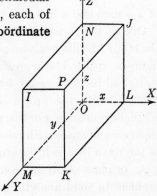

Fig. 14.1

L, M, and N, respectively. Then the directed lengths

$$x = \overline{OL}, \quad y = \overline{OM}, \quad z = \overline{ON},$$

are the **coördinates of the point P.**

Conversely, if the coördinates (x, y, z) of the point P are given, we can locate this point P in the following way: measure off from the origin, on the x-axis, the directed distance $\overline{OL} = x$; from L measure off, on a line through L parallel to the y-axis, the directed distance $\overline{LK} = y$; and finally, from K, on a line parallel to the z-axis, lay off $\overline{KP} = z$. The point P so determined is the point whose coördinates are (x, y, z).

The three coördinate planes divide space into eight parts, called **octants,** which may be distinguished by the signs of the coördinates of the points in them. In particular, the octant in which all the coördinates of a point are positive is known as the *first octant.*

14.2 Figures. To represent a figure in space on a plane, we shall use what is known as a parallel projection. In this projection, we represent the x- and z-axes by two mutually perpendicular lines and the y-axis by a line that makes an angle of $135°$ with each of the other two (Fig. 14.1). Distances parallel to the xz-plane are represented correctly to scale but distances parallel to the y-axis are foreshortened in the ratio $\sqrt{2}$ to 2. When this projection is used to draw figures on coördinate paper, the x- and z-axes should be represented along the rulings and the y-axis along a diagonal. Equal lengths along the three axes will then be represented by the sides of a square and a half of its diagonal.

One of the serious difficulties that the student will encounter in the study of solid analytic geometry is the visualization of the actual figure in space. The representation of it on a plane is only a makeshift, and he must assure himself from the beginning that he understands clearly the properties of the three-dimensional figure with which he is dealing. For this purpose, it is often convenient to visualize this figure in space with reference to the floor and two adjacent walls of the room in which the student is sitting, as coördinate planes.

As in plane analytic geometry, the first step in the solution of a problem in solid analytic geometry should consist in the construction of an accurate figure.

EXERCISES

Plot the given points:

1. $(5, 0, 0)$, $(2, 2, 0)$, $(0, 1, 1)$, $(6, -3, 2)$, $(-4, 2, 7)$, $(8, -2, -5)$, $(-2, -4, -6)$.

2. $(0, 0, 3)$, $(3, 0, 5)$, $(6, 2, 7)$, $(4, 4, -3)$, $(-2, 6, 1)$, $(3, -4, 2)$, $(-4, -3, 5)$.

3. Find the coördinates of the feet of the perpendiculars from the point $P(x, y, z)$ to (a) the coördinate planes and (b) the coördinate axes.

4. Show that the figure $O-LJIM-P$ (Fig. 14.1) is a rectangular parallelepiped (or box-shaped figure) and find the lengths of all its edges.

5. Find the lengths of the segments LP, MP, and NP (Fig. 14.1) in terms of the coördinates of P.

6. Find the length of the segment OP (Fig. 14.1).

7. What is the locus of a point for which $x = 0$? for which $y = 0$? for which $z = 0$?

8. What is the locus of a point for which $y = 0$, $z = 0$?

9. What is the locus of a point for which $x = 4$?

10. What is the locus of a point for which $x = 2$, $y = 6$?

11. A cube of side a has one vertex at the origin and three of its edges extending in the positive directions along the axes. Find the coördinates of all its vertices.

12. Solve Ex. 11 when the center of the cube is at the origin and its edges are parallel to the coördinate axes.

13. Describe the position in space of the octant for which the signs of the coördinates are $(-, -, +)$.

14. Two points are *symmetric* with respect to a plane if the segment joining them is perpendicular to the plane and is bisected by the plane. Find the coördinates of the points symmetric to $P(x, y, z)$ with respect to each of the coördinate planes.

15. Find the coördinates of the points symmetric to $P(x, y, z)$ with respect to (a) each of the coördinate axes; (b) the origin.

16. Draw the triangular pyramid and find its volume given that its vertices are $(0, 0, 0)$, $(a, 0, 0)$, $(0, a, 0)$, and $(0, 0, a)$.

14.3 Distance between Two Points.

To find the distance between two given points $P_1(x_1, y_1, z_1)$ and $P_2(x_2, y_2, z_2)$, we construct a box-shaped figure by passing planes through P_1 and P_2 parallel to the coördinate planes (Fig. 14.2). The required distance $d = P_1P_2$ is the length of the diagonal of this box and the lengths of the sides of the box are given by the numerical values of P_1U, P_1V, and P_1W.

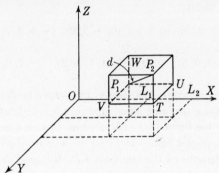

Fig. 14.2

From Fig. 14.2, we have

$$\overline{P_1U} = \overline{L_1L_2} = \overline{OL_2} - \overline{OL_1} = x_2 - x_1,$$

$$\overline{P_1V} = y_2 - y_1, \quad \text{and} \quad \overline{P_1W} = z_2 - z_1. \tag{1}$$

By elementary geometry,

$$P_1P_2{}^2 = P_1T^2 + TP_2{}^2 = P_1U^2 + UT^2 + TP_2{}^2 = P_1U^2 + P_1V^2 + P_1W^2.$$

If we put $P_1P_2 = d$, we have, from (1),

$$d^2 = (x_2 - x_1)^2 + (y_2 - y_1)^2 + (z_2 - z_1)^2.$$

Hence

$$d = \sqrt{(x_2 - x_1)^2 + (y_2 - y_1)^2 + (z_2 - z_1)^2}. \tag{2}$$

This is the formula for the distance between the points

$$P_1(x_1, y_1, z_1) \quad \text{and} \quad P_2(x_2, y_2, z_2).$$

EXERCISES

Find the undirected distances between the given pairs of points:

1. $(0, 0, 0)$, $(12, 4, 3)$.   2. $(0, 0, 0)$, $(4, 2, 4)$.
3. $(5, -3, 2)$, $(7, 3, -1)$.   4. $(1, -4, -1)$, $(2, 4, 3)$.
5. $(5, 1, -4)$, $(-1, -6, 2)$.   6. $(4, 1, 9)$, $(2, -3, 5)$.
7. $(5, 7, 4)$, $(4, 2, 1)$.   8. $(-1, 2, 3)$, $(2, 1, 5)$.

9. Show that $(5, 2, 4)$, $(7, 3, 1)$ and $(4, 5, 2)$ are the vertices of an equilateral triangle.

10. Show that $(7, -4, -6)$, $(5, 1, -3)$ and $(8, 2, -5)$ are the vertices of an isosceles triangle and find the lengths of all its sides.

11. Show that $(1, 6, 2)$, $(7, 9, 4)$ and $(5, -6, 8)$ are the vertices of a right triangle and find its area.

12. Show that $(3, 1, -4)$, $(5, 9, -2)$, $(11, 3, -2)$ and $(5, 3, 4)$ are the vertices of a tetrahedron (or triangular pyramid) whose six edges are all equal in length.

13. Find the equation of the locus of a point whose undirected distance from $(-2, 1, 5)$ is equal to 3. What is the locus of this equation?

14. What locus is defined by the equation $x^2 + y^2 + z^2 = 25$?

15. What locus is defined by the equation $(x - 3)^2 + (y - 5)^2 + (z + 6)^2 = 49$?

16. Find and simplify the equation of the locus of a point whose undirected distances from $(3, 1, -4)$ and $(7, 3, -2)$ are equal. What is the locus of this equation?

14.4 Direction Cosines of a Directed Line. Let $P_1(x_1, y_1, z_1)$ be any point on a given **directed line** l in space. Through P_1 draw the lines P_1A, P_1B, and P_1C, having the same directions as the x-, y-, and z-axes, respectively. Then the angles α, β, and γ, which the positive direction on l makes with the positive direction on P_1A, P_1B, and P_1C, respectively, are called the **direction angles** of l.

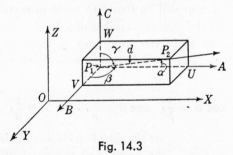

Fig. 14.3

We shall usually deal, not with the direction angles α, β, and γ themselves, but with their cosines. These three cosines, **cos α, cos β,** and **cos γ,** are the **direction cosines** * of the directed line l.

---

* In the following pages we shall frequently use the expression "the direction cosines of a line." It shall be understood by this expression that the positive direction on the line has been assigned and that we are speaking of the direction cosines of the directed line.

Let $P_2(x_2, y_2, z_2)$ be any point on l in the positive direction from P_1 and let U, V, and W be the points in which the planes through P_2 perpendicular to the x-, y-, and z-axes intersect P_1A, P_1B, and P_1C, respectively (Fig. 14.3). Since the triangles P_1UP_2, P_1VP_2, and P_1WP_2 are right triangles (Why?), we now have, from the definition of the cosine of an angle,

$$\cos \alpha = \frac{\overline{P_1U}}{\overline{P_1P_2}}, \quad \cos \beta = \frac{\overline{P_1V}}{\overline{P_1P_2}}, \quad \text{and} \quad \cos \gamma = \frac{\overline{P_1W}}{\overline{P_1P_2}}.$$

If we now put $P_1P_2 = d$, and substitute for $\overline{P_1U}$, $\overline{P_1V}$, and $\overline{P_1W}$ their values from (1), we have

$$\cos \alpha = \frac{x_2 - x_1}{d}, \quad \cos \beta = \frac{y_2 - y_1}{d}, \quad \text{and} \quad \cos \gamma = \frac{z_2 - z_1}{d}, \quad (3)$$

where

$$d = \sqrt{(x_2 - x_1)^2 + (y_2 - y_1)^2 + (z_2 - z_1)^2}.$$

If we square the members of equations (3), add, and substitute for d its value, we find that

$$\cos^2 \alpha + \cos^2 \beta + \cos^2 \gamma = 1 \qquad (4)$$

that is, *the sum of the squares of the direction cosines of any line is equal to unity.* This relation will be found to be of importance whenever we shall deal with the direction cosines of a line.

If, in (3), we let P_1 be the origin and let P_2 be any other point $P(x, y, z)$ in space, and if we further denote the distance OP by ρ, we find that

$$\cos \alpha = \frac{x}{\rho}, \quad \cos \beta = \frac{y}{\rho}, \quad \cos \gamma = \frac{z}{\rho}, \qquad (5)$$

Fig. 14.4

are the direction cosines of the line through the origin and the point P and directed from O toward P.

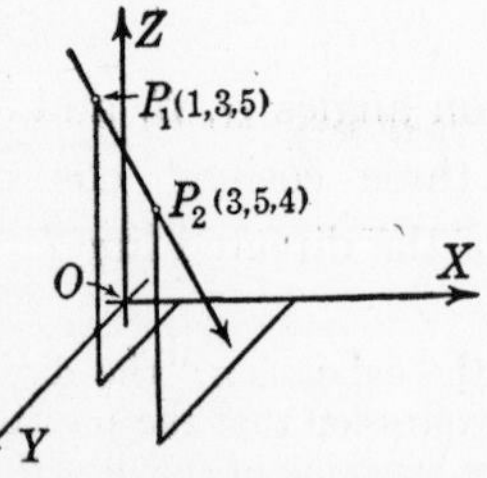

Example. Find the direction cosines of the line through $P_1(1, 3, 5)$ and $P_2(3, 5, 4)$ and directed from P_1 toward P_2.

The distance between these points is

$$d = \sqrt{(3 - 1)^2 + (5 - 3)^2 + (4 - 5)^2} = 3.$$

Hence, from (3), the direction cosines of this line (directed from P_1 toward P_2) are

$$\cos \alpha = \tfrac{2}{3}, \quad \cos \beta = \tfrac{2}{3}, \quad \cos \gamma = -\tfrac{1}{3}.$$

14.5 Direction Numbers of a Line. Any three real numbers a, b, and c, not all zero, are called a set of **direction numbers** of a line if they are proportional to the direction cosines of the directed line. Hence if a, b, and c are a set of direction numbers of a line whose direction cosines are $\cos \alpha$, $\cos \beta$, and $\cos \gamma$ there must exist a constant $k \neq 0$ such that

$$a = k \cos \alpha, \quad b = k \cos \beta, \quad \text{and} \quad c = k \cos \gamma. \tag{6}$$

To find the direction cosines of a line when a set of its direction numbers a, b, and c are given, we must determine the factor of proportionality k. By squaring the members of equations (6), adding, and simplifying by means of equation (4), we obtain

$$a^2 + b^2 + c^2 = k^2(\cos^2 \alpha + \cos^2 \beta + \cos^2 \gamma) = k^2.$$

Hence, $\qquad\qquad k = \pm \sqrt{a^2 + b^2 + c^2}.$

If we substitute this expression for k in equations (6), and solve, we obtain, as the direction cosines of a line with a set of direction numbers a, b, and c,

$$\cos \alpha = \frac{a}{\pm \sqrt{a^2 + b^2 + c^2}}, \quad \cos \beta = \frac{b}{\pm \sqrt{a^2 + b^2 + c^2}},$$

$$\cos \gamma = \frac{c}{\pm \sqrt{a^2 + b^2 + c^2}}. \tag{7}$$

The sign in the denominator is to be taken as positive throughout, or as negative throughout, according as one direction on the line, or the other, is to be taken as the positive direction on the line, as illustrated in Example 1.

It will be left as an exercise for the student (Ex. 23) to show that any set of three real numbers, not all zero, are a set of direction numbers for a line.

When a line is determined by two points, $P_1(x_1, y_1, z_1)$ and $P_2(x_2, y_2, z_2)$, a set of direction numbers for the line is given by

$$x_2 - x_1, \quad y_2 - y_1, \quad z_2 - z_1$$

as is seen from equations (3). Any set of three numbers proportional to these is also a set of direction numbers, as long as the factor of proportionality is not zero.

When we fix the direction cosines of a directed line we have determined which of the two possible directions on the line shall be the positive one. Observe that when we give a set of direction numbers for a line we have not fixed a positive direction. In many problems, however, it is sufficient to use a set of direction numbers rather than the direction cosines.

Example 1. A set of direction numbers of a line are 6, 2, − 3 and the positive direction is chosen on the line so that the angle γ is acute. Find the direction cosines of the line.

On substituting these values of a, b, and c in equations (7), we have

$$\cos \alpha = \frac{6}{\pm \sqrt{36 + 4 + 9}} = \frac{6}{\pm 7}, \quad \cos \beta = \frac{2}{\pm 7}, \quad \cos \gamma = \frac{-3}{\pm 7}.$$

Since the angle γ is acute, its cosine is positive. Hence, from the last of the above equations, the sign in the denominator must be negative and we have

$$\cos \alpha = -\tfrac{6}{7}, \quad \cos \beta = -\tfrac{2}{7}, \quad \cos \gamma = \tfrac{3}{7}.$$

Example 2. Find a set of direction numbers of the line determined by the points $P_1(4, -1, -4)$, $P_2(2, 5, -8)$.

Here $x_2 - x_1 = -2, y_2 - y_1 = 6$, and $z_2 - z_1 = -4$. Hence $-2, 6, -4$ is one set of direction numbers. Dividing each member of this set by -2, we obtain the set $1, -3, 2$. This set will serve equally well and, in fact, consists of smaller numbers numerically.

EXERCISES

Find a set of direction numbers for each of the following lines. Assuming the positive direction to be from the first point to the second, also find the direction cosines of each line:

1. $(0, 0, 0)$, $(1, -8, 4)$.   2. $(2, 9, 6)$, $(6, 2, 2)$.
3. $(5, 7, -1)$, $(-7, 3, 2)$.   4. $(-1, 4, 7)$, $(5, 2, 4)$.
5. $(4, -2, 3)$, $(7, 2, 4)$.   6. $(2, 9, -3)$, $(3, 4, 5)$.

Find the direction cosines of a line having the given set of direction numbers, given that γ is acute:

7. $6, -7, 6$.   8. $9, 6, -2$.   9. $2, -1, 2$.
10. $-3, -18, -14$.   11. $-5, -3, -6$.   12. $4, 1, 3$.

Find the direction cosines of a line given that the angle not specified is acute:

13. $\alpha = 45°$, $\beta = 60°$.   **14.** $\alpha = 90°$, $\gamma = 120°$.

15. $\beta = 2\pi/3$, $\gamma = \pi/3$.   **16.** $\alpha = 2\pi/3$, $\beta = 3\pi/4$.

17. Find the direction cosines of each of the coördinate axes.

18. A line through the origin is directed into the first octant and makes equal angles with the coördinate axes. Find its direction cosines.

19. The coördinates of a point P_1 are $(1, 17, -9)$. Find the coördinates of P_2, given that the length of the directed segment $\overline{P_1P_2}$ is 28 and its direction cosines are $\frac{2}{7}$, $-\frac{6}{7}$, $\frac{3}{7}$.

20. Using direction numbers, show that $(2, 1, -1)$, $(-1, 2, 1)$ and $(-10, 5, 7)$ lie on a line.

21. Show that the point $(5, 7, -1)$ lies on the line joining $(2, 1, 5)$ and $(8, 13, -7)$ and is equidistant from these points.

22. Using direction cosines and the distance formula, show that $\left(\dfrac{x_1 + x_2}{2}, \dfrac{y_1 + y_2}{2}, \dfrac{z_1 + z_2}{2} \right)$ are the coördinates of the midpoint of the segment joining $P_1(x_1, y_1, z_1)$ and $P_2(x_2, y_2, z_2)$.

23. Show that any three real numbers a, b, and c (not all zero) are a set of direction numbers of the line through the origin and the point (a, b, c).

14.6 The Angle between Two Directed Lines. If we draw two lines at random in space, these two lines, usually, will not intersect. In order that we may speak of the angle between two such lines, we make the following definition: *The angle between two directed lines in space that do not meet is equal to the angle between the positive directions of two intersecting lines having the same directions as the given lines.*

In particular, if the given lines are parallel, the angle between them is zero or π according as their positive directions are the same or opposite.

Let l_1 and l_2 (Fig. 14.5) be two given directed lines and let ϕ be the angle between them. We shall now express $\cos \phi$ in terms of the direction cosines of l_1 and l_2.

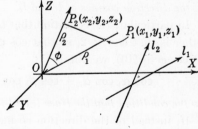

Fig. 14.5

Through the origin O, draw the lines OP_1 and OP_2, having the same directions as l_1, and l_2, respectively. Then, from the above definition of the angle between two directed lines, we have

$$\text{angle } P_1OP_2 = \phi.$$

Let the coördinates of P_1 be (x_1, y_1, z_1) and of P_2 be (x_2, y_2, z_2). Let the length of the segment $OP_1 = \rho_1$ and of $OP_2 = \rho_2$. Draw P_1P_2 and apply the law of cosines (Art. 0.13) to the triangle P_1OP_2. We have

$$P_1P_2{}^2 = \rho_1{}^2 + \rho_2{}^2 - 2\rho_1\rho_2 \cos \phi$$

or
$$\cos \phi = \frac{\rho_1{}^2 + \rho_2{}^2 - P_1P_2{}^2}{2\rho_1\rho_2}. \tag{8}$$

But $\qquad \rho_1{}^2 = x_1{}^2 + y_1{}^2 + z_1{}^2 \quad \text{and} \quad \rho_2{}^2 = x_2{}^2 + y_2{}^2 + z_2{}^2$

and $\qquad P_1P_2{}^2 = (x_2 - x_1)^2 + (y_2 - y_1)^2 + (z_2 - z_1)^2.$

On making these substitutions in the numerator of (8), and simplifying, we obtain

$$\cos \phi = \frac{x_1x_2 + y_1y_2 + z_1z_2}{\rho_1\rho_2}. \tag{9}$$

From (5), we have

$$\cos \alpha_1 = \frac{x_1}{\rho_1}, \quad \cos \beta_1 = \frac{y_1}{\rho_1}, \quad \cos \gamma_1 = \frac{z_1}{\rho_1},$$

and $\qquad \cos \alpha_2 = \frac{x_2}{\rho_2}, \quad \cos \beta_2 = \frac{y_2}{\rho_2}, \quad \cos \gamma_2 = \frac{z_2}{\rho_2}.$

On making these substitutions in (9), we have the equation,

$$\cos \phi = \cos \alpha_1 \cos \alpha_2 + \cos \beta_1 \cos \beta_2 + \cos \gamma_1 \cos \gamma_2, \tag{10}$$

which expresses *the cosine of ϕ, the angle between l_1 and l_2, in terms of the direction cosines of l_1 and l_2.*

In particular, the condition that l_1 and l_2 are perpendicular to each other is that $\phi = \pi/2$, so that $\cos \phi = 0$. On substituting this value of $\cos \phi$ in (10), we obtain

$$\cos \alpha_1 \cos \alpha_2 + \cos \beta_1 \cos \beta_2 + \cos \gamma_1 \cos \gamma_2 = 0 \tag{11}$$

as *the condition that the lines l_1 and l_2 are perpendicular.*

If, instead of the direction cosines of l_1 and l_2, we have direction numbers a_1, b_1, c_1 and a_2, b_2, c_2, respectively, for the lines we first find the direction cosines of l_1 and l_2 from (7), then substitute these values in (10). This gives

$$\cos \phi = \pm \frac{a_1 a_2 + b_1 b_2 + c_1 c_2}{\sqrt{a_1^2 + b_1^2 + c_1^2}\,\sqrt{a_2^2 + b_2^2 + c_2^2}} \qquad (12)$$

as *the value of* $\cos \phi$ *in terms of the direction numbers of* l_1 *and* l_2.

Since l_1 and l_2 are perpendicular if, and only if, $\cos \phi = 0$, it follows that

$$a_1 a_2 + b_1 b_2 + c_1 c_2 = 0 \qquad (13)$$

is the condition that l_1 *and* l_2 *are perpendicular.*

Example 1. Find the angle between the line through $P_1(1, -2, 4)$ and $P_2(3, 8, -7)$ and the line through $P_1'(1, 5, -2)$ and $P_2'(7, -2, 4)$. Assume that these lines are directed from P_1 toward P_2 and from P_1' toward P_2' respectively.

From (3), the direction cosines of the first of these lines are $\frac{2}{15}$, $\frac{10}{15}$, and $-\frac{11}{15}$; and those of the second are $\frac{6}{11}$, $-\frac{7}{11}$, and $\frac{6}{11}$. On substituting these values of the direction cosines of the given lines in (10), we have

$$\cos \phi = \frac{2 \cdot 6 + 10 \cdot (-7) - 11 \cdot 6}{15 \cdot 11} = \frac{-124}{165} = -0.7515.$$

From the tables, by the aid of the reduction formulas, we find that $\phi = 139°$ approximately.

Example 2. Find direction numbers for a line that is perpendicular to each of two lines having direction numbers 4, 1, 3 and 6, 3, 5, respectively.

Denote the required direction numbers by a, b, c. We have, from (13),

$$4a + b + 3c = 0$$

and

$$6a + 3b + 5c = 0.$$

If we solve these equations for a and b in terms of c, we have $a = -2c/3$ and $b = -c/3$. Since only the ratios of these numbers are significant, we may give c any value, except zero, that we please. If we put $c = -3$, we obtain 2, 1, -3 as the required direction numbers.

EXERCISES

Find the angle between the lines whose direction cosines are:

1. $\dfrac{7}{11}, \dfrac{-6}{11}, \dfrac{6}{11}; \dfrac{-1}{9}, \dfrac{4}{9}, \dfrac{8}{9}.$ 2. $\dfrac{-2}{11}, \dfrac{-6}{11}, \dfrac{-9}{11}; \dfrac{4}{9}, \dfrac{4}{9}, \dfrac{-7}{9}.$

3. $\dfrac{-2}{3}, \dfrac{2}{3}, \dfrac{-1}{3}; \dfrac{14}{23}, \dfrac{-3}{23}, \dfrac{-18}{23}.$ **4.** $\dfrac{6}{19}, \dfrac{-10}{19}, \dfrac{-15}{19}; \dfrac{12}{13}, \dfrac{-4}{13}, \dfrac{3}{13}.$

Find the acute angle between the lines with direction numbers:

5. 7, 4, 4; 6, 10, 15.   **6.** 12, 3, $-$ 4; 2, 11, $-$ 10.

7. 5, $-$ 2, $-$ 14; 1, 2, $-$ 2.   **8.** 3, $-$ 5, 2; 4, 1, 3.

9. Show that $(-2, 4, 3)$, $(2, 8, 1)$, $(4, 1, 9)$ and $(8, 5, 7)$ are vertices of a rectangle and find its area.

10. Show that $(-2, -1, -3)$, $(6, 3, -2)$, $(1, 1, 3)$ and $(9, 5, 4)$ are vertices of a parallelogram and find its acute angle.

Using direction numbers, show that the three given points are vertices of a right triangle. Find, also, direction numbers for a line perpendicular to all the sides of the triangle:

11. $(5, 4, 1)$, $(4, 1, -1)$, $(1, -2, 5)$.

12. $(4, 5, -3)$, $(-1, 3, 6)$, $(2, -1, 3)$.

13. Show that the three pairs of opposite edges of the tetrahedron (or triangular pyramid) whose vertices are $(4, 2, 2)$, $(3, 3, 4)$, $(4, 5, 5)$ and $(5, -2, 9)$ are mutually perpendicular.

14. Show that a set of direction numbers of a line perpendicular to two non-parallel lines with direction numbers a_1, b_1, c_1, and a_2, b_2, c_2, are

$$\begin{vmatrix} b_1 & c_1 \\ b_2 & c_2 \end{vmatrix}, \quad \begin{vmatrix} c_1 & a_1 \\ c_2 & a_2 \end{vmatrix}, \quad \begin{vmatrix} a_1 & b_1 \\ a_2 & b_2 \end{vmatrix}.$$

15. Use Ex. 14 to find a set of direction numbers of a line perpendicular to the lines with direction numbers 1, 2, 7 and 3, $-$ 2, 5.

MISCELLANEOUS EXERCISES

1. Do the points $(3, -6, -7)$, $(7, -1, 3)$ and $(-5, 5, 9)$ lie on a line?

2. Show in two ways that $(3, -6, -7)$, $(-2, 8, -9)$ and $(-5, 2, -3)$ are vertices of a right triangle.

3. Show in two ways that $(3, 6, -4)$, $(5, 2, 2)$ and $(-6, 5, 3)$ are vertices of an isosceles triangle.

4. Show that $(4, 3, 4)$, $(6, 5, 3)$, $(-4, 4, 3)$ and $(-6, 2, 4)$ are vertices of a parallelogram and find the lengths of the diagonals.

5. Find x, given that the lines joining $(2, 3, 5)$ to $(x, 7, 3)$ and to $(5, 9, 11)$ are perpendicular.

6. Find a point in the xy-plane whose distances from $(8, 3, 3)$, $(3, 1, 8)$ and $(6, 4, 4)$ are equal.

7. Find the angles of the triangle whose vertices are $(4, 1, 4)$, $(2, 3, 3)$ and $(6, -5, -5)$.

8. Find the direction cosines of a line perpendicular to the sides of the triangle in Ex. 7.

9. Show that the tetrahedron whose vertices are $(a, 0, 0)$, $(0, a, 0)$, $(0, 0, a)$, and (a, a, a) is regular, that is, that its sides are all equal in length.

10. Find the angle between two opposite edges of the tetrahedron in Ex. 9.

11. Find the point equidistant from the vertices of the tetrahedron in Ex. 9.

SELECTED EXERCISES

1. Discuss Ex. 14 when the lines are parallel.

2. Find the condition that there exists a line perpendicular to three given lines.

3. Find an expression for the sine of the angle between two lines whose direction cosines are given.

4. The vertices of a triangle are $P_1(x_1, y_1, z_1)$, $P_2(x_2, y_2, z_2)$, and $P_3(x_3, y_3, z_3)$. Find the direction cosines of a line perpendicular to the three sides of this triangle.

5. Show that the area of the triangle in Ex. 4 is

$$\frac{1}{2}\sqrt{\begin{vmatrix} y_1 & z_1 & 1 \\ y_2 & z_2 & 1 \\ y_3 & z_3 & 1 \end{vmatrix}^2 + \begin{vmatrix} z_1 & x_1 & 1 \\ z_2 & x_2 & 1 \\ z_3 & x_3 & 1 \end{vmatrix}^2 + \begin{vmatrix} x_1 & y_1 & 1 \\ x_2 & y_2 & 1 \\ x_3 & y_3 & 1 \end{vmatrix}^2}$$

6. If two pairs of opposite edges of a tetrahedron are perpendicular, show that the third pair is also perpendicular.

CHAPTER

——————————————

$X\ V$

Planes and Lines

15.1 Normal Equation of a Plane. Let ABC (Fig. 15.1) be the given plane and let N be the foot of the perpendicular from the

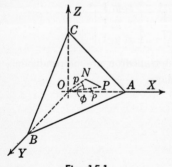

Fig. 15.1

origin to the plane. Draw the directed line segment $\overline{ON}$, denote its length by p and its direction cosines by $\cos \alpha$, $\cos \beta$, and $\cos \gamma$.

Let $P(x, y, z)$ be any point in the plane. Draw $\overline{OP}$, and denote the length of $\overline{OP}$ by ρ and its direction cosines by $\cos \alpha'$, $\cos \beta'$, and $\cos \gamma'$. Denote also the angle NOP by ϕ.

Since ON is perpendicular to the plane and N and P lie in the plane, the angle ONP is a right angle. (Why?) Hence, $\cos \phi = p/\rho$, or

$$p = \rho \cos \phi. \tag{1}$$

From equation (10), Art. 14.6, we have

$$\cos \phi = \cos \alpha' \cos \alpha + \cos \beta' \cos \beta + \cos \gamma' \cos \gamma.$$

On substituting this value of cos ϕ in (1) and multiplying out the second member, we find that

$$p = \rho \cos \alpha' \cos \alpha + \rho \cos \beta' \cos \beta + \rho \cos \gamma' \cos \gamma. \tag{2}$$

From equations (5), Art. 14.4, we have

$$\rho \cos \alpha' = x, \qquad \rho \cos \beta' = y, \qquad \rho \cos \gamma' = z.$$

If we make these substitutions in (2), we obtain the result

$$x \cos \alpha + y \cos \beta + z \cos \gamma - p = 0, \tag{3}$$

which is the required *equation of the plane in the normal form.*

Exercise. If the point $P(x, y, z)$ does not lie in the given plane, show that the foot of the perpendicular from P on the line ON is a point N' distinct from N and hence that the coördinates of P do not satisfy equation (3).

15.2 General Form of the Equation of a Plane. The normal form (3) of the equation of a plane is of the first degree in x, y, and z with real coefficients. We shall now show, conversely, that *the locus of any equation of the first degree in x, y, and z with real coefficients,*

$$Ax + By + Cz + D = 0, \tag{4}$$

where A, B, and C are not all zero, is a plane.

The locus of equation (4) is not changed if we divide each of its terms by the non-zero constant $\pm \sqrt{A^2 + B^2 + C^2}$. We thus obtain

$$\frac{A}{\pm \sqrt{A^2 + B^2 + C^2}} x + \frac{B}{\pm \sqrt{A^2 + B^2 + C^2}} y + \frac{C}{\pm \sqrt{A^2 + B^2 + C^2}} z$$

$$+ \frac{D}{\pm \sqrt{A^2 + B^2 + C^2}} = 0. \tag{5}$$

By Art. 14.5, the coefficients of x, y, and z in (5) are the direction cosines of a line, so that we may put

$$\frac{A}{\pm \sqrt{A^2 + B^2 + C^2}} = \cos \alpha$$

$$\frac{B}{\pm \sqrt{A^2 + B^2 + C^2}} = \cos \beta \tag{6}$$

$$\frac{C}{\pm \sqrt{A^2 + B^2 + C^2}} = \cos \gamma.$$

If we substitute these values of the coefficients of x, y, and z in (5), and compare the result with equation (3), we find that equation (5), and hence equation (4) which has the same locus, is the equation of a plane. It follows, moreover, from the comparison with (3), that this plane is perpendicular to the line whose direction cosines are given by (6) and that it lies at a distance from the origin equal to

$$p = \frac{-D}{\pm \sqrt{A^2 + B^2 + C^2}}. \tag{7}$$

Equation (4) is called the **general form** of the equation of a plane. To reduce it to the normal form (5), we divide each of its terms by $\pm \sqrt{A^2 + B^2 + C^2}$. In order to fix the sign of the radical by which we divide each term of (4) to get (5), *we shall take the sign to agree with that of C if C $\neq$ 0, to agree with that of B if C = 0, and to agree with that of A if B = 0 and C = 0.* If $C \neq 0$, this means that we are fixing the direction of the normal so that cos γ is positive. Thus, we are taking the upward direction along the normal as the positive direction.

Of frequent importance in the applications is the following theorem which follows at once from the foregoing discussion: *the coefficients of x, y, and z in the equation of a plane are the direction numbers of a line perpendicular to the plane.*

15.3. The Traces of a Plane. The lines in which a given plane intersects the coördinate planes are called its **traces** on those planes.

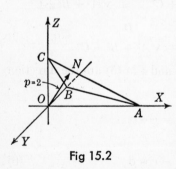

Fig 15.2

A plane is usually represented on the figure by means of its traces on the coördinate planes, as in Fig. 15.2. If, however, it passes through (or very near to) the origin, or if it is parallel to one of the coördinate axes, it should be represented, instead, by a parallelogram having two of its sides extending along two of its traces on the coördinate planes.

Example. Reduce the equation of the plane $x - 2y + 2z - 6 = 0$ to the normal form. Find the direction cosines of the normal and the distance of the plane from the origin. Determine its traces on the coördinate planes.

To reduce the equation of the plane to the normal form, we divide through by $\sqrt{1^2 + (-2)^2 + 2^2} = 3$. The result is $\frac{1}{3}x - \frac{2}{3}y + \frac{2}{3}z - 2 = 0$.

The direction cosines of the normal to the plane are found, by comparing this equation with (3), to be $\frac{1}{3}, -\frac{2}{3}, \frac{2}{3}$ and the distance of the plane from the origin is similarly found to be 2.

The equations of the traces of the given plane on the coördinate planes are:

On the xy-plane	$-x - 2y - 6 = 0,$	$z = 0;$
On the xz-plane	$x + 2z - 6 = 0,$	$y = 0;$
On the yz-plane	$-2y + 2z - 6 = 0,$	$x = 0.$

EXERCISES

Find the equation in the normal form of the plane for which α, β, γ, and p have the values stated:

1. $60°, 60°, 45°; 3.$
2. $90°, 45°, 135°; 5.$
3. $\pi/6, 2\pi/3, \pi/2; -2.$
4. $\pi/3, 3\pi/4, 2\pi/3; -7.$

Find the equations of the planes having the given set of direction numbers for their normals and lying at the given undirected distance from the origin:

5. $6, 3, 2; 4.$
6. $4, -7, 4; 2.$
7. $2, 11, -10; 3.$
8. $4, -8, -1; 5.$
9. $-9, 2, 6; 6.$
10. $3, 5, 2; \sqrt{38}.$

Find the equation of the plane, given that the coördinates of the foot of the perpendicular from the origin on the plane are:

11. $(6, 6, -7).$
12. $(5, -2, -14).$

Write the equation of the plane in the normal form. Find the direction cosines of the normal and the directed distance from the origin to the plane. Write two equations for each of the three traces of the plane on the coördinate planes:

13. $2x - y + 2z - 12 = 0.$
14. $8x - 9y + 12z - 34 = 0.$
15. $6x - 10y - 15z + 57 = 0.$
16. $2x - y - z - 12 = 0.$

17. Show analytically that the locus of a point equidistant from $(2, 1, -4)$ and $(5, 3, 1)$ is a plane perpendicular to the line joining these points.

18. Find the point of intersection of the planes $5x + 3y - 2z + 11 = 0$, $7x - y + 2z - 19 = 0$, and $3x - 5y - 4z + 7 = 0$.

15.4. Angle between Two Planes. It is proved, in elementary geometry, that the magnitudes of the four dihedral angles formed by two intersecting planes are numerically

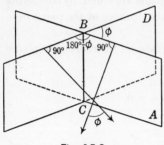

Fig. 15.3

equal, respectively, to the four corresponding angles formed by the two lines that can be drawn through any point in space perpendicular to the given planes (Fig. 15.3). It is by means of this theorem that the angles between two planes are usually measured in advanced mathematics.

If positive directions are assigned to the two perpendiculars, we shall choose, as **the angle between the planes,** a dihedral angle formed by them that is equal in magnitude to *the angle between the positive directions of these perpendiculars.*

Thus, if the equations of the planes are given in the normal form

$$x \cos \alpha_1 + y \cos \beta_1 + z \cos \gamma_1 - p_1 = 0,$$

and
$$x \cos \alpha_2 + y \cos \beta_2 + z \cos \gamma_2 - p_2 = 0,$$

then, by Art. 15.1, the direction cosines of the normals to the planes are $\cos \alpha_1$, $\cos \beta_1$, $\cos \gamma_1$, and $\cos \alpha_2$, $\cos \beta_2$, $\cos \gamma_2$, respectively, and the angle between the planes, being equal in magnitude to the angle between the positive directions of the normals, is found, from equation (11), Art. 14.6, to be

$$\cos \phi = \cos \alpha_1 \cos \alpha_2 + \cos \beta_1 \cos \beta_2 + \cos \gamma_1 \cos \gamma_2, \quad (8)$$

where ϕ is the angle between the planes and α_1, β_1, γ_1 and α_2, β_2, γ_2 are the direction angles of the normals to the planes.

Similarly, if the equations of the planes are given in the general form

$$A_1 x + B_1 y + C_1 z + D_1 = 0$$

and
$$A_2 x + B_2 y + C_2 z + D_2 = 0,$$

then A_1, B_1, C_1 and A_2, B_2, C_2 are sets of direction numbers of the normals to the planes and the angle between the planes is found, from equation (13), Art. 14.6, to be

$$\cos \phi = \pm \frac{A_1 A_2 + B_1 B_2 + C_1 C_2}{\sqrt{A_1^2 + B_1^2 + C_1^2} \, \sqrt{A_2^2 + B_2^2 + C_2^2}}. \quad (9)$$

In particular, the condition that the planes are perpendicular is that $\cos \phi = 0$, so that

$$A_1A_2 + B_1B_2 + C_1C_2 = 0. \tag{10}$$

If the given planes are parallel, they are both perpendicular to the same line, and we have

$$\frac{A_1}{A_2} = \frac{B_1}{B_2} = \frac{C_1}{C_2}. \tag{11}$$

These equalities fail and must be replaced if any direction number is zero. If, for example, $A_1 = 0$ then $A_2 = 0$. Then if the remaining direction numbers are not zero, we replace (11) by $B_1/B_2 = C_1/C_2$.

15.5. Plane through a Given Point Perpendicular to a Given Line. Let $P_1(x_1, y_1, z_1)$ be the given point and let a, b, c be direction numbers of the given line.

From the last theorem of Art. 15.2, it is seen that the plane

$$ax + by + cz + D = 0 \tag{12}$$

is perpendicular to the given line for all values of D.

We determine D from the condition that the plane (12) passes through P_1. This condition is

$$ax_1 + by_1 + cz_1 + D = 0.$$

If we substitute the value of D from this equation in (12), and collect terms, we have

$$a(x - x_1) + b(y - y_1) + c(z - z_1) = 0. \tag{13}$$

This is the required equation of the plane through $P_1(x_1, y_1, z_1)$ perpendicular to the line whose direction numbers are $a, b,$ and c.

15.6. Distance from a Plane to a Point. Let $P_1(x_1, y_1, z_1)$ be the given point and let the equation of the given plane be

$$Ax + By + Cz + D = 0. \tag{14}$$

From (13), the equation of a plane through P_1 parallel to the given plane (14) is

$$A(x - x_1) + B(y - y_1) + C(z - z_1) = 0. \tag{15}$$

The directed distances from the origin to the planes (14) and (15) are, by (7),

$$p_1 = \frac{-D}{\pm \sqrt{A^2 + B^2 + C^2}} \quad \text{and} \quad p_2 = \frac{Ax_1 + By_1 + Cz_1}{\pm \sqrt{A^2 + B^2 + C^2}}.$$

The difference

$$d = p_2 - p_1$$

between these distances is equal to the required distance from the plane (14) to the given point P_1, that is,

$$d = \frac{Ax_1 + By_1 + Cz_1 + D}{\pm \sqrt{A^2 + B^2 + C^2}}, \qquad (16)$$

where the sign in the denominator is fixed by the rule given in Art. 15.2.

The value of d, as found from this equation, is a directed distance. It is positive or negative according as the segment of the perpendicular, measured from the plane to the point P_1, is in the positive or the negative direction along the normal.

EXERCISES

Find the acute angle between the two planes:

1. $2x - 2y - z - 8 = 0$,
$x - 8y + 4z + 10 = 0$.

2. $7x - 6y + 6z - 2 = 0$,
$5x - 2y - 14z + 8 = 0$.

3. $6x + 3y - 6z + 7 = 0$,
$7x + 4y - 4z + 9 = 0$.

4. $2x - 9y - 6z - 5 = 0$,
$12x - 4y + 3z - 8 = 0$.

5. Write the equations of the two planes through $(3, -1, 2)$ parallel respectively to the two planes in Ex. 3.

6. Find the directed distance from each of the planes in Ex. 1 to the point $(1, 8, 2)$.

7. Which of the points $(3, 1, 7)$ and $(4, 2, 1)$ lies on the same side of the plane $2x + 5y - z - 9 = 0$ as $(2, 3, 4)$ does?

Find the undirected distance between the parallel planes:

8. $2x - 14y + 5z - 5 = 0$,
$2x - 14y + 5z + 40 = 0$.

9. $6x + 2y - 3z + 22 = 0$,
$6x + 2y - 3z - 13 = 0$.

10. Find two planes parallel to $9x - 2y - 6z - 4 = 0$ whose distances from $(4, -2, 5)$ are numerically equal to 5.

11. Find k, given that the plane $(k + 6)x + (2k - 3)y - (k + 4)z + 3k - 5 = 0$ is perpendicular to the plane $4x - 5y + 3z + 9 = 0$.

12. Show that the condition that the plane $Ax + By + Cz + D = 0$ is perpendicular to the plane $z = 0$ is $C = 0$. Find the condition that it is perpendicular to (a) $x = 0$; (b) $y = 0$.

15.7 Planes Satisfying Three Conditions. The position of a plane is usually fixed by assigning three conditions that it must satisfy. We may, for example, require it to pass through three given points, or to pass through a given point and be perpendicular to each of two given planes, and so forth.

The method of determining the equation of a plane that satisfies three such conditions is illustrated by the following examples.

Example 1. Find the equation of the plane that passes through the points $(3, 2, -3)$, $(-1, 3, 5)$, and $(5, 4, -2)$.

The condition that any one of these points lies in the plane

$$Ax + By + Cz + D = 0$$

is that its coördinates satisfy the equation of the plane. If we substitute the coördinates of the given points successively in the equation of the plane, we obtain the three equations

$$3A + 2B - 3C + D = 0$$
$$-A + 3B + 5C + D = 0$$
$$5A + 4B - 2C + D = 0.$$

If we solve these three equations for B, C, and D in terms of A, we obtain $B = -\frac{4}{3}A$, $C = \frac{2}{3}A$, $D = \frac{5}{3}A$.

We may now assign to A *any value we please except zero*. To avoid fractions, we put $A = 3$; then $B = -4$, $C = 2$, and $D = 5$. The required equation of the plane is, accordingly,

$$3x - 4y + 2z + 5 = 0.$$

As a check, the student should verify that the coördinates of each of the given points satisfy this equation.

Example 2. Find the equation of the plane that passes through the points $(6, 1, 2)$ and $(3, 4, 4)$ and is perpendicular to the plane $x + 3y + 2z - 7 = 0$.

The conditions that the plane $Ax + By + Cz + D = 0$ passes through the given points are found, by substituting the coördinates of the points in the equation of the plane, to be

$$6A + B + 2C + D = 0$$
$$3A + 4B + 4C + D = 0.$$

The condition that it is perpendicular to the given plane is

$$A + 3B + 2C = 0.$$

We cannot solve these equations for B, C, and D in terms of A since the resulting equations are incompatible. We can, however, solve for A, C, and D in terms of B. The results are $A = 0$, $C = -\frac{3}{2}B$, $D = 2B$.

If we put $B = 2$ we have $C = -3$ and $D = 4$. The required equation is, accordingly, $2y - 3z + 4 = 0$.

15.8 Intercept Equation of a Plane. The directed distances from the origin to the points of intersection of a plane with the coördinate

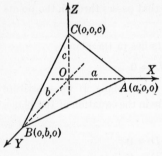

Fig. 15.4

axes are called the **intercepts** of the plane on those axes.

Let a, b, and c (which, we shall suppose, are all different from zero) be the intercepts of the plane

$$Ax + By + Cz + D = 0 \qquad (17)$$

on the x-, y-, and z-axis, respectively.

To find the equation of this plane in terms of its intercepts, we first observe that it passes through the points $A(a, 0, 0)$, $B(0, b, 0)$, and $C(0, 0, c)$ (Fig. 15.4). Hence the coördinates of each of these points satisfy the equation of the plane, and we have

$$Aa + D = 0, \qquad Bb + D = 0, \qquad Cc + D = 0.$$

If we solve these equations for A, B, and C in terms of D, and then put $D = -1$, we have

$$A = \frac{1}{a}, \qquad B = \frac{1}{b}, \qquad C = \frac{1}{c}, \qquad D = -1.$$

On substituting these values of A, B, C, and D in (17), we obtain

$$\frac{x}{a} + \frac{y}{b} + \frac{z}{c} = 1 \qquad (18)$$

as the *intercept form of the equation of a plane.*

EXERCISES

Write the equation of the plane in the intercept form:

1. $3x + 2y + 4z - 24 = 0$.   **2.** $3x - 15y - 5z - 45 = 0$.

3. $7x - 2y - 3z + 42 = 0$.   **4.** $4x + 3y - 5z - 7 = 0$.

Write the equation of the plane that passes through the three given points:

5. $(4, 0, 0)$, $(0, -3, 0)$, $(0, 0, 2)$.

6. $(4, -1, 3)$, $(-1, -2, 7)$, $(3, 2, -4)$.

7. $(2, 4, 2)$, $(3, 1, 1)$, $(5, 3, 2)$.   **8.** $(1, 4, 4)$, $(6, 3, 2)$, $(4, -1, 6)$.

9. Find the equation of the plane that passes through $(4, 3, 8)$ and $(-7, -4, -2)$ and has its z-intercept equal to 4.

10. Find the equation of the plane that passes through $(3, 7, 1)$ and $(2, 3, 7)$ and has its z-intercept equal to 4 times its y-intercept.

Find the equation of the plane that passes through the two given points and is perpendicular to the given plane:

11. $(1, 4, 3)$, $(2, -5, 6)$, $2x + 3y - 3z + 7 = 0$.

12. $(8, 3, 2)$, $(4, -1, 4)$, $7x - 3y + 4z - 5 = 0$.

13. $(5, -1, -2)$, $(3, 3, -6)$, $2x - y + 6z + 8 = 0$.

14. $(2, -3, 1)$, $(7, -1, 4)$, $2x - y + 6z + 8 = 0$.

Find the equation of the plane that passes through the given point and is perpendicular to the two given planes:

15. $(3, 5, 1)$, $2x - y - 4z + 6 = 0$, $2x + 3y + 2z - 5 = 0$.

16. $(7, 5, -2)$, $6x + 5y - 2z - 9 = 0$, $2x + 4y - z - 3 = 0$.

17. $(4, 1, 3)$, $x - 2y - 3z + 4 = 0$, $3x + 4y + 5z - 6 = 0$.

18. $(3, -9, 2)$, $6x + y - 2z + 1 = 0$, $2x - 5y + 2z + 7 = 0$.

19. Find the equation of the plane that passes through $(3, 2, 9)$, is perpendicular to $4x + 3y - 2z - 5 = 0$ and has the sum of the reciprocals of its intercepts equal to 0.

20. Find the equations of two planes through $(4, -3, 5)$ and $(2, -1, 6)$ each of which makes an angle of $45°$ with the plane $x - y + 4z + 5 = 0$.

THE LINE IN SPACE

15.9 Planes and Lines. We have seen, in Art. 15.2, that a single linear equation in x, y, and z, with real coefficients,

$$Ax + By + Cz + D = 0,$$

defines a plane. Geometrically, a line in space is determined by the intersection of two distinct non-parallel planes. Hence, analytically, a line in space is determined by the equations, taken simultaneously, of two distinct non-parallel planes,

$$A_1x + B_1y + C_1z + D_1 = 0, \qquad A_2x + B_2y + C_2z + D_2 = 0$$

that have this line as their intersection. Thus, if a point lies on this line its coördinates must satisfy *both* of these equations, and conversely.

In the articles that follow, we shall study pairs of equations which fix the position of a line in space. We shall write these equations in several forms depending on the information that is given us about the line or on the uses to which we intend to put these equations.

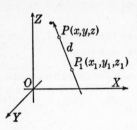

Fig. 15.5

15.10 Line through a Given Point Having a Given Direction. The Symmetric Form.

Let $P_1(x_1, y_1, z_1)$ be the given point and let $\cos \alpha$, $\cos \beta$, and $\cos \gamma$ be the direction cosines of the given directed line.

Let $P(x, y, z)$ be any point on the given line and let $d = \overline{P_1P}$ be the length of the directed segment from P_1 to P. From equations (3), Article 14.4, we have

$$x - x_1 = d \cos \alpha, \quad y - y_1 = d \cos \beta, \quad z - z_1 = d \cos \gamma. \quad (19)$$

If we solve these three equations for d, and equate the values for d so obtained, we have, as the equations of the line,

$$\frac{x - x_1}{\cos \alpha} = \frac{y - y_1}{\cos \beta} = \frac{z - z_1}{\cos \gamma}. \quad (20)$$

These equations constitute the **symmetric form** of the equations of a line. They consist of three equations

$$\frac{x - x_1}{\cos \alpha} = \frac{y - y_1}{\cos \beta}, \quad \frac{y - y_1}{\cos \beta} = \frac{z - z_1}{\cos \gamma}, \quad \frac{x - x_1}{\cos \alpha} = \frac{z - z_1}{\cos \gamma}.$$

Only two of these equations are essential, however, since any one of them can be deduced from the other two.

If, in (20), we multiply all the denominators by any non-zero constant that we please, the equalities still hold. The denominators now become, not the direction cosines, but the direction numbers of the line. If we denote these direction numbers by a, b, and c, we may write the resulting equations of the line in the form

$$\frac{x - x_1}{a} = \frac{y - y_1}{b} = \frac{z - z_1}{c}. \quad (21)$$

These equations which are also called the **symmetric form** are frequently more convenient to use than equations (20) which involve the actual direction cosines.

If the given line is perpendicular to any one of the coördinate axes, equations (20) and (21) fail. If for example, the line is perpendicular to the x-axis, $\cos \alpha = 0$, then by using equations (19) we obtain the following equations instead of equations (20):

$$x - x_1 = 0, \qquad \frac{y - y_1}{\cos \beta} = \frac{z - z_1}{\cos \gamma}. \tag{20$'$}$$

If the line is perpendicular to both the x- and y-axes, then $\cos \alpha = 0$, $\cos \beta = 0$, and the required equations are

$$x - x_1 = 0, \qquad y - y_1 = 0. \tag{20$''$}$$

15.11 The Two-point Form. Let $P_1(x_1, y_1, z_1)$ and $P_2(x_2, y_2, z_2)$ be any two fixed points on the line. By Art. 14.5, the numbers $x_2 - x_1$, $y_2 - y_1$, and $z_2 - z_1$ are direction numbers of this line. Hence, we may use them, in (21), as the direction numbers a, b, and c of the line. The resulting equations are

$$\frac{x - x_1}{x_2 - x_1} = \frac{y - y_1}{y_2 - y_1} = \frac{z - z_1}{z_2 - z_1}. \tag{22}$$

These equations demonstrate the **two-point form** of the equations of the line.

As in Art. 15.10, if the line is perpendicular to any one of the coördinate axes, equations (22) fail. If, for example, the line is perpendicular to the z-axis, $z_2 = z_1$ and (22) must be replaced by

$$\frac{x - x_1}{x_2 - x_1} = \frac{y - y_1}{y_2 - y_1}, \qquad z - z_1 = 0. \tag{22$'$}$$

15.12 The Parametric Form. If, in equations (21), we equate each of the equal fractions to k and solve for x, y, and z, we obtain

$$x = x_1 + ak, \quad y = y_1 + bk, \quad z = z_1 + ck. \tag{23}$$

These three equations are **parametric equations** of the line in terms of the parameter k. The point determined by assigning to k any value we please is a point that lies on the line.

15.13 The General Form. When a line is determined by a pair of equations

$$A_1x + B_1y + C_1z + D_1 = 0$$
$$A_2x + B_2y + C_2z + D_2 = 0$$

(24)

we say that the line is given in the **general form.**

To reduce the general form (24) of the equations of a line to the symmetric form and to the parametric form, we may proceed as in the following example.

Example. Write the equations of the line of intersection of the planes $3x + 3y - 4z + 7 = 0$ and $x + 6y + 2z - 6 = 0$ in the symmetric form and in the parametric form.

To determine the equations of the line in the symmetric form and in the parametric form we need to determine a set of direction numbers of the line and the coördinates of one point on the line.

To determine a set of direction numbers of the line we make use of the fact that the required line is perpendicular to the normals of the two intersecting planes. The coefficients of x, y, and z in the equations of the planes are sets of direction numbers of the normals to the planes. Hence, if we let a, b, and c be the required set of direction numbers for the line and use the condition that two lines are perpendicular (Art. 14.6), we obtain

$$3a + 3b - 4c = 0$$
$$a + 6b + 2c = 0.$$

If we solve these equations for a and b in terms of c we have $a = 2c$ and $b = -2c/3$. Since only the ratios of a, b, and c are significant, we set $c = 3$ and obtain $6, -2, 3$ as a set of direction numbers of the line.

To determine a point on the line, we may assume for one of its coördinates any value we please and determine its other two coördinates by means of the given equations. For example, if we put $z = 1$, the equations to determine x and y are

$$3x + 3y + 3 = 0, \quad x + 6y - 4 = 0.$$

On solving these equations we find that $x = -2, y = 1$. Hence $(-2, 1, 1)$ is a point that lies on the line.

Substituting the above results in equations (21) and (22), we obtain

$$\frac{x + 2}{6} = \frac{y - 1}{-2} = \frac{z - 1}{3}$$

and $x = -2 + 6k$, $y = 1 - 2k$, $z = 1 + 3k$ as the equations of the line in the symmetric and parametric forms respectively.

To obtain the direction cosines of the line we divide each of the direction numbers by $\pm \sqrt{6^2 + (-2)^2 + 3^2} = \pm 7$. The sign which is to be used depends upon which direction on the line is the positive direction. If the positive direction is upward, the direction cosines are $+\frac{6}{7}$, $-\frac{2}{7}$, $+\frac{3}{7}$; if downward, the direction cosines are $-\frac{6}{7}$, $+\frac{2}{7}$, $-\frac{3}{7}$.

An alternative method of obtaining a set of direction numbers of the line is by use of the results obtained in Ex. 14, Art. 14.6. Using this result, we obtain

$$\begin{vmatrix} 3 & -4 \\ 6 & 2 \end{vmatrix}, \quad \begin{vmatrix} -4 & 3 \\ 2 & 1 \end{vmatrix}, \quad \begin{vmatrix} 3 & 3 \\ 1 & 6 \end{vmatrix}$$

or 30, -10, 15. Dividing this set by 5, we obtain the set 6, -2, 3 used above.

15.14 Family of Planes through a Line. Projecting Planes. All of the planes of the family

$$A_1x + B_1y + C_1z + D_1 + k(A_2x + B_2y + C_2z + D_2) = 0, \qquad (25)$$

where k is the parameter, contain the line defined by equations (24). For, if $P_1(x_1, y_1, z_1)$ is any point on this line, its coördinates satisfy both of the equations (24) and thus, when substituted in (25), reduce this equation to $0 + k(0) = 0$, which is true for all values of k.

By assigning a suitable value to k in equation (25), we can determine a plane that passes through the line (24) and satisfies one additional condition; for example, we can make it pass through a given point not on the line or we can make it be perpendicular to a given plane.

The planes through a line that are perpendicular to the xy-, yz-, and zx-planes, respectively, are called the **projecting planes** of the line on these coördinate planes. The equations of the projecting planes of a given line may be found as in the following Example 1.

Example 1. Find the projecting planes of the line $4x - 2y + 3z + 1 = 0$, $5x + 3y + 2z - 3 = 0$ on the coördinate planes.

The family of planes through this line is, by (25),

$$4x - 2y + 3z + 1 + k(5x + 3y + 2z - 3) = 0.$$

If we collect the coefficients of x, y, and z in this equation, we may write the equation in the form

$$(4 + 5k)x + (-2 + 3k)y + (3 + 2k)z + 1 - 3k = 0. \qquad (26)$$

The condition that a plane of this family is perpendicular to the xy-plane (that is, to the plane $z = 0$) is, by (10), that the coefficient of z in its equation is equal to zero.

If we put the coefficient of z in (26) equal to zero, we have $3 + 2k = 0$, from which $k = -\frac{3}{2}$. On substituting this value of k in (26) and simplifying, we obtain

$$7x + 13y - 11 = 0$$

which is the equation of the projecting plane of the line on the xy-plane.

The equations of the projecting planes of the line on the yz-plane and on the xz-plane are found similarly, by equating to zero the coefficients of x and of y in (26), to be

$$22y - 7z - 17 = 0 \quad \text{and} \quad 22x + 13z - 3 = 0,$$

respectively.

Exercise. Show that by eliminating x, y, and z, respectively, from the equations in Example 1, we obtain the yz-, xz-, and xy- projecting planes.

Example 2. Find the plane through the line in Example 1 and the point $(1, 1, -2)$.

Since the given point lies in the required plane, the value of k must be chosen so that the coördinates of this point satisfy equation (26). On substituting the coördinates of the point in (26) and solving, we obtain $k = 3$. If we now substitute this value of k in (26) and simplify, we have

$$19x + 7y + 9z - 8 = 0$$

as the equation of the required plane.

EXERCISES

Write the equations of the following lines and find their direction cosines, given that γ is acute:

  1. Through $(5, 1, -3)$, direction numbers $6, -9, 2$.

  2. Through $(-3, 7, -2)$, direction numbers $-4, 7, 4$.

  3. Through $(-6, 1, 4)$ and $(8, 3, -1)$.

  4. Through $(2, -7, 6)$ and $(12, 4, 4)$.

  5. Through $(4, -1, 3)$ parallel to the line through $(6, 4, 2)$ and $(3, -2, 8)$.

  6. Through $(3, -1, 4)$ perpendicular to the plane $8x - 9y - 12z + 4 = 0$.

7. Through $(4, 1, 3)$ perpendicular to the two lines with direction numbers 2, 2, 3 and 1, 4, -3.

8. Through $(7, 2, -5)$ parallel to the line of intersection of the planes $3x + 4y - 5z + 7 = 0$ and $6x - 4y - z + 2 = 0$.

9. Write the equation of the line through $(5, -1, -3)$ and $(3, -4, 2)$ in parametric form.

10. Show that the line in Ex. 9 lies in the plane $6x + y + 3z - 20 = 0$.

Hint. A line lies in a plane if two points on it lie in the plane.

Find the projecting planes of the given lines on each of the coördinate planes. Find, also, the point in which the line intersects each of the coördinate planes. Find the direction cosines of the line, given that γ is acute:

11. $4x + y - z - 9 = 0,$
$6x + 4y + z - 26 = 0.$

12. $6x - 2y - 5z - 18 = 0,$
$9x + 4y + 3z + 36 = 0.$

13. $x + 3y - 4z + 8 = 0,$
$2x + 3y + 4z + 28 = 0.$

14. $2x - y - 6z = 0,$
$4x + 3y + 3z - 30 = 0.$

15. Find the acute angle between the lines given in Ex. 11 and Ex. 13.

16. Find the equation of the plane through $(1, 6, -3)$ perpendicular to the line in Ex. 11.

17. Find the equation of the plane through the line in Ex. 11 and the point $(1, 3, -12)$.

TRANSFORMATION OF COÖRDINATES

In the following two articles, we shall derive the equations, analogous to those found in Chapter Seven, for a translation or a rotation of axes in space.

★ **15.15 Translation of Axes.**
Let the coördinates of a point P with respect to one set of axes OX, OY, OZ be (x, y, z) and, with respect to a second set $O'X'$, $O'Y'$, $O'Z'$, having the same positive directions, respectively, as the first, be (x', y', z'). Let the coördinates of O' with respect to the first set of axes be (h, k, l).

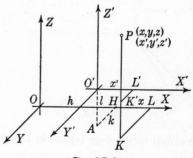

Fig. 15.6

We have, from Fig. 15.6,

$$x = \overline{OL} = \overline{OH} + \overline{HL} = \overline{OH} + \overline{O'L'} = h + x'.$$

In a similar way, we find that

$$y = k + y' \quad \text{and} \quad z = l + z'.$$

Hence the required equations for a translation of axes to the new origin $O'(h, k, l)$ are

$$x = x' + h, \quad y = y' + k, \quad z = z' + l. \tag{27}$$

Example. Transform the equation $x^2 + y^2 + z^2 - 2x + 6y - 10z + 26 = 0$ to parallel axes through the point $(1, -3, 5)$.

We first write the equation in the form

$$x^2 - 2x + 1 + y^2 + 6y + 9 + z^2 - 10z + 25 = 1 + 9 + 25 - 26$$

or
$$(x - 1)^2 + (y + 3)^2 + (z - 5)^2 = 9.$$

If we now transform the origin to the given point according to the equations

$$x = x' + 1, \quad y = y' - 3, \quad z = z' + 5,$$

we obtain, as the required equation referred to the new axes,

$$x'^2 + y'^2 + z'^2 = 9.$$

★ **15.16 Rotation of Axes.** Let the coördinates of a point P with respect to one set of axes OX, OY, OZ be (x, y, z) and, with respect to a second set OX', OY', OZ',

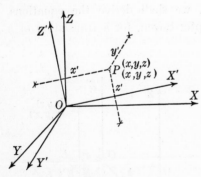

having the same origin, be (x', y', z'). Let the direction cosines of OX', OY', and OZ', referred to the first set of axes, be $\cos \alpha_1$, $\cos \beta_1$, $\cos \gamma_1$; $\cos \alpha_2$, $\cos \beta_2$, $\cos \gamma_2$; and $\cos \alpha_3$, $\cos \beta_3$, $\cos \gamma_3$, respectively.

Since the $y'z'$-plane is perpendicular to OX', and passes through O (so that its distance, p, from the origin is zero), the

Fig. 15.7

normal form of its equation is, by Art. 15.1,

$$x \cos \alpha_1 + y \cos \beta_1 + z \cos \gamma_1 = 0.$$

Since this plane is the $y'z'$-plane, the directed distance of the point P from it is the x'-coördinate of P. Hence we have, by Art. 15.6,

$$x' = x \cos \alpha_1 + y \cos \beta_1 + z \cos \gamma_1.$$

Similarily, $$y' = x \cos \alpha_2 + y \cos \beta_2 + z \cos \gamma_2 \qquad (28)$$

and $$z' = x \cos \alpha_3 + y \cos \beta_3 + z \cos \gamma_3.$$

The nine direction cosines in formulas (28) satisfy the following six equations.

Since the three cosines in the first, the second, and the third of equations (28) are the direction cosines of OX', OY', and OZ', respectively, we have, by (4), Art. 14.4,

$$\cos^2 \alpha_1 + \cos^2 \beta_1 + \cos^2 \gamma_1 = 1$$
$$\cos^2 \alpha_2 + \cos^2 \beta_2 + \cos^2 \gamma_2 = 1 \qquad (29)$$
$$\cos^2 \alpha_3 + \cos^2 \beta_3 + \cos^2 \gamma_3 = 1.$$

Moreover, since the three lines OX', OY', and OZ' are perpendicular to each other, we have, by (12), Art. 14.6,

$$\cos \alpha_1 \cos \alpha_2 + \cos \beta_1 \cos \beta_2 + \cos \gamma_1 \cos \gamma_2 = 0$$
$$\cos \alpha_2 \cos \alpha_3 + \cos \beta_2 \cos \beta_3 + \cos \gamma_2 \cos \gamma_3 = 0 \qquad (30)$$
$$\cos \alpha_3 \cos \alpha_1 + \cos \beta_3 \cos \beta_1 + \cos \gamma_3 \cos \gamma_1 = 0.$$

From Fig. 15.7, it will be seen that the direction cosines of OX, OY, and OZ, referred to the second set of axes, are $\cos \alpha_1$, $\cos \alpha_2$, $\cos \alpha_3$; $\cos \beta_1$, $\cos \beta_2$, $\cos \beta_3$; and $\cos \gamma_1$, $\cos \gamma_2$, $\cos \gamma_3$, respectively. Hence, by the reasoning used in deriving equations (28), we obtain

$$x = x' \cos \alpha_1 + y' \cos \alpha_2 + z' \cos \alpha_3$$
$$y = x' \cos \beta_1 + y' \cos \beta_2 + z' \cos \beta_3 \qquad (31)$$
$$z = x' \cos \gamma_1 + y' \cos \gamma_2 + z' \cos \gamma_3.$$

These equations express x, y, and z in terms of x', y', and z'.

EXERCISES

Find the equation of the given surface when the origin is translated to the point $(5, -2, 4)$:

1. $2x + y - 5z + 12 = 0.$ **2.** $7x - 3y - 8z - 9 = 0.$

3. $x^2 + y^2 + z^2 - 10x + 4y - 8z + 11 = 0.$

4. $2x^2 - 3y^2 - 5z^2 - 20x - 12y + 40z - 72 = 0.$

5. By a translation of axes, remove the first-degree terms from $5x^2 - 2y^2 + 3z^2 + 10x + 12y - 30z + 42 = 0.$

6. Show that the lines $\dfrac{x}{6} = \dfrac{y}{3} = \dfrac{z}{2}$, $\dfrac{x}{2} = \dfrac{y}{-6} = \dfrac{z}{3}$, and $\dfrac{x}{3} = \dfrac{y}{-2} = \dfrac{z}{-6}$ are mutually perpendicular. Write the equations of a rotation of axes having these lines as x', y', and z' axes, respectively.

7. Find the equation of the surface $10x^2 + 7y^2 + 19z^2 + 8yz - 20zx + 28xy = 36$ when the axes are rotated so that the lines whose direction cosines are $\dfrac{1}{3}, \dfrac{2}{3}, \dfrac{2}{3}; \dfrac{2}{3}, -\dfrac{2}{3}, \dfrac{1}{3};$ and $\dfrac{2}{3}, \dfrac{1}{3}, \dfrac{-2}{3}$ are taken, respectively, as the x', y', and z' axes.

8. Show that the equations of a rotation of axes in which the z-axis remains fixed may be written in the form $x = x' \cos \phi - y' \sin \phi$, $y = x' \sin \phi + y' \cos \phi$, $z = z'$.

MISCELLANEOUS EXERCISES

1. Write the equation of the plane through $(7, -1, 3)$ perpendicular to the line $\dfrac{x}{2} = \dfrac{y}{4} = \dfrac{z}{-3}$.

2. Write the equation of the plane $6x - 9y - 2z = 54$ (*a*) in the intercept form; (*b*) in the normal form.

3. Find the directed distances from the plane $7x + 6y - 6z + 5 = 0$ to the points $(1, 4, -3)$ and $(1, -5, 3)$. Do these points lie on the same or on opposite sides of the plane?

4. Write the equations of two planes parallel to $6x - 3y - 2z + 5 = 0$ whose undirected distances from $(1, -3, 5)$ are equal to 4.

5. Write the equations of the line through $(1, 7, 3)$ and $(3, 1, -1)$.

6. Write the equations in the parametric form of the line through $(2, -3, 5)$ perpendicular to the plane given in Ex. 4.

7. Write the equations in the general form of the line through $(1, 8, -2)$ parallel to the line of intersection of the planes $3x + y + 2z - 4 = 0$ and $4x - y - z - 1 = 0$.

8. Write the equations of the line through $(5, 1, -3)$ that is perpendicular to both of the lines $\dfrac{x}{3} = \dfrac{y}{1} = \dfrac{z}{4}$ and $\dfrac{x}{1} = \dfrac{y}{5} = \dfrac{z}{2}$.

9. Find the equations of the projecting planes of the line $4x + 3y - z - 10 = 0$, $2x + 2y - 3z - 10 = 0$ on the coördinate planes and the points at which this line meets the coördinate planes.

10. Write the equation of the plane that contains the line $3x - 2y + 5z - 1 = 0$, $2x - 6y + 3z + 4 = 0$ and is perpendicular to the plane $x + y + z - 30 = 0$.

11. Does the line $\dfrac{x-4}{-2} = \dfrac{y+2}{6} = \dfrac{z-8}{9}$ lie in the plane $6x + 5y - 2z + 2 = 0$?

12. Find the point of intersection of the planes $2x + 3y + 5z + 1 = 0$, $4x - y + 3z + 9 = 0$, $2x + y + 6z + 12 = 0$.

Sketch the solid figure bounded by the given planes.

13. The coördinate planes and $5x + 2y + 3z - 30 = 0$.
14. The coördinate planes, $z = 4$ and $2x + 5y = 10$.
15. The coördinate planes, $2x + 3y = 12$, and $3x + 2z = 18$.
16. The coördinate planes, $x = 5$, $y = 3$, $2y = 5z$.
17. The planes $x = 0$, $z = 0$, $4x + 7y = 28$, $9y = 4z$.

SELECTED EXERCISES

1. Derive the expression for the distance from the plane $A_1x + B_1y + C_1z + D_1 = 0$ to the point $P_1(x_1, y_1, z_1)$ by determining the coördinates of the foot of the perpendicular from P_1 to the plane and the distance of this point from P_1.

2. Find the point in which the plane through $P_1(x_1, y_1, z_1)$ perpendicular to the line $\dfrac{x - x_2}{a} = \dfrac{y - y_2}{b} = \dfrac{z - z_2}{c}$ meets this line. Hence derive an expression for the distance from this line to the point P_1.

3. Find the equations of the planes that bisect the pairs of vertical dihedral angles formed by the intersecting planes $A_1x + B_1y + C_1z + D_1 = 0$ and $A_2x + B_2y + C_2z + D_2 = 0$.

4. Let the equations of two non-parallel, non-intersecting lines be

$$\frac{x - x_1}{\cos \alpha_1} = \frac{y - y_1}{\cos \beta_1} = \frac{z - z_1}{\cos \gamma_1} \quad \text{and} \quad \frac{x - x_2}{\cos \alpha_2} = \frac{y - y_2}{\cos \beta_2} = \frac{z - z_2}{\cos \gamma_2}.$$

Write the equation of a plane through the first line parallel to the second and of a plane through the second parallel to the first.

5. Show that the distance between the planes found in Ex. 4 is the distance between the given lines, and find this distance.

6. Find the condition that four given planes meet in a point.

7. Find the equation of the plane through three given non-collinear points $P_1(x_1, y_1, z_1)$, $P_2(x_2, y_2, z_2)$, and $P_3(x_3, y_3, z_3)$ and express the result by equating to zero a fourth-order determinant.

8. Find the length of the perpendicular from the point $P_4(x_4, y_4, z_4)$ to the plane found in Ex. 7.

9. Using the results of Ex. 8, and of Ex. 5, page 223, show that the volume of the tetrahedron having the points P_1, P_2, P_3, and P_4 as vertices is numerically equal to

$$\frac{1}{6} \begin{vmatrix} x_1 & y_1 & z_1 & 1 \\ x_2 & y_2 & z_2 & 1 \\ x_3 & y_3 & z_3 & 1 \\ x_4 & y_4 & z_4 & 1 \end{vmatrix}$$

10. Discuss all cases arising in the algebraic solution of

$$\begin{aligned} A_1x + B_1y + C_1z &= D_1 \\ A_2x + B_2y + C_2z &= D_2 \quad \text{where} \\ A_3x + B_3y + C_3z &= D_3 \end{aligned} \qquad \begin{vmatrix} A_1 & B_1 & C_1 \\ A_2 & B_2 & C_2 \\ A_3 & B_3 & C_3 \end{vmatrix} = 0.$$

Interpret each case geometrically.

Types of Surfaces and Curves

16.1 Surfaces and Curves. In Art. 15.9 we pointed out that a plane in space is defined by a single linear equation in x, y, and z with real coefficients and that a line in space is defined by two such linear equations.

This is an elementary illustration of a very general and fundamental principle in the analytic geometry of space. When we wish to study analytically a surface in space, we shall think of its position as fixed by a single equation

$$f(x, y, z) = 0.$$

When this equation is linear the surface is a plane, as pointed out at the beginning of this article. When, on the other hand, we wish to fix the position of a curve in space, we shall use two equations,

$$f(x, y, z) = 0, \qquad F(x, y, z) = 0$$

such that each of these equations, taken by itself, is the equation of a surface that contains the curve under consideration. The points that lie on this curve will then possess the property that their coördinates will satisfy the equations of both of these surfaces. When these two equations are linear we have two planes, whose curve of intersection is a straight line (unless the planes are parallel).

In this chapter, we shall discuss certain types of surfaces and of curves in space that are of especial importance in the applications of analytic geometry.

16.2 Cylinders. A surface generated by a line which moves so that it is always parallel to a fixed line and always intersects a fixed curve is called a **cylinder.** Any position of the generating line is an *element* of the cylinder and the fixed curve which all of these elements intersect is the *directrix curve*.

In elementary solid geometry, special attention is given to the circular cylinders; that is, to cylinders that have circles as directrix curves. Although the circular cylinders are included among the surfaces we shall study, most of the cylinders that will be considered in this course are not circular cylinders.

Consider, for example, the surface in space defined by the equation

$$y^2 = 2px. \tag{1}$$

The section of this surface by the xy-plane is the parabola

$$y^2 = 2px, \qquad z = 0. \tag{2}$$

Let $P'(x, y, 0)$ be any point on this parabola. Draw the line through P' parallel to the z-axis and let $P(x, y, z)$ be any point

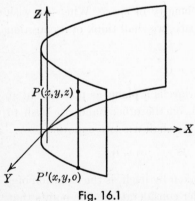

Fig. 16.1

on this line. Then the x- and y-coördinates of P are equal, respectively, to those of P'. By hypothesis, the coördinates of P' satisfy equations (2) and, since the first of these equations does not contain z, it follows that the coördinates of P will also satisfy (1); that is, every point P on the line through P' parallel to the z-axis lies on the surface (1).

If we now let P' describe the

parabola (2), the line $P'P$ will describe a cylinder having the parabola (2) as directrix curve and having its elements parallel to the z-axis. The coördinates of every point on this cylinder (and no others) satisfy equation (1). Hence this cylinder is the required locus of equation (1). It is called a **parabolic cylinder.**

By extending the reasoning used in the foregoing discussion, we are led to the following theorem: *If the equation of a surface does not contain the variable z, then the surface is a cylinder with elements parallel to the z-axis and having the curve of section by the plane $z = 0$ as directrix curve.* Similarly, if y, or x, is absent from the equation, then the surface is a cylinder with elements parallel to the y-axis, or the x-axis, respectively.

EXERCISES

Sketch the cylindrical surfaces:

1. $x^2 + y^2 = 16.$ **2.** $4x^2 + 25y^2 = 100.$ **3.** $3x + 7y = 21.$

4. $x^2 = 6y.$ **5.** $2xz = 9.$ **6.** $16x^2 - 49z^2 = 784.$

7. $y^2 + z^2 + 6y = 0.$ **8.** $y = z^3.$ **9.** $y^2 = z^3.$

10. $z = \cos x.$ **11.** $x^2 - 5x + 6 = 0.$ **12.** $z = \log_{10} x.$

16.3 Surfaces of Revolution. The surface generated by revolving a plane curve about a line in its plane is a **surface of revolution.** The line about which this curve revolves is the *axis of revolution* and any position of the revolving curve is a *meridian section.*

Let us find, for example, the equation of the right circular cone generated by revolving the line defined by the equations

$$x = cz, \qquad y = 0, \qquad (3)$$

around the z-axis.

Let $P_1(x_1, 0, z_1)$ be any point on the given line and let $N_1(0, 0, z_1)$ be the foot of the perpendicular from P_1 to the z-axis. As the given line revolves around the z-axis, P_1 describes a circle with center at N_1, radius N_1P_1, and lying in a plane perpendicular to the z-axis (Fig. 16.2).

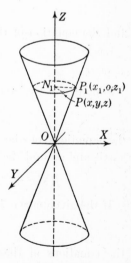

Fig. 16.2

Let $P(x, y, z)$ be any point on this circle. Since it lies in a plane through P_1 parallel to the xy-plane, we have

$$z = z_1.$$

Since it also lies on a circle with center at N_1 and radius $N_1P = N_1P_1 = x_1$, we have further

$$\sqrt{x^2 + y^2} = x_1.$$

Since P_1 lies on the line (3), it follows that

$$x_1 = cz_1$$

and, on substituting in this equation the values already found for x_1 and z_1, we obtain

$$\sqrt{x^2 + y^2} = cz, \quad \text{or} \quad x^2 + y^2 = c^2z^2,$$

which is the required equation of the right circular cone.

By the same reasoning, we find that, if

$$f(x, z) = 0, \qquad y = 0,$$

are the equations of any curve in the xz-plane, the equation of the surface formed by revolving this curve around the z-axis is

$$f(\sqrt{x^2 + y^2}, z) = 0,$$

and the equation of the surface formed by revolving it around the x-axis is

$$f(x, \sqrt{y^2 + z^2}) = 0.$$

Similarly, if we have given a curve in the xy-plane,

$$f(x, y) = 0, \qquad z = 0,$$

the equations of the surfaces formed by revolving it around the y-axis and around the x-axis, respectively, are

$$f(\sqrt{x^2 + z^2}, y) = 0 \quad \text{and} \quad f(x, \sqrt{y^2 + z^2}) = 0.$$

If the given curve lies in the yz-plane, so that its equations are:

$$f(y, z) = 0, \qquad x = 0,$$

the equations of the surfaces formed by revolving it around the z-axis and around the y-axis are, respectively,

$$f(\sqrt{x^2 + y^2}, z) = 0 \quad \text{and} \quad f(y, \sqrt{x^2 + z^2}) = 0.$$

EXERCISES

Find the equation of the surface of revolution formed by revolving the given curve around the axis indicated:

1. $x^2 + z^2 = a^2$, $y = 0$; x-axis.   **2.** $bz + ay = ab$, $x = 0$; y-axis.

3. $z^2 = 4x$, $y = 0$; x-axis.   **4.** $z^2 = 4x$, $y = 0$; z-axis.

5. $9x^2 + 4y^2 = 36$; $z = 0$; x-axis.   **6.** $9x^2 + 4y^2 = 36$, $z = 0$; y-axis.

7. $z = e^x$, $y = 0$; x-axis.   **8.** $z = \cos x$, $y = 0$; x-axis.

9. $z = \cos x$, $y = 0$; z-axis.   **10.** $y^2 = x^3$, $z = 0$; x-axis.

11. $y = x^3$, $z = 0$; x-axis.   **12.** $(x-2a)^2 + z^2 = a^2$, $y = 0$; z-axis.

16.4 The Sphere. A sphere is the locus of a point in space that moves so that its distance from a fixed point, the center, is equal to a constant, the radius.

It follows at once from this definition that the equation of a sphere with center at the point C (h, k, l) and radius a is

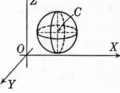

Fig. 16.3

$$(x - h)^2 + (y - k)^2 + (z - l)^2 = a^2. \quad (4)$$

For, the left-hand member of this equation is the square of the distance of the point (x, y, z) on the locus from the center $C(h, k, l)$ and this is equal to the square of the radius.

In particular, if the center of the sphere is at the origin, equation (4) reduces to the simple form

$$x^2 + y^2 + z^2 = a^2. \quad (5)$$

The equation

$$x^2 + y^2 + z^2 + Gx + Hy + Iz + K = 0 \quad (6)$$

is called the **general form** of the equation of the sphere.

To determine the center and radius of the sphere defined by equation (6), we complete the square of the terms in x, y, and z, separately, and write the equation in the form

$$\left(x + \frac{G}{2}\right)^2 + \left(y + \frac{H}{2}\right)^2 + \left(z + \frac{I}{2}\right)^2 = \frac{G^2 + H^2 + I^2 - 4K}{4}.$$

By comparing this equation with (4), we find that its locus is a sphere with center $\left(-\dfrac{G}{2}, -\dfrac{H}{2}, -\dfrac{I}{2}\right)$

and radius $a = \tfrac{1}{2}\sqrt{G^2 + H^2 + I^2 - 4K}.$

The sphere defined by equation (6) is thus a *real sphere*, a *point sphere*, or an *imaginary sphere*, according as

$$G^2 + H^2 + I^2 - 4K \gtreqless 0.$$

EXERCISES

Write the equation of the sphere having the given point as center and the given radius:

1. $(2, 3, 6)$, $a = 7$. **2.** $(14, -2, 5)$, $a = 16$.

3. $(-5, 7, 1)$, $a = 8$. **4.** $(5, -6, 4)$, $a = 6$.

Find the coördinates of the center and the radius of the given sphere:

5. $x^2 + y^2 + z^2 - 2x + 6y - 8z + 1 = 0$.

6. $x^2 + y^2 + z^2 + 10x + 4y + 2z - 19 = 0$.

7. $x^2 + y^2 + z^2 + 8x - 2y - 6z + 30 = 0$.

8. $x^2 + y^2 + z^2 - 2x - 6y + 2z + 11 = 0$.

Find the equation of the sphere, given:

9. Center $(3, -1, -5)$, tangent to the xy-plane.

10. Tangent to all the coördinate planes, lying in the first octant, center in the plane $3x + 2y - z - 8 = 0$.

11. Having $(4, 3, -5)$ and $(10, 1, -1)$ as ends of a diameter.

12. Center at $(-2, 4, 3)$, passing through $(2, 1, 7)$.

13. With center at $(4, 7, 2)$ and tangent to the plane $2x - y + 2z + 4 = 0$.

14. Passing through $(-1, 3, 6)$ and $(1, 5, -2)$; center on the line $x - 2y + 3z + 1 = 0$, $3x + y - 2z - 6 = 0$.

15. Passing through the points $(3, 2, -1)$, $(0, 1, -1)$, $(2, 5, 3)$ and $(3, 5, 2)$.

16. Show that, for all values of θ and ϕ, the point $x = a \sin \phi \cos \theta$, $y = a \sin \phi \sin \theta$, $z = a \cos \phi$ lies on the sphere $x^2 + y^2 + z^2 = a^2$.

Note. The above three equations are called the *parametric equations* of the given sphere in terms of the parameters θ and ϕ.

16.5 Quadric Surfaces. The locus of an equation of the second degree in x, y, and z, that is, an equation of the form

$$Ax^2 + By^2 + Cz^2 + Dyz + Ezx + Fxy + Gx + Hy + Iz + K = 0,$$

wherein A, B, C, D, E, and F are not all zero, is called a *quadric surface*.

It is seen at once from equation (6) that a sphere is a quadric surface. In the following articles, we shall state the standard forms of the equations of the most important quadric surfaces other than the sphere, and point out a few of the outstanding properties of these surfaces.

16.6 The Ellipsoid. The locus of the equation

$$\frac{x^2}{a^2} + \frac{y^2}{b^2} + \frac{z^2}{c^2} = 1$$

is an *ellipsoid*.

This surface is symmetric with respect to each of the coördinate planes since, if we change the sign of any one of the coördinates,

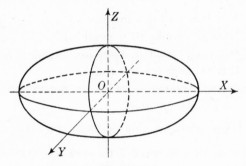

Fig. 16.4

we do not change the equation. These planes are called the *principal planes* of the ellipsoid and their point of intersection, the origin, is its *center*.

The segments of the coördinate axes that lie inside the surface are the *axes* of the ellipsoid. By solving the equations of the axes as simultaneous with that of the surface, we find that the intercepts on the x-, y-, and z-axis are, respectively, $\pm a$, $\pm b$, and $\pm c$. If $a > b > c > 0$, these numbers are called the lengths of the *semi-major*, the *semi-mean*, and the *semi-minor axis*, respectively, of the ellipsoid.

The usual way to determine the form of a surface from its equation is to study the curves of section of the surface by a family of parallel planes. For the ellipsoid, we shall use the sections by planes perpendicular to the z-axis.

The equations of the section of the given ellipsoid by a plane $z = k$ are found, by putting $z = k$ in the equation and simplifying, to be

$$\frac{x^2}{a^2} + \frac{y^2}{b^2} = 1 - \frac{k^2}{c^2}, \quad z = k,$$

or, if $k \neq \pm c$,

$$\frac{x^2}{\frac{a^2}{c^2}(c^2 - k^2)} + \frac{y^2}{\frac{b^2}{c^2}(c^2 - k^2)} = 1, \quad z = k.$$

If $k^2 < c^2$, these are the equations of an ellipse of semi-axes $\frac{a}{c}\sqrt{c^2 - k^2}$ and $\frac{b}{c}\sqrt{c^2 - k^2}$. The largest ellipse of section is thus in the plane $z = 0$. As k increases in numerical value, the ellipse of section becomes smaller and shrinks to a point when $k^2 = c^2$. If $k^2 > c^2$, the ellipse is imaginary; that is, there are no points on the surface in any plane defined by such a value of k.

If $a = b > c$, the ellipsoid is called an **oblate spheroid** and, if $a > b = c$, it is a **prolate spheroid**.

Exercise 1. Discuss the sections of the ellipsoid by the planes $x = k$.

Exercise 2. Given that the surface of the earth is an oblate spheroid with equatorial semi-axes of 3963 miles and polar semi-axis of 3950 miles, choose a suitable set of axes and write the equation of this spheroid.

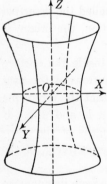

16.7 The Hyperboloid of One Sheet. The surface defined by the equation

$$\frac{x^2}{a^2} + \frac{y^2}{b^2} - \frac{z^2}{c^2} = 1$$

is a *hyperboloid of one sheet.*

This surface also has the coördinate planes as planes of symmetry (Why?), or *principal planes,* and the origin as *center.* It intersects the x-axis at $(\pm\, a, 0, 0)$ and the y-axis at $(0, \pm\, b, 0)$ but it has no point in common with the z-axis. (Why?)

Fig. 16.5

The section of this hyperboloid by the plane $z = k$ is the ellipse defined by the equations

$$\frac{x^2}{a^2} + \frac{y^2}{b^2} = 1 + \frac{k^2}{c^2}, \quad z = k.$$

This ellipse is smallest for $k = 0$ and increases indefinitely in size as the numerical value of k increases. The surface thus extends indefinitely far from the origin.

Exercise 1. Show that the sections of the hyperboloid of one sheet by the planes $x = k$, when $k \neq \pm a$, are hyperbolas. Locate, and find the lengths of, the transverse and conjugate axes. What are the curves of section by the planes $x = \pm a$?

Exercise 2. Discuss, as in Ex. 1, the sections of the hyperboloid of one sheet by the planes $y = k$.

16.8 The Hyperboloid of Two Sheets. This name is given to the locus of the equation

$$\frac{x^2}{a^2} - \frac{y^2}{b^2} - \frac{z^2}{c^2} = 1.$$

This surface has the coördinate planes as *principal planes* and the origin as *center*. Its x-intercepts are $\pm a$ but it does not meet either of the other coördinate axes.

The equation of its curve of section by the plane $x = k$ are

$$\frac{y^2}{b^2} + \frac{z^2}{c^2} = \frac{k^2}{a^2} - 1, \quad x = k.$$

If $k^2 < a^2$, this curve is an imaginary ellipse and has no points on it. If $k^2 = a^2$, the curve is a point ellipse and, if $k^2 > a^2$, the curve is a

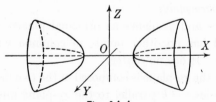

Fig. 16.6

real ellipse which increases indefinitely in size as k^2 increases indefinitely. The surface thus consists of two distinct parts which extend indefinitely far away from the yz-plane.

Exercise. Discuss the section of the hyperboloid of two sheets by the plane $y = k$ and by the plane $z = k$. Find the coördinates of the vertices and the foci and the equations of the asymptotes.

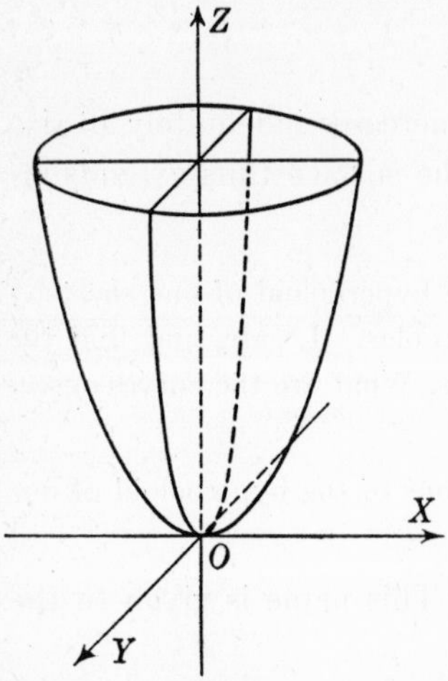

Fig. 16.7

16.9 The Elliptic Paraboloid. The locus of the equation

$$\frac{x^2}{a^2} + \frac{y^2}{b^2} = z$$

is an *elliptic paraboloid*.

The surface is symmetric with respect to the xz- and yz-planes but not with respect to the xy-plane. It has no center. It touches the xy-plane at the origin but does not extend below it.

The section of this surface by the plane $z = k$, when $k > 0$, is an ellipse whose semi-axes are $a\sqrt{k}$ and $b\sqrt{k}$. This ellipse thus increases indefinitely in size as k increases. The sections of the surface by planes perpendicular to the x-axis, or to the y-axis, are parabolas.

Exercise. Show that the latera recta of the parabolas of section of the elliptic paraboloid by the family of planes $y = k$ are equal.

16.10 The Hyperbolic Paraboloid. The surface

$$\frac{x^2}{a^2} - \frac{y^2}{b^2} = z$$

is a *hyperbolic paraboloid*.

It has the xz- and yz-planes as principal planes, passes through the origin, and has no other points in common with any of the coördinate axes. It has no center.

Its section by the xy-plane is composed of the two lines $y = \pm bx/a$, $z = 0$. The planes $z = k$ parallel to the xy-plane intersect it in hyperbolas that have their transverse axes parallel to the x-axis if $k > 0$ and parallel to the y-axis if $k < 0$. The planes $y = k$ intersect the surface in parabolas which are concave upward; the planes $x = k$, in parabolas which are concave downward.

If $a = b$, the surface is said to be a **rectangular hyperbolic paraboloid**. In this special case, the equation of the surface may be written in the form

$$x^2 - y^2 = a^2 z. \tag{7}$$

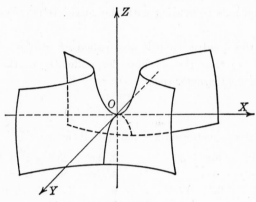

Fig. 16.8

If we now rotate the x- and y-axes, in their own plane, through an angle of $-45°$ by means of the equations (5), Art. 7.4, of a rotation of axes; that is, if we apply to x and y the transformation

$$x = \frac{x'}{\sqrt{2}} + \frac{y'}{\sqrt{2}}, \quad y = \frac{-x'}{\sqrt{2}} + \frac{y'}{\sqrt{2}}$$

equation (7) reduces to

$$2x'y' = a^2 z'. \tag{8}$$

In the applications of solid analytic geometry, the equation of the rectangular hyperbolic paraboloid is frequently encountered in this form.

16.11 The Quadric Cone. The surface defined by the equation

$$\frac{x^2}{a^2} + \frac{y^2}{b^2} = \frac{z^2}{c^2}$$

is symmetric with respect to each of the coördinate planes. Its trace in the yz-plane consists of the two lines $y = \pm\, bz/c$, $x = 0$ and, in the

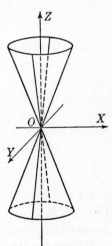

Fig. 16.9

xz-plane, of the two lines $x = \pm az/c$, $y = 0$. Its intersection with the xy-plane is a single point, the origin. The section of the surface by any plane $z = k$, parallel to the xy-plane is an ellipse the lengths of whose semi-axes, ak/c and bk/c, are proportional to the distance of the plane from the xy-plane. This surface is a cone with vertex at the origin and axis coinciding with the z-axis. It is called a **quadric cone.**

If $a \neq b$, the quadric cone is also called an *oblique circular cone* and if $a = b$, so that the sections perpendicular to the z-axis are circles, it is a *right circular cone.*

EXERCISES

Sketch the given quadric surface and state its name:

1. $9x^2 + 4y^2 + 36z^2 = 36$.	**2.** $4x^2 + 25y^2 - z^2 = 100$.
3. $16x^2 + 9y^2 = 144z$.	**4.** $2x^2 - 5y^2 - 3z^2 = 30$.
5. $3x^2 + 4y^2 + 6z^2 = 12$.	**6.** $x^2 + 2y^2 - 5z^2 + 10 = 0$.
7. $4x^2 + y^2 + 9z^2 = 36$.	**8.** $4x^2 + 9y^2 = z^2$.
9. $4x^2 - 9y^2 = 6z$.	**10.** $y^2 + 4z^2 = 2x$.
11. $4y^2 + 25z^2 = 25 + x^2$.	**12.** $xy = 2z$.
13. $9x^2 - z^2 = 4y^2$.	**14.** $25y^2 - 16z^2 = 400 - x^2$.
15. $16x^2 + 4y^2 = 9z^2$.	**16.** $3y^2 + z^2 = 6x$.
17. $4z^2 - 2x - 9y^2 = 0$.	**18.** $25 - 4x^2 - 4y^2 = 4z^2$.
19. $9z^2 - 4x^2 - 4y^2 + 16 = 0$.	**20.** $25 - 9x^2 + 4z^2 + y^2 = 0$.

16.12 Curves in Space. We have seen (Art. 15.9) that the position of a line in space is defined by considering simultaneously the equations of two planes that intersect in this line. Similarly, if a curve in space is the intersection of two surfaces, we take the equations of these two surfaces, considered simultaneously, as the equations defining this curve.

Thus, the first of the two equations

$$x^2 + y^2 + z^2 = 16, \qquad x + 2y + 3z = 6 \qquad (9)$$

is the equation of a sphere and the second, of a plane that intersects this sphere in a circle. The two equations taken simultaneously are, accordingly, the equations of this circle.

If, between the two equations of a curve, we eliminate successively x, y, and z, we obtain the equations of three cylinders (Art. 16.2) whose elements are perpendicular to the yz-, zx-, and xy-planes, respectively. These cylinders each contain the given curve and are called the **projecting cylinders** of the curve on these three planes.

The projecting cylinders of the circle (9), for example, on the coordinate planes are found, by solving the second equation for x, y, and z successively and substituting in the first equation, to be

$$(6 - 2y - 3z)^2 + y^2 + z^2 = 16$$

$$x^2 + \left(3 - \frac{x}{2} - \frac{3z}{2}\right)^2 + z^2 = 16$$

$$x^2 + y^2 + \left(2 - \frac{x}{3} - \frac{2y}{3}\right)^2 = 16.$$

16.13 Parametric Equations of a Curve in Space. A second way of defining a curve in space, which is often more convenient than the one given in Art. 16.12, is to express the coördinates of the points on it in terms of a parameter. Thus

$$x = f_1(t), \qquad y = f_2(t), \qquad z = f_3(t) \tag{10}$$

are the parametric equations of a curve in space in terms of the parameter t.

For example, we have seen (Art. 15.12) that the equations

$$x = x_1 + ak, \qquad y = y_1 + bk, \qquad z = z_1 + ck$$

are parametric equations, in terms of the parameter k, of the line through the point (x_1, y_1, z_1) having the direction numbers a, b, c.

Similarly, the equations

$$x = a \, (\sin \alpha \cos \phi - \cos \alpha \cos \beta \sin \phi)$$
$$y = a \, (\cos \alpha \cos \phi + \sin \alpha \cos \beta \sin \phi)$$
$$z = a \sin \beta \sin \phi,$$

where ϕ is the parameter, are parametric equations of a circle with center at the origin and radius a. For, by substituting the values of x, y, and z from the given equations in the following two equations, and simplifying, the student may readily verify that, for all values of ϕ, the points defined by the parametric equations lie in the plane

$$x \cos \alpha \sin \beta - y \sin \alpha \sin \beta + z \cos \beta = 0$$

and on the sphere

$$x^2 + y^2 + z^2 = a^2,$$

so that the locus of the given parametric equations is the circle of intersection of this plane with the sphere. Since the plane passes through the origin, which is the center of the sphere, the center of the circle is at the origin and its radius is a, the radius of the sphere.

The helix. As a third example, consider the curve defined by the parametric equations,

$$x = a \cos \phi \qquad y = a \sin \phi \qquad z = b\phi, \qquad (11)$$

where ϕ is the parameter. This curve is called a **helix**. It winds around, and ascends, the right circular cylinder $x^2 + y^2 = a^2$ like the thread on a bolt, or the handrailing on a circular staircase.

EXERCISES

Sketch the following curves and write the equations of their projecting cylinders on the coördinate planes:

1. $y^2 + z^2 = a^2$, $x + y = 3a$.   **2.** $x^2 + z^2 = a^2$, $x^2 + y^2 + z^2 = 5a^2$.

3. $x^2 + y^2 = az$, $z = 2x$.   **4.** $x^2 + z^2 = a^2$, $y^2 + z^2 = a^2$.

5. $x^2 + y^2 + z^2 = a^2$, $x^2 + y^2 = 2ax$.

6. $x^2 + y^2 + z^2 = 2a^2$, $x^2 + y^2 = az$.

7. Draw the graph of the helix $x = a \cos \phi$, $y = a \sin \phi$, $z = \phi$ from $\phi = -2\pi$ to $\phi = 2\pi$.

Sketch the following curves and find, for each curve, the equations of two surfaces that contain it:

8. $x = 5 - 6t$, $y = 2t$, $z = t^2$.

9. $x = a \cos \phi$, $y = a \sin \phi$, $z = 3a \sin \phi$.

10. $x = \dfrac{e^t + e^{-t}}{2}$, $y = \dfrac{e^t - e^{-t}}{2}$, $z = \dfrac{e^{2t} - e^{-2t}}{2}$.

11. $x = at$, $y = at^2$, $z = at^3$.

12. $x = a \cos \phi$, $y = b \sin \phi$, $z = c\phi$.

13. $x = \phi \cos \phi$, $y = \phi \sin \phi$, $z = a\phi$.

16.14 The Sketching of Solids Bounded by Surfaces. Frequently in applications of solid analytic geometry, particularly in calculus, it is necessary to sketch a particular solid bounded by a given set of surfaces. This means that at least some part of each of the given surfaces must be drawn on the same figure in such a way that the required solid shows up as clearly as possible. To do this one must always show all the parts of the curves of intersection of the bounding surfaces that constitute edges of the required solid. Additional clarity in the figure can usually be obtained by drawing traces of the bounding surfaces by appropriate planes parallel to the coördinate planes. If the required figure has traces in the coördinate planes themselves these traces should always be shown. Many times it is sufficient to draw some part of the required solid, (for example, the part in the first octant) and then to visualize the remaining part by means of symmetry. This process will be illustrated by means of examples.

Example 1. Sketch the solid bounded by $x^2 + 4y^2 = z$ and $z = 4$.

The first surface is an elliptic paraboloid which opens up along the z-axis. Its trace in the xy-plane is just the origin. Its trace in the xz-plane is the parabola whose equations are $y = 0$, and $x^2 = z$. Its trace in the yz-plane is the parabola whose equations are $x = 0$ and $4y^2 = z$. These parabolas are shown in Fig. 16.10a.

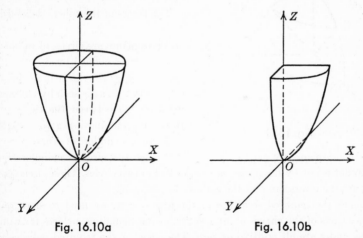

Fig. 16.10a   Fig. 16.10b

The plane $z = 4$ bounds the solid above. The curve defined by $z = 4$ and $x^2 + 4y^2 = z$ is an ellipse for it lies in the plane $z = 4$ and its projecting cylinder on the xy-plane is the elliptic cylinder $x^2 + 4y^2 = 4$. This ellipse is shown in the figure. Similarly, the planes $z = k$ for $0 < k < 4$ all intersect the elliptic paraboloid in ellipses.

This is an example of a problem where we could have shown only the portion in the first octant (Fig. 16.10b), for the remaining parts follow by symmetry. Observe that, though the paraboloid extends indefinitely far, only the part below the plane $z = 4$ is required in this figure.

In sketching solids bounded by surfaces, it is advisable first to sketch the figure lightly in pencil. This gives a good outline for the final sketch and makes it easy to correct errors. In drawing the final sketch the curves that form the edges of the required solid are usually shown in heavy lines. Dotted lines are used for edges and lines of the figure which cannot be seen but are visualized.

Example 2. Sketch the solid which lies in the first octant and is inside the sphere $x^2 + y^2 + z^2 = 25$ and inside the cone $x^2 + y^2 = z^2$.

The surface defined by $x^2 + y^2 = z^2$ is a right circular cone about the z-axis. Its trace in the xy-plane is the point circle defined by $x^2 + y^2 = 0$

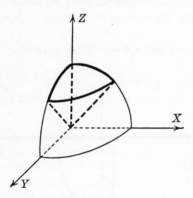

Fig. 16.11

and $z = 0$. The trace in the xz-plane is the pair of lines defined by $x^2 - z^2 = 0$ and $y = 0$. The trace in the yz-plane is the pair of lines defined by $y^2 - z^2 = 0$ and $x = 0$.

The traces of the sphere defined by $x^2 + y^2 + z^2 = 25$ in each of the co-ordinate planes are circles of radius 5.

The curves defined by $x^2 + y^2 = z^2$ and $x^2 + y^2 + z^2 = 25$ lie in the planes $z = \pm 5\sqrt{2}/2$, as is seen by eliminating x and y between the two equations. By eliminating z to get the projecting cylinder of these curves

on the xy-plane, we get $2x^2 + 2y^2 = 25$ which is a circular cylinder. This cylinder is cut by the planes $z = \pm 5\sqrt{2}/2$ in two circles. These circles constitute the intersection of the cone and the sphere.

Since the required solid lies in the first octant, we need to show only those parts of the curves of intersection of the bounding surfaces for which x, y, and z are all positive or zero. The edges of the required volume are shown by the heavier lines (Fig. 16.11).

Exercise. Show by symmetries that the entire volume inside both the sphere and the cone is in magnitude eight times that of the solid shown in Fig. 16.11.

Example 3. Sketch the solid in the first octant inside the surfaces defined by $x^2 + y^2 + z^2 = a^2$ and $x^2 + y^2 = ax$.

The traces of the sphere $x^2 + y^2 + z^2 = a^2$ in each of the coördinate planes are circles of radius a. Only the parts of these in the planes bounding the first octant are shown in Fig. 16.12.

By writing the equation of the surface defined by $x^2 + y^2 = ax$ in the form

$$(x - a/2)^2 + y^2 = a^2/4$$

we see that it is a circular cylinder with elements perpendicular to the xy-plane. Its trace in the xy-plane is a circle of radius $a/2$ and center at $(a/2, 0, 0)$. This circle is also the projection on the xy-plane of the curve of intersection of the cylinder and the sphere.

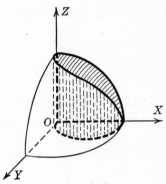

Fig. 16.12

In Fig. 16.12 the parts that lie in the first octant of the sections of the bounding cylinder and sphere by several planes parallel to the yz-plane are shown.

Exercise. Show by symmetries that the entire volume inside both the sphere and the cylinder is in magnitude four times that of the solid shown in Fig. 16.12.

EXERCISES

Sketch the solid bounded by the given surfaces:

1. $x^2 + y^2 = 4$, $z = 0$, $z = 4$.   2. $x^2 + y^2 = z^2$, $z = 4$.
3. $x^2 + y^2 = 9$, $z = 0$, $z = y$, $y \geqq 0$.
4. $9x^2 + 9y^2 = z^2$, $x + z = 7$.
5. $x^2 + y^2 = 4$, $z = 0$, $z = x + 2$.
6. $y^2 = x$, $z = 0$, $z = x$, $x = 5$.
7. $z^2 - 4x^2 + 9y^2 = 36$, $x = 0$, $x = 3$.
8. $y^2 + 2z^2 = 4x$, $x + y = 8$.
9. $4x^2 + 9y^2 = 36 - 9z$, $x = 0$.

Sketch the indicated part of the solid bounded by the given surfaces:

10. $x^2 + y^2 + z^2 = 25$, $z = 3$. The upper solid.
11. $x^2 + y^2 = 16$, $x^2 + y^2 + z^2 = 25$. Inside the cylinder and for which $y \geqq 0$ and $z \geqq 0$.
12. $x^2 + y^2 = 9z^2$, $x^2 + y^2 + z^2 = 160$. Inside the cone and for which $y \geqq 0$ and $z \geqq 0$.

13. $x^2 + y^2 = 25$, $y^2 + z^2 = 25$. In the first octant.

14. $x^2 + 4y^2 + 9z^2 = 36$, $x^2 + 4y^2 = 27z$. Inside the paraboloid and in the first octant.

15. $x^2 + y^2 = 4z$, $x^2 + y^2 = 8x$. In the first octant.

16. $y^2 + z = 4$, $x + y = 2$, $x = 0$, $z = 0$. In the first octant.

17. $y^2 + z^2 = x^2$, $x^2 + y^2 + z^2 = 10x$. Inside the cone and in the first octant.

18. $x^2 + y^2 = 4 - z$, $x^2 + y^2 = z^2$. Inside the cone and in the first octant.

16.15 Cylindrical Coördinates. In this article and the following one, we shall describe two systems of coördinates in space, each of

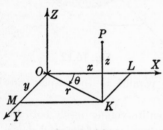

Fig. 16.13

which bears some resemblance to polar coördinates in the plane. Both of these systems have been found useful in the applications of analytic geometry, particularly in the study of surfaces. Many equations which arise in the physical sciences are more easily studied when they are written in one of these coördinate systems.

Let P be any point in space with rectangular coördinates (x, y, z) and let $K(x, y, 0)$ be the foot of the perpendicular from P on the xy-plane. Let (r, θ) be the polar coördinates in the xy-plane of the point K when O is taken as the origin and OX as the initial line. Then the three numbers (r, θ, z) are called the *cylindrical coördinates* of P.

From Art. 5.3, we have at once for the values of x, y, and z in terms of the cylindrical coördinates

$$x = r \cos \theta, \quad y = r \sin \theta, \quad z = z. \tag{12}$$

Similarly, for the values of r, θ, and z in terms of the rectangular coördinates of P, we have

$$r = \pm \sqrt{x^2 + y^2}, \quad \theta = \arctan \frac{y}{x}, \quad z = z, \tag{13}$$

where the quadrant in which the angle θ lies is to be determined by plotting the given point on the figure, as in Art. 5.3.

16.16 Spherical Coördinates. If the distance ρ of a point P from the origin is known, then P lies on a sphere with center at the origin and radius ρ. We have learned from the study of geography that the position of a point on the surface of a sphere can be determined by two angles (its longitude and latitude). The spherical coördinates of a point consist, accordingly, of a distance and two angles, which we shall define in the following way.

Let $P(x, y, z)$ be any point in space and let $K(x, y, 0)$ be the foot of the perpendicular from P on the xy-plane. Draw OP, OK, and KP. Let

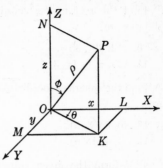

Fig. 16.14

$$\overline{OP} = \rho, \quad \text{angle } XOK = \theta, \quad \text{and} \quad \text{angle } ZOP = \phi.$$

Then (ρ, θ, ϕ) are the **spherical coördinates** of P. We call ρ the **radius vector**, θ, the **longitude**, and ϕ, the **co-latitude** of P.

To find the values of (x, y, z) in terms of (ρ, θ, ϕ), we note that angle $KOP = 90° - \phi$, so that $\overline{OK} = \rho \cos KOP = \rho \sin \phi$.

From the right triangles OLK and ONP, we now have

$$x = \rho \sin \phi \cos \theta, \qquad y = \rho \sin \phi \sin \theta, \qquad z = \rho \cos \phi, \qquad (14)$$

as the equations expressing x, y, and z in terms of ρ, θ, and ϕ.

If we solve these equations for ρ, θ, and ϕ, we obtain

$$\rho = \sqrt{x^2 + y^2 + z^2}, \quad \theta = \arctan \frac{y}{x}, \quad \phi = \arccos \frac{z}{\sqrt{x^2 + y^2 + z^2}} \qquad (15)$$

as the equations expressing ρ, θ, and ϕ in terms of x, y, and z.

EXERCISES

Find the rectangular coördinates of the point whose cylindrical coördinates are:

   1. $(16, 120°, 5)$.   **2.** $(12, 315°, -2)$.

   3. $(4, \pi/3, 3)$.   **4.** $(16, \pi/6, 11)$.

Find the cylindrical coördinates of the point whose rectangular coördinates are:

   5. $(3, 3, -2)$.   **6.** $(-2\sqrt{3}, 2, 5)$.   **7.** $(-3, -\sqrt{3}, -8)$.

   8. $(0, 7, 2)$.

Find the rectangular coördinates of the point whose spherical coördinates are:

9. $(12, 30°, 30°)$.   **10.** $(16, 120°, 30°)$.
11. $(24, \pi/6, 4\pi/3)$.   **12.** $(14, \pi/3, \pi/2)$.

Find the spherical coördinates of the point whose rectangular coördinates are:

13. $(0, 3\sqrt{3}, 3)$.   **14.** $(-5\sqrt{3}, 5, 0)$.
15. $(4, 4, 4\sqrt{6})$.   **16.** $(-1, -1, -1)$.

Transform the given equation from cylindrical to rectangular coördinates. Sketch the surface:

17. $r = 9$.   **18.** $\theta = 135°$.   **19.** $r = 4\cos\theta$.   **20.** $r = 2z$.

Transform the given equation from spherical to rectangular coördinates. Sketch the surface:

21. $\rho = 5$.   **22.** $\phi = 60°$.   **23.** $\rho\sin\phi\sin\theta + 2 = 0$.
24. $\rho = 4\cos\phi$.

Write each of the following equations in cylindrical and in spherical coördinates. Sketch the surface:

25. $x^2 + y^2 + z^2 = 36$.   **26.** $x^2 + y^2 = 49$.
27. $9x^2 + 9y^2 + 4z^2 = 25$.   **28.** $y = 6$.
29. $x^2 + y^2 = 4z^2$.   **30.** $4x^2 + 4y^2 - 9z^2 = 36$.
31. $x^2 + y^2 = 4x$.   **32.** $xy = z$.

33. Find the direction cosines of the line from the origin to the point whose spherical coördinates are (ρ, θ, ϕ).

34. Write the equations expressing the cylindrical in terms of the spherical coördinates.

35. Derive a formula for the distance between two points whose spherical coördinates are $(\rho_1, \theta_1, \phi_1)$ and $(\rho_2, \theta_2, \phi_2)$.

MISCELLANEOUS EXERCISES

Sketch the following surfaces and state their names:

1. $x = 1$.   **2.** $xy = 1$.
3. $x^2 - z^2 = 4$.   **4.** $z^2 + 4y^2 = 4$.
5. $y^2 = z + 4$.   **6.** $y^2 - z^2 = 0$.
7. $4x^2 - 4y^2 = 16 + z^2$.   **8.** $z^2 - 4x^2 = 9y^2$.
9. $z + x^2 = 4y^2$.   **10.** $z^2 + 16y^2 = 9x^2 - 9$.

Sketch the following surfaces whose equations are in cylindrical coördinates:

11. $r = a \sin \theta$.   **12.** $r^2 \cos 2\theta = a^2$.

13. $r = a(1 - \sin \theta)$.   **14.** $r^2 + 4z^2 = 16$.

15. $r^2 = 4z$.   **16.** $r^2 - z^2 = 25$.

17. Find the equation of the tangent plane to the sphere $x^2 + y^2 + z^2 = 50$ at the point $(4, -3, 5)$.

18. Find the equation of the right circular cylinder whose axis is the line $x = -6, y = 8$ and whose radius is 10.

The following quadric surfaces have their vertices or centers at points other than the origin. State their names and sketch them.

19. $(x - 2)^2 + (y - 4)^2 = (z + 3)^2$.

20. $(x + 3)^2 + 4(y - 2)^2 + 9(z + 1)^2 = 36$.

21. $x^2 + 4y^2 = z - 4$.

22. $(y - 4)^2 - (z + 2)^2 = (x - 1)^2 + 4$.

23. $9(z - 1)^2 + 4(x + 2)^2 = 4(y - 3)^2 + 36$.

24. $x^2 + 4y^2 - 4x + 8y = 8z$.

By eliminating the parameters θ and ϕ from the three given parametric equations of a surface, find the rectangular equation of the surface and state the name of the surface:

25. $x = a \sin \phi \cos \theta$, $y = b \sin \phi \sin \theta$, $z = c \cos \phi$.

26. $x = a \sec \phi \cos \theta$, $y = b \sec \phi \sin \theta$, $z = c \tan \phi$.

27. $x = a \tan \phi \cos \theta$, $y = b \tan \phi \sin \theta$, $z = c \sec \phi$.

28. $x = a \sin \phi \cos \theta$, $y = b \sin \phi \sin \theta$, $z = c \sin^2 \phi$.

29. Show that, for any given value of k, the line of intersection (a) of the planes $\dfrac{x}{a} - \dfrac{y}{b} = k$, $z = k\left(\dfrac{x}{a} + \dfrac{y}{b}\right)$, and (b) of the planes $\dfrac{x}{a} + \dfrac{y}{b} = k$, $z = k\left(\dfrac{x}{a} - \dfrac{y}{b}\right)$ lies on the hyperbolic paraboloid $\dfrac{x^2}{a^2} - \dfrac{y^2}{b^2} = z$.

30. Show that, for any given value of k, the line of intersection (a) of the planes $\dfrac{x}{a} - \dfrac{z}{c} = k\left(1 + \dfrac{y}{b}\right)$, $1 - \dfrac{y}{b} = k\left(\dfrac{x}{a} + \dfrac{z}{c}\right)$, and (b) of the planes $\dfrac{x}{a} - \dfrac{z}{c} = k\left(1 - \dfrac{y}{b}\right)$, $1 + \dfrac{y}{b} = k\left(\dfrac{x}{a} + \dfrac{z}{c}\right)$ lies on the hyperboloid of one sheet $\dfrac{x^2}{a^2} + \dfrac{y^2}{b^2} - \dfrac{z^2}{c^2} = 1$.

Note. The family of lines defined by the two equations in Ex. 29a, 29b, 30a, or 30b is called a *regulus*.

TABLES

I. Four-place Table of Logarithms 268
II. Four-place Table of Natural Trigonometric Functions 270
III. Exact Values of the Trigonometric Functions of Certain Angles 271
IV. Three-place Table of Square Roots 271
V. Three-place Table of Exponential Functions 272

TABLE I. FOUR–PLACE LOGARITHMS

N	0	1	2	3	4	5	6	7	8	9
10	0000	0043	0086	0128	0170	0212	0253	0294	0334	0374
11	0414	0453	0492	0531	0569	0607	0645	0682	0719	0755
12	0792	0828	0864	0899	0934	0969	1004	1038	1072	1106
13	1139	1173	1206	1239	1271	1303	1335	1367	1399	1430
14	1461	1492	1523	1553	1584	1614	1644	1673	1703	1732
15	1761	1790	1818	1847	1875	1903	1931	1959	1987	2014
16	2041	2068	2095	2122	2148	2175	2201	2227	2253	2279
17	2304	2330	2355	2380	2405	2430	2455	2480	2504	2529
18	2553	2577	2601	2625	2648	2672	2695	2718	2742	2765
19	2788	2810	2833	2856	2878	2900	2923	2945	2967	2989
20	3010	3032	3054	3075	3096	3118	3139	3160	3181	3201
21	3222	3243	3263	3284	3304	3324	3345	3365	3385	3404
22	3424	3444	3464	3483	3502	3522	3541	3560	3579	3598
23	3617	3636	3655	3674	3692	3711	3729	3747	3766	3784
24	3802	3820	3838	3856	3874	3892	3909	3927	3945	3962
25	3979	3997	4014	4031	4048	4065	4082	4099	4116	4133
26	4150	4166	4183	4200	4216	4232	4249	4265	4281	4298
27	4314	4330	4346	4362	4378	4393	4409	4425	4440	4456
28	4472	4487	4502	4518	4533	4548	4564	4579	4594	4609
29	4624	4639	4654	4669	4683	4698	4713	4728	4742	4757
30	4771	4786	4800	4814	4829	4843	4857	4871	4886	4900
31	4914	4928	4942	4955	4969	4983	4997	5011	5024	5038
32	5051	5065	5079	5092	5105	5119	5132	5145	5159	5172
33	5185	5198	5211	5224	5237	5250	5263	5276	5289	5302
34	5315	5328	5340	5353	5366	5378	5391	5403	5416	5428
35	5441	5453	5465	5478	5490	5502	5514	5527	5539	5551
36	5563	5575	5587	5599	5611	5623	5635	5647	5658	5670
37	5682	5694	5705	5717	5729	5740	5752	5763	5775	5786
38	5798	5809	5821	5832	5843	5855	5866	5877	5888	5899
39	5911	5922	5933	5944	5955	5966	5977	5988	5999	6010
40	6021	6031	6042	6053	6064	6075	6085	6096	6107	6117
41	6128	6138	6149	6160	6170	6180	6191	6201	6212	6222
42	6232	6243	6253	6263	6274	6284	6294	6304	6314	6325
43	6335	6345	6355	6365	6375	6385	6395	6405	6415	6425
44	6435	6444	6454	6464	6474	6484	6493	6503	6513	6522
45	6532	6542	6551	6561	6571	6580	6590	6599	6609	6618
46	6628	6637	6646	6656	6665	6675	6684	6693	6702	6712
47	6721	6730	6739	6749	6758	6767	6776	6785	6794	6803
48	6812	6821	6830	6839	6848	6857	6866	6875	6884	6893
49	6902	6911	6920	6928	6937	6946	6955	6964	6972	6981
50	6990	6998	7007	7016	7024	7033	7042	7050	7059	7067
51	7076	7084	7093	7101	7110	7118	7126	7135	7143	7152
52	7160	7168	7177	7185	7193	7202	7210	7218	7226	7235
53	7243	7251	7259	7267	7275	7284	7292	7300	7308	7316
54	7324	7332	7340	7348	7356	7364	7372	7380	7388	7396

TABLE I. FOUR-PLACE LOGARITHMS *Continued*

N	0	1	2	3	4	5	6	7	8	9
55	7404	7412	7419	7427	7435	7443	7451	7459	7466	7474
56	7482	7490	7497	7505	7513	7520	7528	7536	7543	7551
57	7559	7566	7574	7582	7589	7597	7604	7612	7619	7627
58	7634	7642	7649	7657	7664	7672	7679	7686	7694	7701
59	7709	7716	7723	7731	7738	7745	7752	7760	7767	7774
60	7782	7789	7796	7803	7810	7818	7825	7832	7839	7846
61	7853	7860	7868	7875	7882	7889	7896	7903	7910	7917
62	7924	7931	7938	7945	7952	7959	7966	7973	7980	7987
63	7993	8000	8007	8014	8021	8028	8035	8041	8048	8055
64	8062	8069	8075	8082	8089	8096	8102	8109	8116	8122
65	8129	8136	8142	8149	8156	8162	8169	8176	8182	8189
66	8195	8202	8209	8215	8222	8228	8235	8241	8248	8254
67	8261	8267	8274	8280	8287	8293	8299	8306	8312	8319
68	8325	8331	8338	8344	8351	8357	8363	8370	8376	8382
69	8388	8395	8401	8407	8414	8420	8426	8432	8439	8445
70	8451	8457	8463	8470	8476	8482	8488	8494	8500	8506
71	8513	8519	8525	8531	8537	8543	8549	8555	8561	8567
72	8573	8579	8585	8591	8597	8603	8609	8615	8621	8627
73	8633	8639	8645	8651	8657	8663	8669	8675	8681	8686
74	8692	8698	8704	8710	8716	8722	8727	8733	8739	8745
75	8751	8756	8762	8768	8774	8779	8785	8791	8797	8802
76	8808	8814	8820	8825	8831	8837	8842	8848	8854	8859
77	8865	8871	8876	8882	8887	8893	8899	8904	8910	8915
78	8921	8927	8932	8938	8943	8949	8954	8960	8965	8971
79	8976	8982	8987	8993	8998	9004	9009	9015	9020	9025
80	9031	9036	9042	9047	9053	9058	9063	9069	9074	9079
81	9085	9090	9096	9101	9106	9112	9117	9122	9128	9133
82	9138	9143	9149	9154	9159	9165	9170	9175	9180	9186
83	9191	9196	9201	9206	9212	9217	9222	9227	9232	9238
84	9243	9248	9253	9258	9263	9269	9274	9279	9284	9289
85	9294	9299	9304	9309	9315	9320	9325	9330	9335	9340
86	9345	9350	9355	9360	9365	9370	9375	9380	9385	9390
87	9395	9400	9405	9410	9415	9420	9425	9430	9435	9440
88	9445	9450	9455	9460	9465	9469	9474	9479	9484	9489
89	9494	9499	9504	9509	9513	9518	9523	9528	9533	9538
90	9542	9547	9552	9557	9562	9566	9571	9576	9581	9586
91	9590	9595	9600	9605	9609	9614	9619	9624	9628	9633
92	9638	9643	9647	9652	9657	9661	9666	9671	9675	9680
93	9685	9689	9694	9699	9703	9708	9713	9717	9722	9727
94	9731	9736	9741	9745	9750	9754	9759	9763	9768	9773
95	9777	9782	9786	9791	9795	9800	9805	9809	9814	9818
96	9823	9827	9832	9836	9841	9845	9850	9854	9859	9863
97	9868	9872	9877	9881	9886	9890	9894	9899	9903	9908
98	9912	9917	9921	9926	9930	9934	9939	9943	9948	9952
99	9956	9961	9965	9969	9974	9978	9983	9987	9991	9996

TABLE II. NATURAL TRIGONOMETRIC FUNCTIONS

Radians	Degrees	Sine	Tangent	Cotangent	Cosine		
.0000	0	.0000	.0000	——	1.0000	90	1.5708
.0175	1	.0175	.0175	57.290	.9998	89	1.5533
.0349	2	.0349	.0349	28.636	.9994	88	1.5359
.0524	3	.0523	.0524	19.081	.9986	87	1.5184
.0698	4	.0698	.0699	14.301	.9976	86	1.5010
.0873	5	.0872	.0875	11.430	.9962	85	1.4835
.1047	6	.1045	.1051	9.5144	.9945	84	1.4661
.1222	7	.1219	.1228	8.1443	.9925	83	1.4486
.1396	8	.1392	.1405	7.1154	.9903	82	1.4312
.1571	9	.1564	.1584	6.3138	.9877	81	1.4137
.1745	10	.1736	.1763	5.6713	.9848	80	1.3963
.1920	11	.1908	.1944	5.1446	.9816	79	1.3788
.2094	12	.2079	.2126	4.7046	.9781	78	1.3614
.2269	13	.2250	.2309	4.3315	.9744	77	1.3439
.2443	14	.2419	.2493	4.0108	.9703	76	1.3265
.2618	15	.2588	.2679	3.7321	.9659	75	1.3090
.2793	16	.2756	.2867	3.4874	.9613	74	1.2915
.2967	17	.2924	.3057	3.2709	.9563	73	1.2741
.3142	18	.3090	.3249	3.0777	.9511	72	1.2566
.3316	19	.3256	.3443	2.9042	.9455	71	1.2392
.3491	20	.3420	.3640	2.7475	.9397	70	1.2217
.3665	21	.3584	.3839	2.6051	.9336	69	1.2043
.3840	22	.3746	.4040	2.4751	.9272	68	1.1868
.4014	23	.3907	.4245	2.3559	.9205	67	1.1694
.4189	24	.4067	.4452	2.2460	.9135	66	1.1519
.4363	25	.4226	.4663	2.1445	.9063	65	1.1345
.4538	26	.4384	.4877	2.0503	.8988	64	1.1170
.4712	27	.4540	.5095	1.9626	.8910	63	1.0996
.4887	28	.4695	.5317	1.8807	.8829	62	1.0821
.5061	29	.4848	.5543	1.8040	.8746	61	1.0647
.5236	30	.5000	.5774	1.7321	.8660	60	1.0472
.5411	31	.5150	.6009	1.6643	.8572	59	1.0297
.5585	32	.5299	.6249	1.6003	.8480	58	1.0123
.5760	33	.5446	.6494	1.5399	.8387	57	.9948
.5934	34	.5592	.6745	1.4826	.8290	56	.9774
.6109	35	.5736	.7002	1.4281	.8192	55	.9599
.6283	36	.5878	.7265	1.3764	.8090	54	.9425
.6458	37	.6018	.7536	1.3270	.7986	53	.9250
.6632	38	.6157	.7813	1.2799	.7880	52	.9076
.6807	39	.6293	.8098	1.2349	.7771	51	.8901
.6981	40	.6428	.8391	1.1918	.7660	50	.8727
.7156	41	.6561	.8693	1.1504	.7547	49	.8552
.7330	42	.6691	.9004	1.1106	.7431	48	.8378
.7505	43	.6820	.9325	1.0724	.7314	47	.8203
.7679	44	.6947	.9657	1.0355	.7193	46	.8029
.7854	45	.7071	1.0000	1.0000	.7071	45	.7854
		Cosine	Cotangent	Tangent	Sine	Degrees	Radians

270

TABLE III. EXACT VALUES OF TRIGONOMETRIC FUNCTIONS OF CERTAIN ANGLES

Radians	Degrees	Sine	Cosine	Tangent	Cotangent	Secant	Cosecant
0	0	0	1	0	——	1	——
$\frac{1}{6}\pi$	30	$\frac{1}{2}$	$\frac{1}{2}\sqrt{3}$	$\frac{1}{3}\sqrt{3}$	$\sqrt{3}$	$\frac{2}{3}\sqrt{3}$	2
$\frac{1}{4}\pi$	45	$\frac{1}{2}\sqrt{2}$	$\frac{1}{2}\sqrt{2}$	1	1	$\sqrt{2}$	$\sqrt{2}$
$\frac{1}{3}\pi$	60	$\frac{1}{2}\sqrt{3}$	$\frac{1}{2}$	$\sqrt{3}$	$\frac{1}{3}\sqrt{3}$	2	$\frac{2}{3}\sqrt{3}$
$\frac{1}{2}\pi$	90	1	0	——	0	——	1
$\frac{2}{3}\pi$	120	$\frac{1}{2}\sqrt{3}$	$-\frac{1}{2}$	$-\sqrt{3}$	$-\frac{1}{3}\sqrt{3}$	-2	$\frac{2}{3}\sqrt{3}$
$\frac{3}{4}\pi$	135	$\frac{1}{2}\sqrt{2}$	$-\frac{1}{2}\sqrt{2}$	-1	-1	$-\sqrt{2}$	$\sqrt{2}$
$\frac{5}{6}\pi$	150	$\frac{1}{2}$	$-\frac{1}{2}\sqrt{3}$	$-\frac{1}{3}\sqrt{3}$	$-\sqrt{3}$	$-\frac{2}{3}\sqrt{3}$	2
π	180	0	-1	0	——	-1	——

TABLE IV. SQUARE ROOTS

N	0	1	2	3	4	5	6	7	8	9
0	0.00	1.00	1.41	1.73	2.00	2.24	2.45	2.65	2.83	3.00
1	3.16	3.32	3.46	3.61	3.74	3.87	4.00	4.12	4.24	4.36
2	4.47	4.58	4.69	4.80	4.90	5.00	5.10	5.20	5.29	5.39
3	5.48	5.57	5.66	5.74	5.83	5.92	6.00	6.08	6.16	6.24
4	6.32	6.40	6.48	6.56	6.63	6.71	6.78	6.86	6.93	7.00
5	7.07	7.14	7.21	7.28	7.35	7.42	7.48	7.55	7.62	7.68
6	7.75	7.81	7.87	7.94	8.00	8.06	8.12	8.19	8.25	8.31
7	8.37	8.43	8.49	8.54	8.60	8.66	8.72	8.77	8.83	8.89
8	8.94	9.00	9.06	9.11	9.17	9.22	9.27	9.33	9.38	9.43
9	9.49	9.54	9.59	9.64	9.70	9.75	9.80	9.85	9.90	9.95

TABLE V. EXPONENTIAL FUNCTIONS

x	e^x	e^{-x}	x	e^x	e^{-x}
0.00	1.00	1.000	0.5	1.65	.607
0.01	1.01	0.990	0.6	1.82	.549
0.02	1.02	.980	0.7	2.01	.497
0.03	1.03	.970	0.8	2.23	.449
0.04	1.04	.961	0.9	2.46	.407
0.05	1.05	.951	1.0	2.72	.368
0.06	1.06	.942	1.1	3.00	.333
0.07	1.07	.932	1.2	3.32	.301
0.08	1.08	.923	1.3	3.67	.273
0.09	1.09	.914	1.4	4.06	.247
0.10	1.11	.905	1.5	4.48	.223
0.11	1.12	.896	1.6	4.95	.202
0.12	1.13	.887	1.7	5.47	.183
0.13	1.14	.878	1.8	6.05	.165
0.14	1.15	.869	1.9	6.69	.150
0.15	1.16	.861	2.0	7.39	.135
0.16	1.17	.852	2.1	8.17	.122
0.17	1.19	.844	2.2	9.03	.111
0.18	1.20	.835	2.3	9.97	.100
0.19	1.21	.827	2.4	11.0	.0907
0.20	1.22	.819	2.5	12.2	.0821
0.21	1.23	.811	2.6	13.5	.0743
0.22	1.25	.803	2.7	14.9	.0672
0.23	1.26	.795	2.8	16.4	.0608
0.24	1.27	.787	2.9	18.2	.0550
0.25	1.28	.779	3.0	20.1	.0498
0.26	1.30	.771	3.1	22.2	.0450
0.27	1.31	.763	3.2	24.5	.0408
0.28	1.32	.756	3.3	27.1	.0369
0.29	1.34	.748	3.4	30.0	.0334
0.30	1.35	.741	3.5	33.1	.0302
0.31	1.36	.733	3.6	36.6	.0273
0.32	1.38	.726	3.7	40.4	.0247
0.33	1.39	.719	3.8	44.7	.0224
0.34	1.40	.712	3.9	49.4	.0202
0.35	1.42	.705	4.0	54.6	.0183
0.36	1.43	.698	4.1	60.3	.0166
0.37	1.45	.691	4.2	66.7	.0150
0.38	1.46	.684	4.3	73.7	.0136
0.39	1.48	.677	4.4	81.5	.0123
0.40	1.49	.670	5.0	148.4	.00674
0.41	1.51	.664	6.0	403.4	.00248
0.42	1.52	.657	7.0	1096.6	.000912
0.43	1.54	.651	8.0	2981.0	.000335
0.44	1.55	.644	9.0	8103.1	.000123
0.45	1.57	.638	10.0	22026.5	.000045

Answers to

ODD-NUMBERED EXERCISES

(The answers to certain exercises have been omitted intentionally.)

Review Exercises, Page xxi

1. (a) $\frac{11}{12}$; (b) $\frac{xy - 3y + 2x^2}{x^2 y}$; (c) $\frac{2y + 3}{x^2 - y^2}$; (d) $\frac{2x - 1}{x - 1}$.

3. (a) $\frac{3 + \sqrt{-31}}{4}, \frac{3 - \sqrt{-31}}{4}$; (b) 3, 3; (c) $\frac{-3 + \sqrt{15}}{3}, \frac{-3 - \sqrt{15}}{3}$;

(d) $\frac{-2 + \sqrt{19}}{3}, \frac{-2 - \sqrt{19}}{3}$.

5. (a) $x = 0, y = -1; x = -2, y = -2$; (b) $x = 0, y = -2; x = 0, y = -2$;
(c) $x = 2, y = 3; x = -2, y = 3; x = -2, y = -3; x = 2, y = -3$;
(d) $x = 3, y = 4; x = -3, y = 4; x = -3, y = -4; x = 3, y = -4$.

7. (a) $x = \frac{24}{11}, y = \frac{8}{11}$; (b) $x = \frac{7}{44}, y = \frac{13}{44}$; (c) $x = 3, y = 5, z = -7$;
(d) $x = -1, y = -2, z = -3$.

9. (a) $\log_{10} 100 = 2$; (b) $\log_2 16 = 4$; (c) $\log_{36} 6 = \frac{1}{2}$; (d) $\log_{49} 7 = \frac{1}{2}$;
(e) $\log_8 4 = \frac{2}{3}$; (f) $\log_{81} \frac{1}{3} = -0.25$.

11. (a) $\frac{1}{3} \log_a 16 - \frac{1}{4} \log_a 9 - \frac{3}{2} \log_a 7$; (b) $4 \log_a 3 - 3 \log_a 5$;
(c) $\frac{1}{2} \log_a 5 - 3 \log_a 2 - \frac{1}{3} \log_a 7$.

13. $-4, -1, -10, -2$.   **15.** $2y^2 - 3, -2y - 1, 2/y - 3$.

17. $V = e^3$.   **19.** $A = \pi r^2$.

21. (a) $135°$; (b) $144°$; (c) $143.2°$; (d) $-171.9°$; (e) $600°$.

23. (a) 13 ft.; (b) 2.618 ft.

25. (a) $\sin \theta = \sqrt{7}/4, \tan \theta = -\sqrt{7}/3$; (b) $\sin \theta = -\sqrt{7}/4, \tan \theta = \sqrt{7}/3$.

27. (a) $\pi/2 + 2n\pi, 7\pi/6 + 2n\pi, 11\pi/6 + 2n\pi$; (b) $3\pi/2 + 2n\pi, \pi/6 + 2n\pi$,
$5\pi/6 + 2n\pi$; (c) $\pi/2 + n\pi, \pi/6 + 2n\pi, 5\pi/6 + 2n\pi$; (d) $n\pi, \pi/6 + n\pi$,
$5\pi/6 + n\pi$; (e) $\pi/2 + n\pi$, Arc $\sin \frac{3}{5} + (2n + 1)\pi$; (f) $\pi/3 + n\pi, 2\pi/3 + n\pi$.

Exercises, Page 5

5. 24.   **7.** 63.   **9.** 10.   **11.** $(3, 3), (-3, 3), (-3, -3), (3, -3)$.   **13.** y-axis.
15. (a) Third; (b) second.   **17.** 2.

Exercises, Page 11

1. 0, 0.   **3.** 3, 6.   **5.** $x = 8$.   **7.** 5, 2.   **9.** $-4, -3$.

Exercises, Page 14

1. $(3, 2)$.   **3.** $(3, 1)$.   **5.** $(-1, 1)$.   **7.** $(3, 8), (-4, -13)$.
9. $(-2, 4), (-4, -2)$.   **11.** $(5, 4), (-5, -4), (4, 5), (-4, -5)$.

Exercises, Page 17

1. 6.   **3.** 5.   **5.** -8.   **7.** 5.   **9.** -3.
11. -6.   **13.** $4, -3$.   **15.** $-6, 5$.   **17.** $-7, 3$.   **19.** 5, 13.

Exercises, Page 19

1. 5.   **3.** 10.   **5.** $\sqrt{65}$.   **7.** $\sqrt{34}$, $\sqrt{53}$, $\sqrt{5}$.
9. $4\sqrt{5}$, $\sqrt{34}$, $\sqrt{58}$. **19.** 5.   **21.** -10.   **23.** (2, 5).   **25.** $2x - 3y - 4 = 0$.

Exercises, Page 22

1. (3, 2).   **3.** $(-1, -1)$, (3, 2), (7, 5).   **5.** (1, 9).
7. $(3, -3)$, $(6, -1)$, (4, 0); $\sqrt{41}$, $\sqrt{26}$, $\sqrt{17}$.   **9.** 2 : 3.

Exercises, Page 25

1. $\sqrt{3}/3$. **3.** 0.7536. **5.** 1. **7.** $-\sqrt{3}/3$. **9.** 45°. **11.** 120°. **13.** 12°.
15. 106°.   **17.** $\frac{5}{2}$, 68°.   **19.** $-\frac{4}{5}$, 141°.   **21.** 0, 0°.
23. -0.7739, 142°.   **25.** (8, 5), $\frac{3}{5}$.   **33.** $\sqrt{3}/3$, $-\sqrt{3}/3$.   **35.** $\dfrac{y-2}{x+1} = \dfrac{3}{2}$.

Exercises, Page 28

1. 35°.   **3.** 87°.   **5.** $\frac{1}{7}$.   **9.** Yes.   **11.** 53°.
13. $\alpha = 43°$, $\beta = 84°$, $\gamma = 53°$.   **15.** $\alpha = 107°$, $\beta = 37°$, $\gamma = 36°$.   **17.** 4.

Exercises, Page 33

1. $y + 2 = 0$.   **3.** $x^2 + y^2 = 16$.   **5.** $x^2 + y^2 = 13$.   **7.** $3x - y - 1 = 0$.
9. $2x + 5y - 13 = 0$.   **11.** $y + \sqrt{3}x + 4 = 0$.
13. Circle, center $(3, -2)$, radius 4.
15. Perpendicular bisector of segment joining $(-2, 1)$ and $(4, -5)$.
17. The line through $(-1, 5)$ of slope $-\frac{4}{3}$.
19. $y = 2x$.   **21.** $x^2 + y^2 = 9$.   **23.** $x^2 + y^2 - 9x + 18 = 0$.

Miscellaneous Exercises, Page 34

1. 30.   **3.** 63°.   **5.** 34°, 56°.   **7.** (4, 0), (0, 4), $(-4, 0)$, $(0, -4)$.
9. $(-3, -5)$, 104.
11. $(3, 3\sqrt{3})$, $(-3, 3\sqrt{3})$, $(-6, 0)$, $(-3, -3\sqrt{3})$, $(3, -3\sqrt{3})$.

Exercises, Page 40

1. $2x - y - 8 = 0$. **3.** $2x + y + 2 = 0$. **5.** $y - 7 = 0$. **7.** $x - y + 2 = 0$.
9. $x + y - 8 = 0$.   **11.** $2x - y - 1 = 0$.   **13.** $2x - 3y + 4 = 0$.
15. $2x + y + 1 = 0$.   **17.** (a) $y + 1 = 0$; (b) $x - 4 = 0$.
19. (5, 1), (1, 7), $(-1, -3)$.   **21.** $4x + 7y - 23 = 0$.   **23.** -2.
25. $x + 2y + 5 = 0$, $x + 2y - 15 = 0$, $2x - y = 0$, $2x - y - 5 = 0$, (5, 5).
27. $x + 2y - 9 = 0$, $x - y - 3 = 0$, $x + 5y - 27 = 0$.
29. $2x - y - 10 = 0$, $x + y - 3 = 0$, $5x - y - 23 = 0$, $(\frac{13}{3}, -\frac{4}{3})$.

Exercises, Page 44

1. $y = 2x + 4$.   **3.** $y + 3 = 0$.   **5.** $y = -\dfrac{2}{3}x + 2$, $\dfrac{x}{3} + \dfrac{y}{2} = 1$.

7. $y = \dfrac{4}{3}x - \dfrac{5}{3}$, $\dfrac{x}{\frac{5}{4}} + \dfrac{y}{-\frac{5}{3}} = 1$.   **9.** $-\frac{3}{2}$, 4, 6.

11. $\frac{3}{5}, -5, 3.$ **13.** $-\frac{7}{2}, -\frac{9}{7}, -\frac{9}{2}.$ **15.** $4x - 3y + 23 = 0.$

17. $3x - 8y - 14 = 0, 8x + 3y - 13 = 0.$

19. $2x + 5y + 17 = 0, 5x - 2y - 1 = 0.$

21. $5x - 3y - 31 = 0, 3x + 5y - 5 = 0.$ **23.** $49°.$ **25.** $138°.$

27. $(9, 4), (-5, 14), (-10, 7), (4, -3).$

29. $4x - 3y - 18 = 0, 4x - 3y + 32 = 0, 3x + 4y - 26 = 0, 3x + 4y - 1 = 0,$
$(-2, 8), (3, -2).$

31. $y = m(x - a).$ **33.** $-8, x > -6.$

35. $L = 1.6 + 0.0000192C, 1.60192$ meters.

Exercises, Page 49

1. $\dfrac{x}{2} + \dfrac{\sqrt{3}y}{2} - 5 = 0.$ **3.** $x + 4 = 0.$

5. $\dfrac{\sqrt{2}}{2}x + \dfrac{\sqrt{2}}{2}y + 2 = 0.$ **7.** $\dfrac{x}{2} + \dfrac{\sqrt{3}}{2}y - 5 = 0.$

9. $-\dfrac{\sqrt{2}}{2}x + \dfrac{\sqrt{2}}{2}y + 6 = 0.$ **11.** $-\frac{15}{17}x + \frac{8}{17}y - 2 = 0, 152°, 2.$

13. $\dfrac{2\sqrt{29}}{29}x + \dfrac{5\sqrt{29}}{29}y - 2\sqrt{29} = 0, 68°, 2\sqrt{29}.$

SHOULD BE +

15. $y - \frac{5}{3} = 0, 90°, \frac{5}{3}.$ **17.** $-\dfrac{\sqrt{2}}{2}x + \dfrac{\sqrt{2}}{2}y + 3\sqrt{2} = 0.$

19. (a) $x - y - 9 = 0$; (b) $-\sqrt{3}(x - 7) + y + 2 = 0.$ **21.** 4.

Exercises, Page 51

1. 4, above.   **3.** -3, below.   **5.** $-2\sqrt{29}$, below.

7. No.   **9.** $6x + 3y - 2 = 0.$ **11.** 3.   **13.** $11\sqrt{5}/10.$

15. (a) $4x - 3y + 37 = 0$; (b) $4x - 3y - 13 = 0.$

17. $x + y - 1 = 0, x - y - 13 = 0.$

19. $2x - y - 21 = 0.$ **21.** $x - 2y - 5 = 0.$

23. $x - y + 1 = 0, x + 3y - 15 = 0, 4x + y - 16 = 0.$

Exercises, Page 53

1. 13.   **3.** 93.   **5.** 16.   **7.** $\frac{33}{2}.$ **11.** $\begin{vmatrix} x & y & 1 \\ 4 & 1 & 1 \\ 2 & 5 & 1 \end{vmatrix} = 0.$

Exercises, Page 57

1. $y = \sqrt{3}x + b.$ **3.** $y = mx - 2.$ **5.** $3x - 4y + k = 0.$

7. $x - 2y + k = 0.$ **9.** $x - y + k = 0.$

11. $5x - 3y + 11 + k(2x - 9y + 7) = 0.$ **13.** $x \cos \omega + y \sin \omega \pm 3 = 0.$

21. (a) $3x + y - 17 = 0$; (b) $x - 3y + 1 = 0.$

23. $x - y + 6\sqrt{2} = 0, x - y - 6\sqrt{2} = 0.$

Exercises, Page 58

9. $4x^2 - 9y^2 + 10x + 15y = 0.$

Miscellaneous Exercises, Page 58

1. $y = x + 3$.   **3.** $3, -9$.   **5.** $(0, 10), 53°$.   **7.** $5x - 12y + 43 = 0$.

9. $2x + 10y - 21 = 0$.   **11.** $3x + 11y + k = 0$.

13. $x - y - 2 + k(5x + 7y + 2) = 0$.   **15.** $x \cos \omega + y \sin \omega = 0$.

17. $x - y + 10 = 0, x - y - 6 = 0$.   **19.** $(1, 2)$.

21. 28.   **23.** $(-6, -1)$.

25. $(-1, 3), (7, -1), (5, 4), (-3, 8), 5x + 2y - 33 = 0, x + 2y - 5 = 0$.

Exercises, Page 64

1. $x^2 + y^2 - 8x - 2y + 8 = 0$.   **3.** $x^2 + y^2 + 8x - 6y = 0$.

5. $x^2 + y^2 - 10x + 4y + 4 = 0$.   **7.** $x^2 + y^2 - 24x + 10y = 0$.

9. $x^2 + y^2 + 8x - 14y + 49 = 0$.   **11.** $x^2 + y^2 + 8x + 4y + 11 = 0$.

13. $(-3, 6), 5$, real.   **15.** $(4, -3), 0$, point.   **17.** $(-\frac{7}{2}, -\frac{3}{2}), 7\sqrt{2}/2$, real.

19. $(\frac{5}{4}, \frac{9}{4}), 3\sqrt{2}/4$, real.   **21.** $(0, 2), (0, 10)$; no.

23. $(0, 5), (-3, -4)$.   **25.** $(1, 4), (-4, 3)$.

27. $x^2 + y^2 = a^2$.   **29.** $x^2 + y^2 + 4x + 8y + k = 0$.

Exercises, Page 67

1. $x^2 + y^2 + 4x - 6y = 0$.   **3.** $x^2 + y^2 + 11x - y - 32 = 0$.

5. $x^2 + y^2 + 6x + 4y - 37 = 0$.   **7.** $3x^2 + 3y^2 - 20x - 10y + 20 = 0$.

9. $x^2 + y^2 - 4x - 14y + 36 = 0$.   **11.** $x^2 + y^2 + 7x + 5y - 44 = 0$.

13. $x^2 + y^2 - 2x - 6y - 7 = 0$.

15. $x^2 + y^2 + 14x - 8y + 31 = 0, x^2 + y^2 - 2x - 4y - 29 = 0$.

17. $x^2 + y^2 + 26x + 26y + 169 = 0, x^2 + y^2 + 10x + 10y + 25 = 0$.

19. $5x^2 + 5y^2 - 30x + 40y + 44 = 0$.

Exercises, Page 70

1. $2x^2 + 2y^2 - 2(x_1 + x_2)x - 2(y_1 + y_2)y + x_1^2 + x_2^2 + y_1^2 + y_2^2 = 4c^2$.

3. $x - 3y - 4 = 0$.   **5.** $x^2 + y^2 - 4x + 2y - 4 = 0$.   **7.** $x^2 + y^2 = 64$.

9. $x^2 + y^2 + 2by + b^2 - 4a^2 = 0$.

Miscellaneous Exercises, Page 71

1. $x^2 + y^2 - 3x - 9y - 20 = 0$.   **3.** $x^2 + y^2 - 4x - 2y - 24 = 0$.

5. $x^2 + y^2 - 10x - 6y + 9 = 0$.

7. $x^2 + y^2 - 22x + 2y + 54 = 0, x^2 + y^2 + 10x - 6y - 34 = 0$.

9. $(1, 5), (-1, -3)$.

Exercises, Page 77

19. $4.36, 4.33$.   **21.** $4.88, 9.15$.

Exercises, Page 79

1. $(3\sqrt{3}, 3)$.   **3.** $(4\sqrt{2}, -4\sqrt{2})$.   **5.** $(0, 5)$.   **7.** $(5\sqrt{2}, 45°)$.

9. $(6\sqrt{2}, 225°)$.   **11.** $(4, -30°)$.   **13.** $4\sqrt{3}$.   **15.** $r \cos \theta = 7$.

17. $r(2 \cos \theta + 5 \sin \theta) = 9$.

19. $r = 6 \sin \theta$.   **21.** $x^2 + y^2 = 4$.   **23.** $y = 11$.   **25.** $x^2 + y^2 = 2y$.

Exercises, Page 80

1. $4x - 7y + 11 = 0$.
3. $x + 5 = 0$.
5. $x + y - 4\sqrt{2} = 0$.
7. $r(2 \cos \theta - 5 \sin \theta) + 8 = 0$.
9. $r \cos (\theta - 3\pi/4) + 3 = 0$.
11. (a) $r \cos \theta = 3$; (b) $r \cos \theta = 4$.
13. $r \cos (\theta - \pi/3) = 4$.
15. $r \cos (\theta - 60°) = 4\sqrt{3}$.
17. 20.
19. $(4\sqrt{3}, 90°)$.

Exercises, Page 82

1. $r = 5$.
3. $r = 14 \sin \theta$.
5. $r^2 - 12r \cos (\theta - \pi/3) + 20 = 0$.
7. $(7, 0°), 7$.
9. $(4, - \pi/4), 4$.
11. $(3, 2\pi/3), 2$.
13. $(6, - 30°), 7$.
15. $x^2 + y^2 = 8y$.
17. $x^2 + y^2 + 3\sqrt{2}x - 3\sqrt{2}y = 0$.
19. $x^2 + y^2 - 6x - 6\sqrt{3}y + 27 = 0$.
21. $2x^2 + 2y^2 + 5\sqrt{3}x - 5y + 8 = 0$.
23. $r^2 - 6r \cos (\theta - 60°) + 9 = 9$.
25. $(4, 60°), (4, - 60°)$.

Miscellaneous Exercises, Page 83

1. $(- 3, 3\sqrt{3}), (1.634, 2.516), (- 3.993, - 3.009)$.
3. $r \cos \theta + 6 = 0$.
5. $(4\sqrt{2}, 135°), 4\sqrt{2}$.
7. 10.

Exercises, Page 90

1. $(4, 0), x + 4 = 0, 16$.
3. $(- 7, 0), x - 7 = 0, 28$.
5. $(0, - 10), y - 10 = 0, 40$.
7. $(\frac{3}{5}, 0), 5x + 3 = 0, \frac{12}{5}$.
9. $(0, \frac{7}{8}), 8y + 7 = 0, \frac{7}{2}$.
11. $(0, \frac{15}{28}), 28y + 15 = 0, \frac{15}{7}$.
13. $y^2 = 32x$.
15. $x^2 + 8y = 0$.
17. $y^2 = 20x$.
19. $x^2 = 2y$.
21. $y^2 + 16x = 0$.
23. $(0, 0), (2, 2)$.
25. $(0, 0), (2, - 3)$.
27. $(2, - 10), (8, 20)$.
29. $4x^2 + 4y^2 - 4px - 3p^2 = 0$.
31. 6.
33. 51.
35. $(- 15, 10\sqrt{3}), (- 15, - 10\sqrt{3})$.
37. $x^2 = 16y$.
39. $y^2 - 4x - 6y + 13 = 0$.
41. $x^2 - 6x - 8y + 1 = 0$.
43. $x^2 - 4xy + 4y^2 + 52x + 26y + 91 = 0$.

Exercises, Page 95

1. $(\pm 5, 0), (0, \pm 4), (\pm 3, 0), \frac{32}{5}, \frac{3}{5}$.
3. $(\pm 3, 0), (0, \pm 1), (\pm 2\sqrt{2}, 0), \frac{2}{3}, 2\sqrt{2}/3$.
5. $(0, \pm 5\sqrt{2}), (\pm 5, 0), (0, \pm 5), 5\sqrt{2}, \sqrt{2}/2$.
7. $(\pm 2, 0), (0, \pm\sqrt{3}), (\pm 1, 0), 3, \frac{1}{2}$.
9. $144x^2 + 169y^2 = 24{,}336$.
11. $100x^2 + 64y^2 = 6400$.
13. $16x^2 + 25y^2 = 400$.
15. $2x^2 + 3y^2 = 6$.
17. $x^2 + 25y^2 = 400$.
19. $4x^2 + y^2 = 16$.
21. $3x^2 + 2y^2 = 35$.
23. $4x^2 + 7y^2 = 128$.
25. $(6, 1), (2, 3)$.
29. $x^2 + 4y^2 = a^2$.

Exercises, Page 98

1. $5x^2 + 9y^2 = 45$.
3. $9x^2 + 5y^2 = 180$.
5. $8x^2 + 9y^2 = 288$.
7. $3x^2 + 4y^2 = 108$.
9. $4x^2 + 3y^2 = 300$.
11. $21x^2 + 25y^2 = 225$.
13. $(2, 2), (- 2, 2), (- 2, - 2), (2, - 2), 16$.
15. $15, 6.06, 3.69, 3, 3.69, 6.06, 15$.
17. $\frac{37}{3}, \frac{13}{3}$.

19. 5, 13.   **21.** 94.6 and 91.4 million miles.
23. $4x^2 + 3y^2 + 24x - 24y + 36 = 0.$ **25.** $15x^2 - 6xy + 7y^2 = 96.$
27. $9x^2 + 8y^2 + 18x + 20y - 19 = 0.$
29. $27x^2 - 12xy + 43y^2 - 156x - 172y + 352 = 0.$

Exercises, Page 105

1. $(\pm 12, 0)$, $(\pm 13, 0)$, $\frac{13}{12}$, $\frac{25}{6}$, $12y = \pm 5x.$
3. $(\pm 5, 0)$, $(\pm \sqrt{41}, 0)$, $\sqrt{41}/5$, $\frac{32}{5}$, $5y = \pm 4x.$
5. $(0, \pm 4)$, $(0, \pm 4\sqrt{2})$, $\sqrt{2}$, 8, $y = \pm x.$
7. $(0, \pm 2)$, $(0, \pm \sqrt{13})$, $\sqrt{13}/2$, 9, $3y = \pm 2x.$
9. $(\pm 1, 0)$, $(\pm 2, 0)$, 2, 6, $y = \pm \sqrt{3}x.$
11. $5x^2 - 4y^2 = 20.$ **13.** $16x^2 - 25y^2 = 3600.$ **15.** $4y^2 - 9x^2 = 144.$
17. $x^2 - 4y^2 = 20.$ **19.** $9x^2 - 16y^2 = 144.$ **21.** $y^2 - x^2 = 56.$
23. $4x^2 - y^2 = 96.$ **25.** $(2, 1)$, $(-2, 1)$, $(-2, -1)$, $(2, -1).$
27. $3x^2 - y^2 = 27.$

Exercises, Page 106

1. $3x^2 - y^2 = 27.$ **3.** $2y^2 - x^2 = 54.$ **5.** $21x^2 - 4y^2 = 84.$
7. $(\pm 8, 0)$, $(\pm 10, 0)$, $\frac{5}{4}$, $5x = \pm 32.$ **9.** $(0, \pm 2)$, $(0, \pm 4)$, 2, $y = \pm 1.$
11. $(\pm 5, 0)$, $(\pm \sqrt{29}, 0)$, $\sqrt{29}/5$, $\sqrt{29}x = \pm 25.$
15. 10, 26.   **17.** 3, 5.
21. $9x^2 - 16y^2 - 54x + 64y + 161 = 0.$
23. $3x^2 + 12xy + 8y^2 - 18x - 28y + 11 = 0.$
25. $4x^2 - 5y^2 - 16x + 44y - 16 = 0.$ **27.** $2xy - a^2 = 0.$

Exercises, Page 110

1. $(10, 0°)$, $(\frac{5}{2}, 180°)$, $\frac{3}{5}$, 8, $3r \cos \theta + 20 = 0.$
3. $(4, -90°)$, 1, 16, $r \sin \theta + 8 = 0.$
5. $(2, 0°)$, $(\frac{14}{3}, 0°)$, $\frac{5}{2}$, 14, $5r \cos \theta - 14 = 0.$
7. $(66, 90°)$, $(6, -90°)$, $\frac{6}{5}$, 22, $5r \sin \theta + 66 = 0.$
9. $(12, -90°)$, $(3, -90°)$, $\frac{3}{5}$, 16, $5r \sin \theta + 24 = 0.$

11. $(\frac{5}{2}, 90°)$, 1, 10, $r \sin \theta - 5 = 0.$ **13.** $r = \dfrac{21}{2 - 5 \cos \theta}.$

15. $r = \dfrac{5}{3 - 2 \cos \theta}.$ **17.** $r = \dfrac{30}{3 - 2 \sin \theta}.$

19. $r = \dfrac{10}{2 + 3 \cos \theta}.$ **21.** $r = \dfrac{7}{1 + 2 \cos \theta}$, $r = \dfrac{14}{2 - \cos \theta}.$

Miscellaneous Exercises, Page 111

1. $x^2 = 24y.$ **3.** $y^2 - x^2 = 9.$ **5.** $(3, -6)$, $(12, -12).$ **7.** $5x^2 - 4y^2 = 20.$
9. $b^2x^2 + a^2y^2 = a^2b^2.$

Exercises, Page 118

1. $(2, 2)$, $(-5, 4)$, $(-7, -5)$, $(-2, -1)$, $(-3, 3)$, $(2, 1).$
3. $2x' - 3y' = 0.$ **5.** $5x'^2 + 9y'^2 = 45.$ **7.** $y' = 2x'^2$, 1.1, $-5.1.$

9. $4x'^2 + y'^2 = 16.$ 11. $4x'^2 - 3y'^2 = 7.$ 13. $4x'^2 - 5y'^2 + 100 = 0.$
15. $y'^2 - 4x' = 0, (-3, -5), 4.$ 17. $x'^2 - 5y' = 0, (3, 1), 5.$
19. $7x^2 + 16y^2 - 14x - 96y + 39 = 0, 7x'^2 + 16y'^2 = 112.$
21. $x^2 - 6x + 6y + 12 = 0, x'^2 + 6y' = 0.$
23. $3x^2 - y^2 + 18x - 4y - 4 = 0, 3x'^2 - y'^2 = 27.$
25. 1500 by 2000 rods.

Exercises, Page 121

1. $(4, 6), (-4, -2), (-\sqrt{2}, -3\sqrt{2}), (4\sqrt{2}, -3\sqrt{2}), (-2\sqrt{2}, -2\sqrt{2}),$
$(-4\sqrt{2}, 4\sqrt{2}).$ 3. $x' - 5 = 0.$
5. $4x'^2 - y'^2 = 6.$ 7. $3x'^2 - 2y'^2 + 6 = 0.$ 9. $\sqrt{5}x''^2 + 2y'' = 0.$
11. $7x^2 + 24xy = 144, 16x'^2 - 9y'^2 = 144.$

Exercises, Page 125

1. $(y - 4)^2 + 4(x + 3) = 0, (-3, 4), (-4, 4), x + 2 = 0, y'^2 + 4x' = 0.$
3. $(x - 2)^2 + 8(y + 4) = 0, (2, -4), (2, -6), y + 2 = 0, x'^2 + 8y' = 0.$
5. $3(x - 5)^2 + 4(y - 1)^2 = 12, (5, 1), (3, 1), (7, 1), (4, 1), (6, 1), 3x'^2 + 4y'^2 = 12.$
7. $5(y + 3)^2 - 4(x - 1)^2 = 20, (1, -3), (1, -5), (1, -1), (1, -6), (1, 0),$
$5y'^2 - 4x'^2 = 20.$
9. $16(x - 1)^2 + 7(y + 2)^2 = 112, (1, -2), (1, -6), (1, 2), (1, -5), (1, 1),$
$16x'^2 + 7y'^2 = 112.$
11. $3(x - 3)^2 - (y - 5)^2 = 12, (3, 5), (1, 5), (5, 5), (-1, 5), (7, 5), 3x'^2 - y'^2 = 12.$
13. Two intersecting lines. 15. Imaginary ellipse.

Exercises, Page 127

1. $(y - 4)^2 = 12(x - 2).$ 3. $(x - 1)^2 = 8(y - 5).$ 5. $(y + 7)^2 + 12(x - 6) = 0.$
7. $7(x - 1)^2 + 16(y + 1)^2 = 112.$ 9. $5(x + 2)^2 + (y - 3)^2 = 20.$
11. $3(x - 4)^2 + 4(y + 1)^2 = 108.$ 13. $8(x + 5)^2 - (y - 2)^2 = 32.$
15. $25(y - 2)^2 - 9(x + 1)^2 = 225.$ 17. $4(x - 3)^2 - 9(y - 1)^2 = 324.$

Exercises, Page 129

1. $2x'^2 - 3y'^2 = 8.$ 3. $x'^2 = 4.$ 5. $7x'^2 + 3y'^2 = 9.$ 7. $4x'^2 - y'^2 = 3.$
9. $\sqrt{29}y'^2 - 3x' = 0.$

Exercises, Page 131

1. $x''^2 + 2y''^2 = 6.$ 3. $13x''^2 - 4y''^2 = 81.$ 5. $2x''^2 - 3y''^2 = 24.$
7. $11x''^2 + 6y''^2 = 66.$ 9. $y''^2 - 3x'' = 0.$ 11. $2x''^2 - 11y''^2 = 22.$
13. $4x''^2 - y''^2 = 0.$ 15. $x''^2 = 1.$

Exercises, Page 132

1. Ellipse. 3. Hyperbola. 5. Hyperbola. 7. Ellipse. 9. Parabola.
11. Hyperbola.

Miscellaneous Exercises, Page 132

1. $4x^2 - 3xy - 4a^2 = 0.$ **3.** $x^2 + y^2 - 3ay - a^2 = 0.$
5. $x^2 - 2xy - y^2 - a^2 = 0.$ **7.** $2xy - (a + b)(x + y) + ab = 0.$
9. $5x^2 + 11xy + 14y^2 - 11x - 22y - 12 = 0.$
11. $18x^2 + 17xy - 6y^2 - 73x - 16y + 62 = 0.$

Exercises, Page 148

31. $(x^2 + y^2 + a^2)^2 - 4a^2x^2 = b^4.$ **35.** $T^2 = ka^3.$

Exercises, Page 156

1. $2\pi, 2.$ **3.** $\pi, 2.$ **5.** $\pi, \frac{1}{2}.$ **7.** $\pi/2.$ **9.** $2, 1.$
11. $2\pi.$ **13.** $2\pi, 1.$ **15.** $\pi, 3, \pi/6.$ **17.** $2, 4, \frac{1}{2}.$

Exercise, Page 161

25. (a) $A = 1(1.06)^n$; (b) $A = 1(1 + 0.08n)$; $(0, 1)$; $(10, 1.8)$.

Exercises, Page 169

1. $2x + 3y - 19 = 0.$ **3.** $b^2x^2 - a^2y^2 = a^2b^2.$ **5.** $xy = a^2.$
7. $a^2x = y^3.$ **9.** $x^{\frac{2}{3}} + y^{\frac{2}{3}} = a^{\frac{2}{3}}.$ **11.** $x^2 + y^2 = 25.$
13. $x = y^2 + 3y + 2.$ **15.** $x^3 + 4x^2 - y^2 = 0.$ **17.** $x - y - 1 = 0.$
19. $3x + 2y - 6 = 0.$ **21.** $x + y^2 = 9.$
25. $x = \dfrac{-D - Em}{1 + m^2}, \ y = \dfrac{-Dm - Em^2}{1 + m^2}.$
27. $x = \dfrac{ab^2 - a^3m^2}{b^2 + a^2m^2}, \ y = \dfrac{2ab^2m}{b^2 + a^2m^2}.$
29. $x = \dfrac{a(m^2 - 1)}{m^2 + 1}, \ y = \dfrac{am(m^2 - 1)}{m^2 + 1}.$ **31.** $x = \dfrac{2am^2}{1 + m^2}, \ y = \dfrac{2am^3}{1 + m^2}.$
33. $x = 2\sqrt{1 - 9\sin^2\phi} + k\cos\phi, \ y = (6 - k)\sin\phi.$

Exercises, Page 185

23. $(x^2 + y^2)^2 = a^2x^2 - a^2y^2$; $(x^2 + y^2 + ax)^2 = a^2x^2 + a^2y^2$;
$(x^2 + y^2 + bx)^2 = a^2x^2 + a^2y^2$; $(y - a)^2(x^2 + y^2) = b^2y^2$.
25. No other; $r = a\sin[(\theta + 2\pi)/3]$, $r = a\sin[(\theta + 4\pi)/3]$.

Exercises, Page 188

1. $(4, 60°), (4, 300°).$ **3.** Origin, $(2, 0°), (1, 60°), (1, 300°).$
5. Origin, $(1, 45°).$ **7.** $(2, 30°), (2, 150°), (-2, 30°), (-2, 150°).$
9. $(2, 2), (-2, 2).$ **11.** $(2, 30°), (2, 150°), (6, 210°), (6, 330°).$

Exercises, Page 195

1. (a) $y = 3.07x + 3.86$; (b) $y = 3.21x + 3.86.$
3. (a) $y = -1.88x + 6.19$; (b) $y = -1.89x + 6.21.$

5. (a) $l = 0.227W + 10.3$; (b) $l = 0.226W + 10.4$.
7. (a) $W = 1.07C + 9.31$; (b) $W = 1.09C + 8.68$.
9. (a) $f = 0.065w + 7.67$; (b) $f = 0.065w + 7.67$.
11. (a) $N = 6.27t + 63.7$; (b) $N = 6.18t + 64.0$.

Exercises, Page 200

1. $y = 248x^{-1.67}$.   **3.** $C = 0.00275v^{2.00}$.   **5.** $T = 0.0143d^{1.48}$.
7. $H = 6.54h^{1.53}$.

Exercises, Page 202

1. $y = 1.73(10^{0.303x}) = 1.73e^{0.698x}$.   **3.** $p = 3.01(10^{0.0120t}) = 3.01e^{0.0276t}$.
5. $p = 0.610(10^{0.0218C}) = 0.610e^{0.0502C}$.   **7.** $N = 14.7(10^{0.211t}) = 14.7e^{0.486t}$.

Exercises, Page 206

1. $y = -6.81 - 1.61x + 1.72x^2$.   **3.** $p = 0.736 + 0.227n - 0.0250n^2$.
5. $C = 334 - 3.16p + 0.0114p^2$.   **7.** $N = 36.2 + 12.9h - 2.39h^2 + 0.198h^3$.
9. $x = 0.0975xy + 0.508y$.

Exercises, Page 213

3. (a) $(x, y, 0)$, $(x, 0, z)$, $(0, y, z)$; (b) $(0, 0, z)$, $(0, y, 0)$, $(x, 0, 0)$.
5. $\sqrt{y^2 + z^2}$, $\sqrt{x^2 + z^2}$, $\sqrt{x^2 + y^2}$.   **7.** yz-plane, xz-plane, xy-plane.
9. A plane parallel to the yz-plane and 4 units to the right of it.
11. $(0, 0, 0)$, $(a, 0, 0)$, $(a, a, 0)$, $(0, a, 0)$, $(0, 0, a)$, $(a, 0, a)$, (a, a, a), $(0, a, a)$.
15. (a) $(x, -y, -z)$, $(-x, y, -z)$, $(-x, -y, z)$; (b) $(-x, -y, -z)$.

Exercises, Page 214

1. 13.   **3.** 7.   **5.** 11.   **7.** $\sqrt{35}$.   **11.** 49.
13. $(x + 2)^2 + (y - 1)^2 + (z - 5)^2 = 9$.   **15.** A sphere.

Exercises, Page 218

1. $1, -8, 4$; $\frac{1}{9}, -\frac{8}{9}, \frac{4}{9}$.   **3.** $12, 4, -3$; $-\frac{12}{13}, -\frac{4}{13}, \frac{3}{13}$.
5. $3, 4, 1$; $3\sqrt{26}/26$, $4\sqrt{26}/26$, $\sqrt{26}/26$.
7. $\frac{6}{11}, -\frac{7}{11}, \frac{6}{11}$.   **9.** $\frac{2}{3}, -\frac{1}{3}, \frac{2}{3}$.
11. $\sqrt{70}/14$, $3\sqrt{70}/70$, $3\sqrt{70}/35$.   **13.** $\sqrt{2}/2, \frac{1}{2}, \frac{1}{2}$.   **15.** $\sqrt{2}/2, -\frac{1}{2}, \frac{1}{2}$.
17. $1, 0, 0$; $0, 1, 0$; $0, 0, 1$.   **19.** $(9, -7, 3)$.

Exercises, Page 221

1. $80°$.   **3.** $103°$.   **5.** $34°$.   **7.** $50°$.   **9.** 54.   **11.** $4, -2, 1$.   **15.** $3, 2, -1$.

Miscellaneous Exercises, Page 222

1. No.   **5.** -2.   **7.** $102°, 64°, 14°$.   **11.** $(a/2, a/2, a/2)$.

Exercises, Page 227

1. $\dfrac{x}{2} + \dfrac{y}{2} + \dfrac{\sqrt{2}z}{2} - 3 = 0.$ **3.** $\dfrac{\sqrt{3}x}{2} - \dfrac{y}{2} + 2 = 0.$

5. $6x + 3y + 2z \pm 28 = 0.$ **7.** $2x + 11y - 10z \pm 45 = 0.$

9. $9x - 2y - 6z \pm 66 = 0.$ **11.** $6x + 6y - 7z - 121 = 0.$

13. $\dfrac{2x}{3} - \dfrac{y}{3} + \dfrac{2z}{3} - 4 = 0;\ \frac{2}{3},\ -\frac{1}{3},\ \frac{2}{3};\ 4;\ 2x - y - 12 = 0,\ z = 0;\ x + z - 6 = 0,$
$y = 0;\ y - 2z + 12 = 0,\ x = 0.$

15. $-\dfrac{6x}{19} + \dfrac{10y}{19} + \dfrac{15z}{19} - 3 = 0;\ -\frac{6}{19},\ \frac{10}{19},\ \frac{15}{19};\ 3;\ 6x - 10y + 57 = 0,\ z = 0;$
$2x - 5z + 19 = 0,\ y = 0;\ 10y + 15z - 57 = 0,\ x = 0.$

Exercises, Page 230

1. $59°.$ **3.** $16°.$ **5.** $2x + y - 2z - 1 = 0,\ 7x + 4y - 4z - 9 = 0.$
7. $(4, 2, 1).$ **9.** $5.$ **11.** $3.$

Exercises, Page 232

1. $x/8 + y/12 + z/6 = 1.$ **3.** $x/(-6) + y/21 + z/14 = 1.$
5. $3x - 4y + 6z - 12 = 0.$ **7.** $x + 3y - 8z + 2 = 0.$
9. $2x + 4y - 5z + 20 = 0.$ **11.** $6x + 3y + 7z - 39 = 0.$
13. $10x + 2y - 3z - 54 = 0.$ **15.** $5x - 6y + 4z + 11 = 0.$
17. $x - 7y + 5z - 12 = 0.$ **19.** $5x - 6y + z - 12 = 0.$

Exercises, Page 238

1. $\dfrac{x - 5}{6} = \dfrac{y - 1}{-9} = \dfrac{z + 3}{2};\ \dfrac{6}{11},\ \dfrac{-9}{11},\ \dfrac{2}{11}.$

3. $\dfrac{x + 6}{14} = \dfrac{y - 1}{2} = \dfrac{z - 4}{-5};\ \dfrac{-14}{15},\ \dfrac{-2}{15},\ \dfrac{5}{15}.$

5. $\dfrac{x - 4}{1} = \dfrac{y + 1}{2} = \dfrac{z - 3}{-2};\ \dfrac{-1}{3},\ \dfrac{-2}{3},\ \dfrac{2}{3}.$

7. $\dfrac{x - 4}{6} = \dfrac{y - 1}{-3} = \dfrac{z - 3}{-2};\ \dfrac{-6}{7},\ \dfrac{3}{7},\ \dfrac{2}{7}.$

9. $x = 5 + 2k,\ y = -1 + 3k,\ z = -3 - 5k.$

11. $2x + y - 7 = 0,\ 2x - z - 2 = 0,\ y + z - 5 = 0;$
$(1, 5, 0),\ (\frac{7}{2}, 0, 5),\ (0, 7, -2);\ \frac{1}{3},\ -\frac{2}{3},\ \frac{2}{3}.$

13. $x + 2y + 12 = 0,\ x + 8z + 20 = 0,\ y - 4z - 4 = 0;$
$(-20, 4, 0),\ (-12, 0, -1),\ (0, -6, -\frac{5}{2});\ -\frac{8}{9},\ \frac{4}{9},\ \frac{1}{9}.$

15. $59°.$ **17.** $14x + 6y - z - 44 = 0.$

Exercises, Page 241

1. $2x' + y' - 5z' = 0.$ **3.** $x'^2 + y'^2 + z'^2 = 34.$
5. $5x'^2 - 2y'^2 + 3z'^2 = 20.$ **7.** $2x'^2 - y'^2 + 3z'^2 = 4.$

Miscellaneous Exercises, Page 242

1. $2x + 4y - 3z - 1 = 0.$ **3.** $-\frac{54}{11}, \frac{36}{11},$ Opposite. **5.** $\dfrac{x-1}{1} = \dfrac{y-7}{-3} = \dfrac{z-3}{-2}.$

7. $3x + y + 2z - 7 = 0, 4x - y - z + 2 = 0.$

9. $10x + 7y - 20 = 0, 2x + 7z + 10 = 0, y - 5z - 10 = 0;$
$(-5, 10, 0), (2, 0, -2), (0, \frac{20}{7}, -\frac{10}{7}).$ **11.** Yes.

Exercises, Page 249

1. $x^2 + y^2 + z^2 = a^2.$ **3.** $y^2 + z^2 = 4x.$ **5.** $9x^2 + 4y^2 + 4z^2 = 36.$

7. $y^2 + z^2 = e^{2x}.$ **9.** $z = \cos\sqrt{x^2 + y^2}.$ **11.** $y^2 + z^2 = x^6.$

Exercises, Page 250

1. $x^2 + y^2 + z^2 - 4x - 6y - 12z = 0.$

3. $x^2 + y^2 + z^2 + 10x - 14y - 2z + 11 = 0.$

5. $(1, -3, 4), 5.$ **7.** $(-4, 1, 3), 2\sqrt{-1}.$

9. $x^2 + y^2 + z^2 - 6x + 2y + 10z + 10 = 0.$

11. $x^2 + y^2 + z^2 - 14x - 4y + 6z + 48 = 0.$

13. $x^2 + y^2 + z^2 - 8x - 14y - 4z + 60 = 0.$

15. $x^2 + y^2 + z^2 - 2x - 6y - 2z + 2 = 0.$

Exercises, Page 258

1. $x + y = 3a, (3a - x)^2 + z^2 = a^2, y^2 + z^2 = a^2.$

3. $x^2 + y^2 = 2ax, z = 2x, z^2 + 4y^2 = 4az.$

5. $x^2 + y^2 = 2ax, z^2 + 2ax = a^2, (a^2 - z^2)^2 + 4a^2(y^2 + z^2 - a^2) = 0.$

9. $x^2 + y^2 = a^2, z = 3y.$ **11.** $x^2 = ay, y^3 = az^2.$

13. $a^2x^2 + a^2y^2 = z^2, ax = z \cos (z/a).$

Exercises, Page 263

1. $(-8, 8\sqrt{3}, 5).$ **3.** $(2, 2\sqrt{3}, 3).$ **5.** $(3\sqrt{2}, 45°, -2).$ **7.** $(2\sqrt{3}, 210°, -8).$

9. $(3\sqrt{3}, 3, 6\sqrt{3}).$ **11.** $(-18, -6\sqrt{3}, -12).$ **13.** $(6, 90°, 60°).$

15. $(8\sqrt{2}, 45°, 30°).$ **17.** $x^2 + y^2 = 81.$ **19.** $x^2 + y^2 = 4x.$

21. $x^2 + y^2 + z^2 = 25.$ **23.** $y + 2 = 0.$ **25.** $r^2 + z^2 = 36, \rho = 6.$

27. $9r^2 + 4z^2 = 25, \rho^2(9 \sin^2 \phi + 4 \cos^2 \phi) = 25.$

29. $r^2 = 4z^2, \phi = \arctan (\pm 2).$

31. $r = 4 \cos \theta, \rho \sin \phi = 4 \cos \theta.$

33. $\sin \phi \cos \theta, \sin \phi \sin \theta, \cos \phi.$

35. $P_1P_2^2 = \rho_1^2 + \rho_2^2 - 2\rho_1\rho_2[\sin \phi_1 \sin \phi_2 \cos (\theta_1 - \theta_2) + \cos \phi_1 \cos \phi_2].$

Miscellaneous Exercises, Page 265

17. $4x - 3y + 5z = 50.$ **19.** Cone. **21.** Elliptic paraboloid.

23. Hyperboloid of one sheet. **25.** $\dfrac{x^2}{a^2} + \dfrac{y^2}{b^2} + \dfrac{z^2}{c^2} = 1.$ **27.** $\dfrac{z^2}{c^2} - \dfrac{x^2}{a^2} - \dfrac{y^2}{b^2} = 1.$

Index

polar, 75
principal, 86, 91, 100
radical, 73

Abscissa, 4
Addition of ordinates, 162
Algebraic curves, 135
Amplitude, 152
Angle
  between two lines in space, 219
  between two planes, 228
  from l_1 to l_2, 27
  l_2 makes with l_1, 27
  of lag or lead, 153
Applications
  to elementary geometry, 29
  of ellipse, 95
  of exponential curve, 160
  of parabola, 89
Archimedes, spiral of, 83, 183
Arclight curve, 144
Area of a triangle, 53
Asymptote
  of a curve, 139, 178
  of a hyperbola, 102
Averages, method of, 190
Axes
  of coördinates, 3, 75
  of ellipse, 93
  of ellipsoid, 251
  of hyperbola, 101
  of hyperboloid, 252, 253
  rotation of, 119, 240
  translation of, 114, 189, 239
Axis
  ninety degree, 75
  of a parabola, 86

B

Bifolium, 149
Bipartite cubic, 148
Bisector of an angle, 52

C

Cardioid, 83, 181
Cartesian
  coördinates, 36
  geometry, 3
  oval, 149
Cassini's oval, 149
Catenary, 164
Center
  of circle, 62, 81
  of ellipse, 91
  of ellipsoid, 251
  of hyperbola, 100
  of hyperboloid, 252, 253
  of sphere, 250
Circle, 61
  determined by three conditions, 65
  equations of, 61, 62, 81
  imaginary, 63
  nine-point, 73
  point, 63
Circles
  family of, 72

Circles (*cont.*)
    line of centers, 72
    radical axis, 73
Cissoid, 147
Colatitude, 263
Compound interest law, 161
Conchoid, 182
Condition three lines meet in a point,
    60
Cone
    oblique circular, 256
    quadric, 255
    right circular, 256
Conic
    definition, 84
    degenerate, 85
    determination of type, 132
    discriminant of equation, 133
    general equation, 85, 123
    invariants under rotation, 132
    reduction to standard form, 129
    satisfying given conditions, 126
    standard polar equations, 108, 109
    standard rectangular equations,
        87, 92, 101, 102
Conjugate hyperbolas, 107
Conjugate point, 143
Constructions for
    ellipse, 98, 167
    hyperbola, 106
    parabola, 86, 89
Coördinate
    paper, 5, 76
    planes, 211
Coördinates
    Cartesian, 35
    cylindrical, 262
    oblique, 35
    polar, 75
    rectangular, 3, 211
    spherical, 262
    transformation of, 114, 239
Corresponding focus and directrix,
    98, 106

Cosecant curve, 154
Cosine curve, 151
Cotangent curve, 154
Cruciform curve, 143
Cubical parabola, 148
Curve
    algebraic, 135
    discussion of equation, 135, 177
    higher plane, 135
    parametric equations of, 165
    polar equations of, 175
    transcendental, 135, 150
Curves in space
    equations of, 256, 257
    projecting cylinders of, 257
Cusp, 147
Cycloid, 170
    curtate, 172
    equations of, 171
    prolate, 172
Cylinder, 246
    directrix curve of, 246
    element of, 246
    parabolic, 247
    projecting, of a curve in space, 257
Cylindrical coördinates, 262

D

Damped vibrations, 161
Descartes, 3
Determination of type of a conic, 132
Dihedral angle, 228
Directed line, 15
Directed line segment, 15
Direction
    angles of a line, 215
    cosines of a line, 215
    numbers of a line, 217
Directrix
    of an ellipse, 98
    of a hyperbola, 106
    of a parabola, 86

Discriminant of equation of a conic, 133
Discussion of equation
  of a curve, 135, 177
  of an ellipse, 93
  of a hyperbola, 101
  of a parabola, 87
Distance
  between two points, 18, 213
  from a line to a point, 50
  from a plane to a point, 229

E

Eccentricity of a conic, 108
Elementary geometry, applications to, 29
Ellipse, 91
  applications, 95
  axes, 93
  center, 91
  constructions for, 98, 167
  corresponding focus and directrix, 98
  directrices, 98
  eccentricity, 94
  focal radii, 99
  foci, 91
  imaginary, 125
  latus rectum, 93
  major axis, 93
  minor axis, 93
  point, 125
  polar equations of, 108
  principal axis, 91
  standard equations, 92
  vertices, 93
Ellipsoid
  axes, 251
  center, 251
  principal planes, 251
Elliptic paraboloid, 254

Empirical equations, 189
  exponential type, 201
  hyperbolic type, 197
  linear type, 190
  parabolic type, 197
  polynomial type, 203
Equation
  algebraic, 135
  empirical, 189
  equivalent, 11, 175
  factorable, 57
  of first degree, 42, 225
  general form of, for a conic, 85, 123
  general form of, for a line, 42
  graph of, 6, 145
  linear, 42
  normal, 46, 224
  point-slope, 38
  polar, of a circle, 81
  polar, of a conic, 107
  polar, of a line, 79
  of a quadric surface, 250
  of second degree, 85, 123, 250
  slope-intercept, 41
  transcendental, 135, 150
  two-point, 39, 235
Equilateral hyperbola, 104, 120
Equivalent equations, 11, 175
Equivalent polar coördinates, 76
Excluded intervals, 9, 88, 93, 101, 142, 179
Exponential curves, 158
Exponential type equations, 201

F

Factorable equations, 57
Family
  of circles, 72
  of lines, 54
  of planes, 237
  parameter of, 54

Figures, 4, 212
Focal radius
  of ellipse, 99
  of hyperbola, 107
  of parabola, 90
Focus
  of ellipse, 91
  of hyperbola, 100
  of parabola, 86
Folium, 149
Formulas for least squares, 193
Four-cusped hypocycloid, 174
Function
  inverse, 158
  linear, 44
  polynomial, 137
  quadratic, 117
  rational, 139
  (See Art. 0.5 also.)

G

General equation of first degree
  in three variables, 225
  in two variables, 42
General equation of second degree
  in three variables, 250
  in two variables, 85, 123
General form of equation
  of a circle, 61, 62, 81
  of a conic, 85, 123
  of a line, 42
  of a plane, 225
  of a quadric surface, 250
  of a sphere, 249
Graph of an equation, 6, 145
Graphs, intersections of, 12

H

Helix, 258
Higher plane curves, 135

Hyperbola, 99
  asymptotes, 101
  axes, 101
  center, 100
  conjugate axis, 101
  construction for, 106
  directrices, 106
  eccentricity, 103
  equilateral, 104
  focal radii, 107
  foci, 100
  latus rectum, 103
  polar equations of, 108
  principal axis, 100
  rectangular, 104
  transverse axis, 101
  vertices, 101
Hyperbolas, conjugate, 107
Hyperbolic cosine, 164
Hyperbolic paraboloid, 254
Hyperbolic sine, 164
Hyperbolic spiral, 185
Hyperbolic-type equations, 197
Hypocycloid, 173

I

Imaginary
  circle, 63
  ellipse, 125
  sphere, 250
Inclination, of a line, 23
Initial line, 75
Intercept equation
  of a line, 40
  of a plane, 232
Intercepts
  of a curve, 7, 137, 178
  of a line, 40
  of a plane, 232
Intersections
  of a curve with the axes, 137
  of graphs, 12
  in polar coördinates, 185

Invariants under rotation, 132
Inverse functions, 158
Inverse trigonometric functions, 155
Inversion, 73
Involute of a circle, 174
Isolated point, 143

K

Kappa curve, 83, 181

L

Lag or lead, angle of, 153
Lamé's special quartic, 136
Latus rectum
  of ellipse, 93
  of hyperbola, 103
  of parabola, 86
Least squares, method of, 192
Lemniscate, 83, 149, 181
Limaçon, 181
Line
  of centers, 72
  distance from to a point, 50
  general equation of, 42
  intercept equation, 40
  normal equation, 46
  parallel to an axis, 37
  point-slope equation, 38
  polar equation, 79
  slope-intercept equation, 41
  two-point equation, 39
Line in space
  general equations, 236
  parametric equations, 235
  projecting planes of, 237
  symmetric equations, 234
  through a given point in a given
    direction, 234
  two-point equation, 235
Linear equation, 42

Linear function, 44
Linear-type equation, 190
Lines, family of, 54
Lituus, 184
Loci problems, 68
Locus, equation of, 31
Locus of an equation, 6
Logarithmic
  curves, 157
  paper, 199
  spiral, 83, 184
Longitude, 263

M

Major axis, 93, 251
Mean axis, 251
Meridian section, 247
Method of averages, 190
Method of least squares, 192
Minor axis, 93, 251
Multiplicity of origin on a curve, 143

N

Natural logarithms, 157
Nine-point circle, 73
Ninety-degree axis, 75
Normal equation
  of a line, 46
  of a plane, 224
  reduction to, 48, 226

O

Oblate spheroid, 252
Oblique circular cone, 256
Octant, 212
Ordinate, 4
Ordinates, addition of, 162
Origin
  in polar coördinates, 75

Origin (*cont.*)
  in rectangular coördinates, 4, 211
Oval
  of bipartite cubic, 148
  of Cassini, 149
  of Descartes, 149

P

Parabola, 85
  applications, 89
  axis of, 86
  construction for, 86, 89
  cubical, 148
  directrix, 86
  focal radius, 90
  focus, 86
  latus rectum, 86
  polar equations of, 108
  principal axis, 86
  semi-cubical, 149
  standard equations of, 87
  vertex, 86
Parabolic
  cylinder, 247
  spiral, 185
  type equation, 197
Paraboloid
  elliptic, 254
  hyperbolic, 254
Parallel lines, condition for, 26
Parameter
  of equations of curves, 165
  of a family, 54, 237
Parametric equations, 165
  of circle, 165
  of curve, 165
  of curve in space, 257
  of cycloid, 170
  of ellipse, 166
  of epicycloid, 172
  of folium, 168
  of hypocycloid, 173

  of line in space, 235
  of path of a projectile, 167
  of sphere, 250
Period of a function, 150
Periodic function, 150
Periodicity factor, 152
Perpendicularity, conditions for, 26, 220, 228
Pilaster, 140
Plane
  distance from, to a point, 229
  general equation of, 226
  intercept equation of, 232
  normal equation of, 224
  satisfying three conditions, 231
  traces of, 226
Planes
  angle between two, 228
  condition for perpendicularity, 228
  family of, 237
  projecting, of a line, 237
Point
  circle, 63
  dividing a segment in a given ratio, 20
  ellipse, 125
  sphere, 250
Polar
  axis, 75
  coördinate paper, 76
  coördinates, 75
Polar equation
  of a circle, 81
  of a curve, 175
  of a line, 79
Polar and rectangular coördinates, relations between, 77
Pole, 75
Polynomial function, 137
Polynomial-type equation, 203
Principal axis, of a conic, 86, 91, 100
Principal planes, 251, 252, 253
Probability curve, 162
Projecting planes, 237

Projecting cylinders, 257
Prolate spheroid, 252

Q

Quadrants, 4
Quadratic function, 117
Quadric cone, 256
Quadric surface, 250

R

Radical axis, 73
Radius
    of a circle, 62, 81
    of a sphere, 250
    vector, 76, 263
Ratio, point dividing a segment in a
    given, 20
Rational function, 139
Reciprocal spiral, 185
Rectangular coördinates, 3, 211
Rectangular hyperbolic paraboloid,
    255
Reduction to normal form, 48, 226
Regulus, 265
Relations between rectangular and
    polar coördinates, 77
Removal of xy-term, 127
Residual of a point, 193
Revolution
    axis of, 247
    surface of, 247
Rose curves, 183
Rotation of axes, 119, 240

S

Secant curve, 154
Semi-axes
    of ellipse, 93
    of ellipsoid, 251
    of hyperbola, 101

Semi-cubical parabola, 149
Semi-logarithmic paper, 201
Simplification
    by rotation, 127, 240
    by translation, 124, 239
Sine curve, 150
Slope of a line, 23
Solid bounded by surfaces, 243, 258
Sphere, 249
    equations of, 249
    imaginary, 250
    point, 250
    real, 250
Spherical coördinates, 262
Spheroid, 252
Spiral, 183
    of Archimedes, 183
    hyperbolic, 185
    lituus, 185
    logarithmic, 184
    parabolic, 185
    reciprocal, 185
Standard equations of a conic
    polar, 108
    rectangular, 87, 92, 100, 101
Strophoid, 149
Surface of revolution, 247
Symmetric curve, 136
Symmetric equations of a line, 234
Symmetry, 10, 136, 177

T

Tangent curve, 154
Tangent lines at origin, 143, 178
Tetrahedron, volume of, 244
Three-leaved rose, 178
Top, 149
Traces of a plane, 226
Transcendental curve, 135, 150
Transformation of coördinates, 114,
    239
Translation of axes, 114, 239

Transverse axis of hyperbola, 101
Triangle, area of, 53
Trisection of an angle, 147
Trisectrix, 146
Trochoid, 172
Type of a conic, determination of, 132

X

x-axis, 4, 211
x-coördinate, 4, 212
x-intercept, 7, 137, 232, 251, 252
xy-plane, 211

V

Vectorial angle, 76
Vertex
of ellipse, 93
of hyperbola, 101
of parabola, 85
Volume of a tetrahedron, 244

Y

y-axis, 4, 211
y-coördinate, 4, 212
y-intercept, 7, 137, 232, 251, 252
yz-plane, 211

Z

W

Witch, 149

z-axis, 211
z-coördinate, 212
z-intercept, 232, 251, 252